The
Management
of   Production

The Management of Production

J. D. Radford
B.Sc. (Eng), M.I.Mech.E, F.I.Prod.E,
F.I.W.S.P.

D. B. Richardson
D.I.C., M.I.Mech.E, F.I.Prod.E,
A.M.B.I.M.

Department of Mechanical and Production Engineering,
Brighton College of Technology

SECOND EDITION

Macmillan
London - Melbourne - Toronto
St. Martin's Press
New York

First published 1963
2nd Edition 1968

Published by
MACMILLAN AND CO LTD
Little Essex Street London WC2
and also at Bombay Calcutta and Madras
Macmillan South Africa (Publishers) Pty Ltd Johannesburg
The Macmillan Company of Australia Pty Ltd Melbourne
The Macmillan Company of Canada Ltd Toronto
St Martin's Press Inc New York

Demy 8vo, viii + 320 pages,
144 line illustrations

Printed in Great Britain at the St Ann's Press,
Park Road, Altrincham

Preface

THE FIRST object of this book is to help students preparing for examinations in industrial administration. The second is to provide a down-to-earth guide and reference to a fairly wide variety of people in industry who have either physical or financial control of production.

In preparing the second edition the book has been modified and enlarged to cover the syllabus of the Council of Engineering Institutions' examination in Analysis of Manufacturing Systems and parts of the examination syllabuses of the Institution of Works Managers and the Institute of Work Study Practitioners. It should also be of use to those studying industrial administration for degrees and diplomas in mechanical and production engineering and for students taking endorsements to Higher National Certificates.

We wish to thank those who, by their suggestions and advice, have assisted in the preparation of the book, especially Mr. C. W. Lilburn, B.Sc. and Mr. A. J. Till, B.Sc. (Eng.), F.I.Mech.E., M.I.E.E., A.M.B.I.M. for their helpful criticism and Miss Grace Vine who typed the manuscript.

J. D. Radford
D. B. Richardson

College of Technology,
Brighton,
May 1968

Contents

The Task of Management

EFFECTIVE management is an essential requirement of all forms of successful industrial undertaking. Policy must be formulated, and decisions stemming from the agreed policy must be communicated to those responsible for implementing the decisions and to those affected by them.

The arrangement of the chain of communications is a matter of great and growing importance, and everyone aspiring to an understanding of production management should make at least a brief review of industrial history with particular reference to the development of management techniques. In this book no effort has been made to trace the history of industrial development, but merely to examine the current practice of management in manufacturing companies.

MAKING DECISIONS

Decisions must be taken at all levels in an organization; they are not the prerogative of top management. Unless policies exist which define the types of decisions to be made at various levels, higher levels of management will find much of their time occupied in making decisions which should have been settled by their subordinates. Although, in a well-organized company, the decisions made by senior management will be few in number, they will be of the greatest importance to the future of the company and will determine the policies on which subordinate decisions are taken. By insisting that decisions are taken at the appropriate levels, top management is able to perform its primary task of planning.

The decisions made by middle management, although not so far reaching as those made by the board of directors, are nevertheless important. A works manager may have to decide whether an additional shift is necessary to meet an increase in the production programme; a senior quality engineer may have to decide whether to allow work which is inferior to specification to be sent to the customer. At lower levels machine setters must be encouraged to make decisions; whether, for example, an automatic machine should be stopped and the tools re-set when the surface quality of components begins to deteriorate.

PRESENTATION OF INFORMATION TO MANAGEMENT

If sound decisions are to be made, managers must be presented with as many relevant facts as possible from which to make decisions. Information expressed in terms of absolute quantities is of little help to most managers. Although the daily figures of output may give a general indication to a works manager, it is of more importance if he is presented with information comparing output with programme. The presentation of comparative information to management is of fundamental importance if the organization is to be managed by exception. Management by exception should be the goal of any large organization, because by this means attention is drawn only to those things which are not progressing according to plan and require attention.

Comparative information can be supplied to top management in a number of ways, important methods being the use of graphs, moving annual totals, ratios and budgetary control information. Budgetary control can also be used to supply information to all levels from the board of directors to the shop supervision, enabling planning and performance to be compared and appropriate action to be taken.

Statistical information lends itself to graphical presentation, but

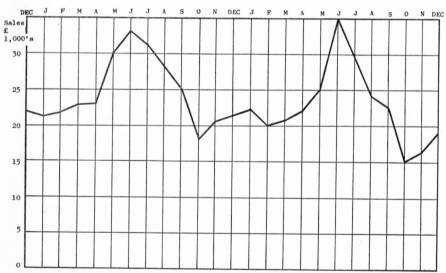

FIG. 1.1 *Graph Showing Monthly Sales over a Period of Two Years*

graphs can sometimes create a false impression if they are not correctly interpreted. Figure 1.1 shows the monthly sales of a company over a period of two years. It will be seen that the shape of the graph follows a similar pattern for the two consecutive years, and it is not obvious at first sight that the value of yearly sales is steadily falling.

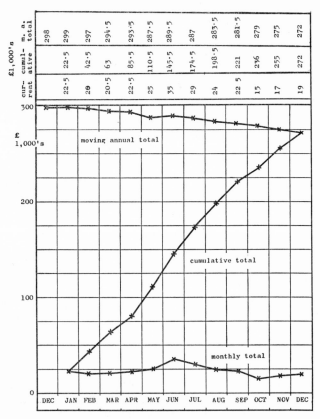

FIG. 1.2 *Z Chart Compiled from Fig.* 1.1, *Showing the Falling Value of the Moving Annual Total.*

Figure 1.2 shows a moving annual total graph compiled from the same information, which demonstrates how, when the effect of seasonal fluctuations is eliminated by considering the total value of sales over a period of one year, the volume of sales is declining. In this case the moving annual total is obviously a more valuable piece of information.

Management ratios are figures expressing important relationships between resources used and results achieved in the form of ratios; they are used to compare present with past performance in the company, or can be used in a decentralized company to compare the performance of the various units. In some industries ratios are compared on an inter-company basis, allowing managers to measure not only their internal performance, but their performance in relation to the rest of the industry. The primary ratio would probably be

$$\frac{\text{operating profit}}{\text{assets employed}},$$

secondary ratios

$$\frac{\text{operating profit}}{\text{value of sales}} \text{ and } \frac{\text{value of sales}}{\text{assets employed}},$$

and departmental ratios would express relationships such as

$$\frac{\text{works cost of sale}}{\text{work-in-progress}} \text{ and } \frac{\text{distribution costs}}{\text{value of sales}},$$

Different ratios will have varying degrees of significance in different businesses, and the factors compared may themselves have rather different meanings according to the industry considered.

Budgetary control enables all levels of management and supervision to know how their departments or sections of the business are proceeding toward the achievement of budgeted targets. These budgets represent the financial requirements of departments during a given period to achieve an estimated profit based on a given volume of sales. Targets are set for all the major sectors of the company's activities to give the most satisfactory overall results. Budgets are often set for a period of one year, and comparisons with targets are made monthly. The effectiveness of budgetary control depends on the accuracy of sales estimates. Budgetary control applications and flexible budgeting are dealt with at greater length in Chapter 11.

To provide the necessary estimates for sales budgets, market research and sales forecasts are used. *Market research* is the study of products in relation to the needs and buying habits of customers. A company must not be satisfied with keeping up with its competitors or following trends in fashion; to increase its share of the market it must look ahead so that its products anticipate the trends and set the fashions. This is a difficult task and one where poor judgement can result in heavy losses, so the soundness of market research is of prime importance. The techniques employed depend on whether the product or something similar is already being marketed, or whether it is completely new. If a similar product is already being manufactured, distributive machinery probably exists, but at this stage it may be worth considering whether alternative methods of distribution would be more efficient. The method of distribution, whether it be to wholesalers, retailers, through agents, by mail order, or to industrial users, will determine whom to approach when making preliminary market surveys. The three main sources of information in this respect are external investigations specifically concerned with the new product, internal sales statistics showing past sales, and published external statistics such as the *Board of Trade Journal* and the annual publication on National Income and Expenditure.

Closely associated with market research is *sales forecasting*, where future demands are estimated to form a basis for short- and long-term policies. The survival of a manufacturing business depends on its ability to assess, with reasonable accuracy, market trends several years ahead. This period is often necessary to enable action to be taken if expansion is required to meet a rising demand or for new products to be developed and tooled.

Forecasters will be able to make use of sales trends, but these must be considered in the light of fashion changes, of competitors' policies, and of the general economic situation expected in home and foreign markets. Elasticity of demand must be considered, as the sales of some products will hardly be affected by economic conditions while others will suffer badly in times of depression. The introduction of new materials frequently upsets existing markets; for instance, the use of plastics has affected the demand for wood or metals in certain fields.

Most new products have a characteristic demand/time curve which reaches a maximum value, after which time the demand remains relatively static or drops until it reaches a steady value, this being the demand for replacements. Once this happens, a sudden increase in demand is usually experienced only when an innovation is marketed. Industries where these trends have been felt to a marked degree are radio and television.

FIXING OBJECTIVES

Objectives are necessary at all levels in a business, and the performance toward objectives must be published at regular intervals so that corrective action may be taken if necessary. Financial objectives have already been mentioned, but for control to be exercised effectively non-financial objectives are also necessary. For example, when calculating a production budget, costs must be based on expected operating efficiencies. To assist supervisors in production shops in achieving the expected levels of efficiency they are provided with objectives covering labour, machine and material utilization, labour efficiency or bonus earnings, output, indirect labour hours and indirect material costs.

Targets must be integrated so that a unity of purpose is developed and that one aspect of the business is not favoured at the expense of another. They must also be realistically set, notably in the light of past performance, so that achievement is a reasonable possibility. Impossible objectives result in an unrealistic budget; unduly modest ones in unnecessarily low operating efficiencies.

IMPLEMENTING DECISIONS

ORGANIZATION STRUCTURE

Decisions once made must be correctly implemented. In some manufacturing industries, where work is mainly of a jobbing nature, a simple line organization has survived and instructions are passed down the line through clearly defined channels of seniority to the operator. Where processes have become more complex, specialist tasks such as quality control, work study and production engineering are undertaken by separate departments. All these departments have dealings with the production shops and with each other, and a functional relationship has developed.

One of the earliest exponents of specialization and functionalization was F. W. Taylor, a remarkable American, who, among other things, is remembered for the introduction of high-speed steel and for piece-work systems based on time study. His idea was to break down a supervisor's job into its component functions and to appoint a foreman to control each function, thereby divorcing planning and performance. It is doubtful if Taylor's idea could be incorporated in its

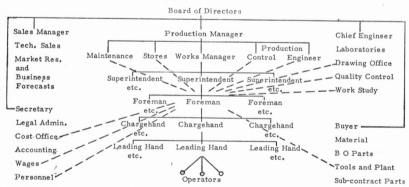

FIG. 1.3 *Functional Organization Chart Showing the Most Important Lines of Communication with a Typical Foreman.*

entirety, due to the confusion which would be created at operator level. The usual arrangement is to exercise functional control through the shop supervision who interpret the instructions from functional departments to the operator. A typical organization chart showing functional influences acting on a production foreman is shown in Figure 1.3.

COMMUNICATIONS

The ability of a management to get things done depends largely on its ability to delegate responsibility at all levels and yet maintain an efficient chain of communication. For communications to be effective, the span of control, that is the number of subordinates responsible to each executive, must be kept within suitable limits. An excessively large span leads to an imperfect knowledge of work performed by subordinates but, on the other hand, a small span creates the impression that every move is being watched and someone is always "breathing down one's neck". Another argument against a small span is its effect on the organization structure. As a result of successive delegation of authority, the number of levels of management from the Board of Directors to the shop floor becomes excessive in a large company. With a long chain of command, communications are poor, implementation of decisions is difficult, and management cannot obtain a clear picture of the effect of its decisions. Labour relations suffer, as with too many layers of management it is difficult to obtain redress of grievances.

Another organizational trend, which in recent years has resulted in deterioration of communications, has been the appointment in some companies of "assistants" to senior executives. Their existence in the organization conflicts with the need for unity of command and often causes confusion and conflict among subordinates unless duties and responsibilities are carefully defined.

In order to preserve a compact structure, large organizations should be divided into smaller units which are relatively autonomous, being tied to the parent company only by financial control. The separate divisions must be large enough to support the type of management they require and be capable of free expansion and development. Decentralization also provides an excellent means of training executives because it offers greater scope for the exercise of initiative than would be possible in a large centralized organization.

CHANGING MANAGEMENT REQUIREMENTS

The rapid growth of highly mechanized processes is already making new demands on managers. Heavier capital investment will require large fixed outputs for profitable operation, and inflexible manufacturing facilities, consequent on mechanization, will call for a smaller margin of managerial error. Due to the amalgamation of the factory into a single complex unit, line relationships will have to be replaced by further functional ones, and poor co-operation between departments and "empire building" will no longer be acceptable. It is probable that greater reliance will be placed on operational research when making industrial decisions. The mathematical nature of operational research and the fast-growing complication of production technology will require large units to have managers with an all-round knowledge, possessing a high standard of mathematical and technical ability.

In heavily capitalized industries a high machine utilization is necessary if profits are to be earned, so it is important that strikes and industrial unrest should be averted wherever possible. Managers of the future will therefore also need a greater appreciation of human nature than some of their predecessors have possessed.

Research, Development and Design

As with so many terms used in production organization and control, the words research, development and design may be taken to mean different things in different industries, or even in different businesses within the same industry. It must be realized that the three words taken in the industrial sense are so closely interrelated that it is virtually impossible to specify where the boundaries exist between them.

Industrial research is conducted in many fields and the diversity of applications, including such widely differing ones as market research and operational research, makes their basic similarity rather obscure. Research has been sub-divided into fundamental, directed basic and applied research, to indicate degrees of direction or control imposed on the research team. However, these terms have only a relative significance, because no research can be completely directed in a set channel, since such direction implies a knowledge of the results of research before it has been conducted. Probably the best definition to cover all types of industrial research is to say that it is the quest for knowledge of the fundamental properties or principles of processes, materials or devices, without reference to an intended item of production.

Accepting this definition of research it is then reasonable to define development as the application of this knowledge to practical problems. In modern industry, where business objectives and requirements are constantly changing, there is a constant need for research to discover new principles which will allow for further development to take place.

Design is the physical form of the developed product. Before product development can proceed there must be some general idea of the finished form, so design and development are as interdependent as are research and development. It is possible, and in many cases probable, that as development proceeds, the design will be considerably changed in order to meet functional and production requirements and customer preferences

APPLICATIONS OF RESEARCH AND DEVELOPMENT

If research and development are to achieve any positive results in a company it is important to realize in which areas investigation is necessary and what objectives should be achieved in each area. Research applications may be broken down into a large number of fields, the most important being product, process, market and operational research. The last two, market research and operational research, are dealt with in greater detail in the first and eighteenth chapters respectively, of this book.

Product research and development are concerned with all aspects of the product design and applications including its functional efficiency, quality, unexplored uses, utilization of waste products, investigation of materials and possible substitutes, standardization and customer satisfaction. The development of existing products in the light of practical experience may be a matter of small refinements or of major re-design. Frequently a completely new design results. An example is the fuel injection pump used on diesel engines. The old reciprocating pump, with the limitations of reciprocating mechanisms and the need for frequent servicing and adjustment, is rapidly giving way to a cheaper and more reliable pump incorporating a rotary principle with most of the reciprocating parts eliminated.

The development of new products often involves very considerable expenditure, and the results expected must be carefully weighed against the expenditure which is likely to be entailed. Frequently an expensive programme of research and development is the only way to ensure survival when competition is keen. In competitive industries it is reasonable to expect a higher percentage of the sales income to be devoted to research. A recent survey made by the Federation of British Industries estimated that research expenditure in the United Kingdom varied from just over 5 per cent of the sales turnover in the light electrical engineering industry, to just over 0·5 per cent in the food industries.

The percentage in the aircraft industry is no doubt much higher, but since this is largely paid for by a government subsidy, the comparison would not be a fair one.

The need to utilize waste products in order to obtain the maximum economy from various processes, and incidentally to avoid the expense of waste disposal, has led to a considerable amount of research and in some cases the growth of new industries has resulted. An example was the need to dispose of the chlorine obtained from the production of caustic soda by the electrolysis of brine. Caustic soda is used in large quantities in the manufacture of paper and soap and the chlorine which was produced could not be liberated into the air for obvious reasons. Manufacture of chlorine bleaches and disinfectants on a large scale helped to dispose of the unwanted chlorine. A new method of producing hydrochloric acid by direct combination of chlorine with hydrogen, produced by the same electrolytic process, also helped to solve the problem and at the same time created a new industrial method of making hydrochloric acid. An even more complete example of utilization of waste products occurs in the coal gas industry where virtually all the valuable by-products are utilized.

Sometimes it is necessary to adapt products in order to capture fresh markets. For example, electrical goods such as dynamos and starters sold for marine or tropical uses require special metal finishes, but in some instances the adoption of these finishes on all the products has led to the marketing of new standard models suitable for all markets. Wherever possible, finishes should be standardized to give the least variety in order to allow a greater degree of mechanization in the electro-plating and enamelling processes. Similarly, products should be developed using standardized parts wherever possible.

Another aspect of product research is the drive to investigate new materials so that the best and most economic materials are used and so that substitutes are available when required. In this way, not only is the best use made of materials, but alternative sources of supply are guaranteed so far as possible.

A most important result of successful product development is the improvement in the company's prestige and in its customer relationships. This can be brought about in a number of ways, the most important being the creation of reliable quality standards which are rigidly adhered to. Other factors resulting in customer satisfaction are the maintenance, if necessary, of a good service and spares organisation, study of design trends and customer preferences and the best form of packaging. Packaging may either be protective or decorative or both. The form of the packaging will depend on the product and the customer, and is a point which is deservedly receiving an increasing amount of attention. Good packaging increases customer appeal, simplifies handling, and ensures the safe transit of the product.

Process research and development are concerned with the study of all aspects of the manufacturing process in order to make the product by the most efficient and economic means and to the required standard of quality. They are applied to the improvement of existing methods, to the development of new methods which reduce manufacturing costs, and to the solution of current production problems. Successful process investigations depend largely on ability to keep abreast of the latest technical developments in production and, where possible, to adapt them to the needs of the company. Extensive sources of new ideas are the technical trade press, the publications of the various professional institutions, abstracts published by research bodies such as the Production Engineering Research Association of

B

Great Britain, and technical exhibitions which are held in most of the large cities. If the maximum benefit is to be derived from these sources, it is essential that production executives should have the opportunity of studying technical literature and of visiting exhibitions. The most important trend to combat is that of tackling all problems in accordance with past custom and practice. Although previous experience plays a large part in successful production engineering, some of the most effective changes have been due to a complete departure from current thought trends. Unfortunately, managements are frequently too slow to realize the potentialities of new ideas. For this reason the automatic transfer machine, which made its earliest appearance in the engine factory of Morris Motors Ltd., at Coventry in 1923, was allowed to die a premature death as a result of unresolved teething troubles, only to be revived in the United States some twenty years later.

Frequently it is advantageous to appoint a process engineer to investigate fully a new process or technique. This person will then become an authority in his limited field. Similarly, when launching a new product it is often useful to appoint a product engineer to look after all the production aspects of the work. In this way there is less likelihood of a decision being made which would be to the detriment of the whole product. The success of these appointments depends mainly on the personalities and technical abilities of the people employed. Since they will have considerable contact with others their ability to create enthusiasm and enlist support will have a marked effect on the outcome of their work. Product and process engineers should have access to a workshop suitable for experimental and development work with a demonstration area where new ideas can be perfected before they are launched in the factory. In fact, many of the larger companies make use of a department whose function it is to conduct research into new techniques, and as a result of the work carried out, to develop or adapt machines for new processes. Progress in development work should be recorded periodically in reports to senior production management so that they may assess the potential usefulness of the project and decide whether or not work on it should continue.

It is essential to the perpetuation of the business that the company should at least keep abreast of developments in competitors' products and processes. A knowledge of products can be obtained by stripping the latest marketed designs to see what developments have taken place, but these designs often represent work which entered the pre-production stage up to three years earlier, so a company which relies only on copying as a means of survival would probably not last long. A knowledge of competitors' processes is even more difficult to obtain, since the process will not generally be apparent from examination of the product. This is another strong reason for pursuing an independent well-directed and co-ordinated programme of process research, but it calls for the employment of a team of able technologists, possessing both practical knowledge and intellectual training to assess the research data obtained and apply them to the job under consideration.

ORGANIZATION OF RESEARCH

In Britain the need for co-ordination of the various research bodies such as universities, research associations and the research departments of manufacturing companies has long been realized and a number of government bodies have been created to assist this purpose. Most of these are administered either by the Ministry of Technology or by the Department of Education and Science.

The Ministry of Technology was created in 1964 and its main object is to encourage the use of advanced technology in British industry. In industries which are developing technologically at a fast rate, such as the computer and electronics industries, appraisal teams have been set up to report to the Ministry and the industries concerned. Appraisal teams have also been created to report on instruments, materials technology and engineering standards. The pattern of government support for technology is still changing and it is probable that the organization will change further as the requirements of industry become better known.

The United Kingdom Atomic Energy Authority and the National Research Development Corporation are now both responsible to the Ministry of Technology. The U.K.A.E.A., which originally undertook research and development into the production of atomic energy, now also produces radioactive materials for industrial use, and is working outside the atomic field on such things as water desalination.

To assist research the Ministry of Technology places contracts with industry, research institutions and universities. Applications for financial assistance with research by firms are usually dealt with by the N.R.D.C., and those from universities and technical institutions by the Science Research Council. The S.R.C. is responsible to the Department of Education and Science, and supports and encourages research in science and technology in universities and colleges by making awards for specific projects and by creating studentships for approved post-graduate courses of study. Close co-ordination exists between the Ministry of Technology and the S.R.C. when allocating awards and contracts to teaching establishments.

In addition to its other functions, the Ministry of Technology has taken over the industrial research and development activities of the former Department of Scientific and Industrial Research. This includes responsibility for ten Government research stations and financial support for forty-eight co-operative industrial research associations.

The research stations conduct research into Building, Forest Products, Hydraulics, Fire Prevention, Chemistry, Engineering, Non-Nuclear Physics, Fish Handling and Water Pollution.

Co-operative research associations exist in most of the main industries and are supported jointly by industry and by grants from the Ministry of Technology. Their research programmes are determined by the requirements of member firms, who are notified of the results of research work carried out. The services of an information bureau and frequently of a technical library are at the disposal of members. When it does not interfere with the general research programme, member firms can also ask for research work to be carried out into their own problems, at cost price, and the firms have a right to preferential use of patents resulting from such research. The services of research associations, particularly to small companies who could not afford the luxury of their own research departments, are of great value, as the rapid growth of these bodies has proved.

Research carried out within the company has a number of obvious advantages when the size of the company permits it, particularly to supplement the work of research associations. Close liaison between research and production teams allows the more rapid conversion of research data to development uses, and a more rapid response is possible to the changing needs of the company in achieving short-term objectives. Also, good research men may be retained for the exclusive use of the company, thereby providing improved security. However, research teams need men of wide general experience to lead them, and if these men are not forthcoming, company research is likely to become restrictive and short-sighted.

REQUIREMENTS OF GOOD DESIGN

It is impossible to specify exactly what constitutes a good design, but the essential requirements are that it is functionally sound, that it can be economically produced and that it is aesthetically acceptable.

The first two requirements are concerned with tangible considerations of quality, performance and cost, but the third is a far more intangible concept based on subjective standards. Fashion trends in design are constantly changing, so that a popular design of five years ago is likely to be obsolete by present standards. The outline form of a product is determined by the function it is to perform and by an indeterminate belief on the part of the designer as to what he thinks looks right.

There is a growing tendency to build decoration into the form of the product rather than on to it. The advent of plastics and other new raw materials, calling for new processes and allowing a great variety of colours has accelerated this trend. Ledges have given way to smooth curves, and ugly, angular joints between mating parts which defied the attentions of the duster have become graceful curves of intersection. Incidentally, the new forms have generally proved easier to "tool-up" and to produce and it is certainly easier to apply a smooth enamelled or plated finish to them.

The growing importance of good design in capturing markets emphasizes the need for good styling. If the design proves unpopular, resulting in its withdrawal from production before the completion of the period allowed for the amortization of the tools, a heavy loss may be incurred. There has been a tendency in Britain to adhere to conventional, conservative design forms, largely due to the relatively small domestic markets for most products. The Americans, however, catering for a larger home market, have introduced far more sweeping and frequent design changes. This provides yet another argument for the adoption of standard products in order to make the best of limited markets. The size of the market is no excuse for lagging in design trends: some leading countries in the field of industrial design, such as the Scandinavian states and Italy, have comparatively small domestic markets.

When considering changing fashions we must not overlook certain fixed designs which have become accepted as hallmarks of quality. Probably the best instance of this is the Rolls-Royce radiator which has remained almost unchanged since the beginning of the century. Tactically, it would be a great error to discard this piece of distinctive, out-of-date design which has survived a host of changes to the surrounding bodywork and yet is still regarded as a thing of beauty. It would be a still greater tactical error if any of the popular car manufacturers tried to copy it.

Colour now plays an important part in design since the acceptance of the wider principles of mass-production. Henry Ford's offer to make a Model-T car of any colour provided it was black is now recognized as a relic of a bygone age. Women particularly, are affected by colour, and it is important that an understanding of this colour-consciousness should underly any new product design for the consumer market.

The need for successful contemporary styling has led to the employment by some firms of consultant designers or their own style designers. In the marketing of consumer goods one of the style designer's most important jobs is the design of the packaging. Packaging should be functionally efficient, and its own advertisement. Many articles are now packed in containers having transparent panels, so that the product helps to advertise itself. Increasingly, companies are coming to realise the false economy of the utilitarian brown cardboard carton and are using more imaginative containers.

FUNCTIONAL CONSIDERATIONS

When considering the functional efficiency of a product we must first decide exactly what is required of it. Taking as an example an electrical control panel, it may be necessary that the various controls can be operated from one position, and where adjustments must be made with reference to instruments or meters the controls must be positioned so that the meter can be easily read while the control is being operated. Emergency stops on all equipment must be placed for rapid operation, and if necessary duplicated. The application of ergonomics to these problems can do much to improve functional efficiency.

Another important consideration is accessibility for servicing. It is difficult to achieve accessibility when a "quart is being crammed into a pint pot", a point which will be appreciated by readers who have tried to service many types of post-war cars. However, by skilful design it should be possible to achieve accessibility and obtain good space utilization.

Except in a few examples of non-utilitarian design, most products are expected to withstand a considerable amount of handling during their lifetime, and it is important that they should be sufficiently rugged to withstand all but exceptionally rough handling. In this sense ruggedness does not imply poor aesthetic design, but rather a construction of adequate strength.

The reliability of a product is the measure of its ability to perform consistently throughout its designed life. This requires a study of raw materials to ensure that the best are chosen for the application in mind. When choosing materials designers can be often guided by the properties quoted in various British Standard specifications. These cover a wide range and form a good basis for a scheme of materials standardization within the company concerned. Having selected the best material, it is necessary to select the most satisfactory manufacturing processes and dimensional limits to enable the product to last its designed life. Here again, British Standard specifications can be of wide use. Specifications exist for many of the normal commodities, covering such diverse fields as dustbin design and safety standards for car-seat belts, and adherence to them ensures a certain standard of performance. In engineering manufacture another British Standard (B.S. 1916) covers a very wide range of limits and fits required to produce any desired union between plain cylindrical metal parts. Selection of optimum fits from this specification ensures that serviceable and economic products are designed. Too frequently, lack of production experience makes draughtsmen over-careful in allowing dimensional tolerances and this leads to an unnecessarily high standard of accuracy being demanded, which adds to production costs.

ECONOMIC AND PRODUCTION CONSIDERATIONS
It is normally uneconomic to mass produce components which require selective assembly. Also the maintenance of an efficient spares organization requires a completely inter-changeable product. Occasionally, when parts are made to very fine mating tolerances, selective assembly may be necessary, but such methods should be used only if production economy demands them.

Estimated production requirements are of course a major factor in determining component design. If a small number is to be produced then castings will probably be made from sand moulds, necessitating maximum stock removal from all functional surfaces. When quantity justifies their use, die castings, involving a high initial tool cost, will show a saving, due to the greater speed of casting and the elimination of subsequent machining operations, and a more elegant component generally results.

The use of standardized parts wherever possible can lead to great savings. Although component standardization is generally applied mainly to internal parts, there is a growing evidence of its application to external parts. In the United States some domestic refrigerator manufacturers, realizing that the end dimensions of their products are limited by the size of the smallest doorways, have standardized on the side panels for entire ranges of their models. Many electronic computers are designed as a number of units. In this way the installation may be added to by fitting extra parts which are designed as self-contained sub-assemblies, and if breakdown occurs the faulty section may be replaced by a new unit. Another important form of standardization is in the field of metal finishing. A limited number of finishes, whether plated or enamelled, enables a greater degree of automation to be achieved, and results in economy in the use of materials, and a reduction in the variety of components.

At the design stage, decisions should be made concerning the sources from which components are to be obtained. Generally speaking, standard parts such as nuts, bolts, rivets and washers are cheaper when purchased from specialist suppliers. Other items may require a greater amount of investigation before making a decision. The choice of buying a sintered metal product from a supplier or of making it in the factory will entail the economic consideration of purchasing expensive special-purpose plant and securing the services of a specialist engineer. These comparisons are normally beyond the scope of the average draughtsman and involve managerial decisions.

A well-designed product will be made from the minimum number of parts and must be capable of repetitive production without undue difficulty. Provision should be made for accurate location points on engineering components, so that when the component is clamped in a fixture for machining, it is possible to repeat accurately the dimensions from a given datum face on each component. A product should be designed with a minimum of material to reduce both machining costs and the original material costs.

When designing engineering components ease of manufacture must always be considered. Some factors which simplify machining are avoidance of blind holes, use of drills, where possible, to produce stepped holes, and fool-proofing features to prevent components being loaded wrongly in jigs and fixtures. Component design is an important factor if automatic methods of production are to be successful. A change to assembly by automatic or semi-automatic processes often demands re-design in order to facilitate the correct feeding and assembly of the components.

It is possible to stipulate the various requirements of design, but the methods by which they may be achieved are not always so easily determined. Unfortunately many designers have little aesthetic sense and often lack sound production experience. The first shortcoming can be remedied by employing industrial designers when the shape of the product is likely to affect its sale. The second shortcoming may be overcome to a certain extent by appointing draughtsmen who have served a trade apprenticeship with the company, although if too much reliance is placed on this sort of appointment the designs tend to follow set patterns that reflect their single company experience.

New designs should be given the widest consideration and be carefully steered through the pre-production stages; one method of doing this is by the appointment of a Design Committee. The members of a typical committee would consist of senior representatives of the Research Department, Design Department, Production Engineering Department, Shop Superintendent, Quality Control Department and, possibly, the Production Control Department. The committee meets regularly until the design is successfully in production. If the product is for a specific industrial market, it may be advantageous to invite the customer to send a representative to these meetings.

PROTOTYPES

Prototypes are essential for most mechanical designs if they are to be successfully developed for quantity production. The form taken by prototypes depends on the complexity of the design and its application. Frequently it is useful to make a wooden "mock-up" which helps to ensure that the product will fit into its appointed place without difficult manipulation. Also, the mock-up provides a useful means for positioning controls and instruments and it enables people concerned with selling the product to comment on its suitability and customer appeal.

The first working prototypes to be used for functional testing will probably be made by jobbing methods, drawn covers being turned or milled from a bar or block of solid material and holes being jig-bored instead of drilled in production jigs. Under these conditions it is likely that a considerable amount of modification will occur during manufacture. For this reason, it is usual for the drawings to be detailed on special sheets, having a number of components on each sheet. The final production component numbers are frequently not allocated until a later stage in order to prevent confusion and to save the need for a laborious drawing alteration procedure. These prototypes can be expected to perform approximately in the same way as the production models, but differences in the manufacturing process or processes may affect the performance of some parts. A hand-made part is sometimes better, and at other times worse, than a similar one made by production tools. Similarly, a prototype assembled in a Model Shop or Short Order Department may be tailor-made to give the desired effect, but a production model assembled by comparatively unskilled labour will not receive the same loving care.

The next stage is the manufacture of pre-production prototypes. These are made from production drawings, and some of the parts may be from the production tools if they are available. Essentially, these prototypes are intended as customer samples and for endurance testing. Any snag experienced in manufacture or assembly should be reported so that corrective action is taken at this stage.

Before the product is ready for production release it is necessary that all tools should be tried out under production conditions, and for this reason it is usual to make a number of production samples. These samples are made by the shops, frequently during overtime working in order that normal production will not suffer.

PATENTS AND REGISTERED DESIGNS

Generally, an invention may be patented for a period of sixteen years, during which time the inventor enjoys monopoly rights to make or license the manufacture of products whose function depends on the invention. It is essential that the subject of a patent should be an original invention which has a practical application. In fact, one of the conditions of granting a patent is that it shall be commercially applied without undue delay. Other conditions attached are intended to prevent suppression of the patent or undue restriction of production.

Although the effective life of a patent is limited to sixteen years it is frequently possible to increase it considerably by patenting refinements or improvements to the original patent.

A design may be registered for a specified period to give protection in a similar way, but a registered design relies on its novelty of form and not on any utilitarian property.

Trade marks are intended as an indication of the source of an article, and anyone using another company's trade mark is liable to an action at Common Law. New trade marks may be registered, and the person registering them has a prior title over others wishing to use the mark; however such title only comes through use. The mark may be in the form of a word, signature, initials or a symbol, but the words used must not describe a characteristic or property which may be possessed by any goods in the same class. Hence an electric lamp manufacturer would not be allowed to register the word "Bright" as a trade mark.

DRAWINGS AND SPECIFICATIONS

Many companies in the past allowed a large range of drawing sizes to be used, which made the problems of storage, filing and reproduction unnecessarily complicated. Since drawing paper, sensitized paper and tracing cloth are all sold in standard 30 in. or 40 in. widths, it is reasonable that standard forms based on these overall dimensions, or simple fractions of them, will give the maximum economy in paper, labour and processing time. In fact, most firms have now standardized on these sizes and all component drawings are usually reproduced on about four standard paper sizes.

Much of the information contained on a drawing is repetitive; for instance the component number, title block, projection and scale will appear on each drawing in the same position. This information may be pre-printed on tracing paper or cloth, thereby showing a considerable saving in draughting time and ensuring uniformity. A British Standard, (B.S. 308:1964, Engineering Drawing Practice) deals at length with standard drawing sizes and with recommended drawing conventions. Most of the conventions recommended are now in general use, and as a result the interpretation of drawings from other firms is facilitated.

The practice of most firms when allocating component numbers ensures that no modified part shall have the same number unless it is interchangeable with the original part. Some companies produce drawings with more than one component on a sheet where the parts are basically similar, differentiating between each by the addition of a suffix letter or number. This system has some points to commend it, but most companies now show each part on a separate sheet, particularly where an overall classification system is in use. General arrangement drawings usually indicate every component by a number or symbol and contain a block which gives the part number of each symbol with its description and the number of such parts used on the assembly. In some jobbing factories this block on the general arrangement drawing is used as a parts list, and no separate parts list is then issued.

Tool drawings consist of a number of parts for use on a particular assembled tool. It is usual, since these drawings are not for production use, to show several parts on the same sheet, so that even a complicated tool can usually be detailed on three or four sheets. The use of standard parts on tools such as drill bushes will reduce draughting time and toolmaking costs.

Two documents originating in the Drawing Office as a result of a new product being released are the Parts List and the Material Register. As has been previously mentioned the detail block on a general arrangement drawing can be used as a parts list, but in batch

| Product   Sheet 1 of 3 | | PARTS   LIST | Alterations   date alt.note | | |
| AB Control Bd. Types A to I | | | date alt.note 15/7/62   6421 | | |

	drg. no.	description	ABA	ABB	ABC	ABD	ABE	ABF	ABG	ABH	ABI		
			product and number off										○
1	2643220	cover	1	1	1	1	1	1	1	1	1	1	
2	2643224	base	1	1	1	1	1	1	1	1	2		
3	2643225	insulator	1	1	1	1	1	1	1	-	-	3	
4	2643228	terminal	3	3	2	2	2	5	5	5	5	4	
5	2643230	ass. regulator	1	1	1	-	-	1	-	-	-	5	
6	2643231	capacitor	1	1	1	-	-	1	-	-	-	6	
7	2643232	terminal	2	2	3	2	2	-	-	-	-	7	
8	2643235	ass. cutout	1	1	-	-	-	1	1	1	1	8	
9	2643238	resistance	1	1	-	-	-	1	1	1	1	9	
10	2643239	connector	2	2	2	2	2	2	2	2	2	10	
11	2643242	lead	3	3	3	3	3	3	-	-	-	11	○
12	2643245	connector	2	2	2	2	2	2	5	5	5	12	
13	2643248	ass. switch	1	-	-	-	1	1	1	-	-	13	form561

FIG. 2.1 *Parts List Showing how Quick Comparison may be made between Similar Models.*

or flow production factories this method is unwieldy, particularly when there is a variety of similar models in use, and the information required is frequently the points of difference between types rather than a complete list of parts. A parts list suitable for a batch production factory is shown in fig. 2.1.

The material register is a list of components in part number order, specifying the material used and the weight of material per part or per hundred parts. A typical sheet from a material register is shown in fig. 2.2 Where a punched-card installation is used, the material register may be kept in card form, in which case alterations only involve replacing individual cards. A complete register may be obtained by simply passing the cards through a tabulating machine

MATERIAL REGISTER for components Nos. 2386535 to 2386554					
	Drawing number	description	material	wt/100 (lb)	
1	2386535	cover	casting 2386536	-	1
2	2386536	casting	mechanite (B.O.)	-	2
3	2386537	sub-assembly	-		3
4	2386538	spindle	3/16" dia. E N I	2·4	4
5	2386539	plate	copper strip 1x¼"	3·5	5
6	2386540	body	casting 2386541	-	6
7	2386541	casting	mechanite (B.O.)	-	7
8	2386542	screw	B O C	-	8
9	2386543	washer	B O C	-	9
10	2386544	collar	⅜" dia. E N 8	4·2	10
11	2386545	sub-assembly	-	-	11
12	2386546	terminal	¼" sq. brass rod	2·8	12
13	2386547	connector	¾x3/32" brass	2·2	13
14	2386548	inspection c.	casting 2386549	-	14
15	2386549	casting	D T D 424	-	15
16	2386550	rivet	B O C	-	16
17	2386551	lamination	0·018 losil sheet	5·6	17
18	2386552	bakelite base	B O C moulding	-	18
19	2386553				19
20	2386554				20
			form 600 date 2.4.62		

FIG. 2.2 *Typical Sheet from a Material Register.*

and printing the punched information on a tabulation sheet. The cards may also be used as a master pack for producing a material schedule from component requirements as described in Chapter 17.

It is usual for both parts lists and material registers, when not kept on punched cards, to be issued in loose-leaf form so that additions or alterations affect one sheet only, which can be removed and replaced by a revised sheet. To facilitate easy reproduction, these documents are frequently typed on pre-printed tracing linen, so that they may be produced in any quantity required by a photo-printing process.

Factory Sites and Buildings

LOCATION OF THE FACTORY

There are many factors which influence the choice of location for a
new factory. Some of the more important of these factors are discussed in the following paragraphs.

1. SOURCES OF RAW MATERIAL

The nearness of the site to raw materials is a major consideration in
industries where the materials are bulky and of relatively low value.
This is the reason for blast furnaces being sited near either coalfields
or deposits of iron ore. It is also responsible for cement works being
situated alongside chalk hills and for some breweries being built
near to supplies of suitable water, thus ensuring that in each case
the bulkiest raw material has not far to travel.

2. LABOUR

In times of full employment adequate supplies of labour may not
be available in certain areas for large-scale development. It may
therefore be advisable to choose a site in an area where traditional
industries are declining, and releasing supplies of labour. The attitude
of workers to modern management techniques is another factor
which may affect the location chosen. There has been at least one
case of a manufacturer losing interest in building in a particular area
and stating the reason was that, in preliminary negotiations with
organized labour, there had been difficulties over the acceptance of
stop-watch work measurement. Fortunately this reactionary attitude
on the part of labour is becoming an exception in most industries.

3. SOURCES OF POWER

With electricity the chief source of industrial power the siting of
factories near to coalfields is now unimportant. Electricity at virtually
a standard price can be obtained almost anywhere in the country.
There are, however, some industries which consume exceptionally
large amounts of power and in these cases the proximity to sources of
cheap power is of paramount importance. The production of
aluminium in this country is negligible compared with its consump-

tion, due to the lack of really cheap electricity which is required for the electrolytic extraction of aluminium from its ore. So important is low-cost electricity to the economical production of aluminium (to win 1 lb of aluminium requires 12 units of electricity) that the town of Kitimat was built in a remote part of British Columbia specifically to produce aluminium near to ample and cheap supplies of hydro-electric power.

4. PROXIMITY TO MARKETS

Nearness to markets is an important factor which considerably reduces costs and it has become of increasing importance now that many technical factors can be satisfied by a wide variety of locations. This factor was one of the main reasons why industry expanded so quickly in and around London in the 1920s and 30s. It also explains the proximity to Birmingham and Coventry of motor accessory and component manufacturing companies. Not only can they economically supply the nearby car assembly plants but liaison between customer and supplier becomes simpler.

5. GOVERNMENT POLICY

The government exercise considerable control over where factories can be built. In the Distribution of Industry Act (1945/48), the Board of Trade was given control over the location of new factory buildings. An Industrial Development Certificate must be obtained before a new factory can be erected or an extension of over 5,000 square feet made to an existing factory. By this means it was possible to discourage the further industrialization of London and certain areas in the Midlands. Financial and other inducements were offered to companies who built factories in less prosperous parts of the country known as Development Areas. The Local Employment Act (1960) has abolished Development Areas, but gives the Board of Trade considerable powers to bring new industries to areas where unemployment is, or is likely to be, persistently high. If a change is required in the use of an existing factory the new Act requires that an Industrial Development Certificate must be obtained.

6. COST OF LAND

The cost of land varies greatly, depending on its location. Rural sites are cheaper than urban ones and land is normally cheaper in the less prosperous or less popular areas of the country. High cost of land may force the building of a multi-storey factory instead of a single storey one; it may also result in inadequate space being provided for expansion or for car parking. The provision of adequate car parks should always be considered when new factories are being planned now that an increasing proportion of workers own cars.

7. EXPANSION ON EXISTING SITE

If horizontal expansion on the existing site is contemplated sufficient land must be purchased to allow for the estimated ultimate size of the building. There are cost-saving advantages to be gained by expanding on an existing site, particularly with small and medium-sized factories. Against these factors must be weighed the cost of extra land which may never be used. Should surplus land be obtained it could be laid out as sports fields, gardens or car parks until required, though there may be difficulties in withdrawing these amenities at a later date.

8. SITE SURVEY

Once the general location of the factory has been decided and the prospective site chosen, it should be surveyed. A sloping site will prove more costly to build on and may result in a split-level factory. The possibility of flooding is obviously undesirable, as is the risk of subsidence, which occurs in certain mining areas. If large amounts of water are going to be used, as in the case of electroplating, the likelihood of successfully sinking an artesian well may be an advantage. The advertisement value of the site is worth consideration; to build a factory adjacent to a main road or railway line is an inexpensive way of keeping the company's name before the public. These and many other factors concerning the suitability of the prospective site will have to be considered relative to the price of the land before a final decision is made. Vacated factories can sometimes be acquired cheaply but their adaptation may prove expensive.

DESIGN AND CONSTRUCTION OF THE FACTORY BUILDING

This is the specialized field of the architect and civil engineer and cannot be dealt with adequately in this book. To produce a satisfactory design the architect must have from his client a clear analysis of what is required of the factory, as well as some idea of the amount of money to be spent. A high degree of co-operation between the architect and the company's engineers will be required. Four walls and a roof over a given floor area may at one time have been satisfactory, but today, particularly in more specialized forms of industry, the building is closely integrated with the manufacturing process. This integration must, however, be carefully considered for if the factory building is too tailor-made it will lack flexibility for expansion and product changes.

SINGLE AND MULTI-STOREY BUILDINGS

A decision on this point will have to be taken at an early stage, probably before the site is purchased. Single-storey buildings have the following advantages:

1. There is greater flexibility so far as plant layout and re-organization is concerned. It is easier to plan the position of plant and equipment in one large area than in a number of small ones.

2. Expansion can be achieved more simply provided site area is available. If space for horizontal expansion is not available, the building might be converted into a multi-storey one, although this may involve expensive structural alterations.

3. Natural light and ventilation can be supplied through the roof.

4. Materials handling costs are lower, as floor to floor moves involving lifts and conveyors are not required.

5. Heavy equipment can be situated anywhere in the factory. In multi-storey factories heavy equipment often cannot be situated on upper floors due to their restricted loading. Adequate floor loadings can be provided for upper floors of multi-storey buildings but will result in more pillars and additional building costs.

6. The risk of serious fire damage is less.

7. Vibration from other machinery is less liable to affect adversely accurate machining operations such as precision grinding.

8. Building costs are less compared with a multi-storey factory of the same gross area.

The advantages of multi-storey buildings can be summarized as follows:

(*a*) Lower site cost for a given manufacturing area.

(*b*) Less heat loss from the building; the losses through the ceilings heat the floors above and result in reduced heating costs.

(*c*) The arrangement is more compact. One British company using a large single-storey factory has found it necessary to provide electric vehicles to transport executives within the building.

(*d*) Cleaner air and better light may be available on the higher floors in some locations.

In most cases the advantages are with single-storey buildings, although they are often constructed with mezzanine floors. By using mezzanine floors works offices, stores and auxiliary equipment, such as transformers, can be taken out of the production area.

FLOOR AREA REQUIRED

A firm figure of the amount of production area needed with associated offices and stores will be required. This will have to be based on the expected production rate. The conversion of sales estimates into floor area will either be by a management estimate derived from experience, or by calculation; in some cases a combination of both methods will be used.

The calculation converts the sales estimate into production equipment hours, which, in turn, is converted into the number of pieces of plant required. The plant is then laid out using scale models or templates and from this layout the floor area is obtained. The machine requirement calculation is dealt with in detail under Machine Loading in Chapter 16, and the use of scale plans in Chapter 4.

The size of the production area required is almost inversely proportional to the number of hours worked per day. A given floor area can produce almost twice as much with a double shift as with a single shift.

EXPANSION

Although some policy of expansion will probably have been determined before the site was selected, estimates of the rate of expansion will be desirable, as well as some idea of how each section will be affected by expansion. For instance, it may be possible to cope with production increases on some sections by introducing a night-shift but on light assembly work employing women, work after 10 p.m. is not legally permitted in the U.K. Therefore if there is to be no assembly nightwork additional space for expansion will be required on the assembly section.

The modern tendency is to house all processes under the same roof, and expansion is normally catered for in single-storey buildings by expanding either the length or breadth of the building. For this purpose walls which can be cheaply removed should be built in areas where expansion is likely to occur. Where processes are housed in separate buildings, certain plan shapes have become popular due to their ease of extension. Some of those often used are in the form of the letters E, H, L and U. An indication of their use is shown in fig 3.1.

Expansion can be provided in a single-storey building by use of a mezzanine floor for light production operations and services. Mezzanine floors can also be built in multi-storey buildings, although in most cases this will not be possible due to insufficient ceiling height. In multi-storey factories additional floors can be added to allow for

C

expansion, provided the foundations and lower structure of the building are adequate.

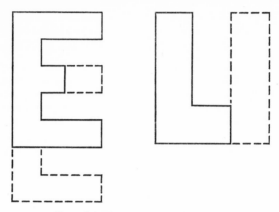

F IG. 3.1 *Extensions to Factories.*
Original Building in Full Lines. Possible Extensions
Dotted.

FLEXIBILITY

Factories are built to last for a long time and people who work in some of our older factories may feel that they have lasted far too long. But whether the factory exists for 50, 100 or even 200 years, it will probably outlive the original product design many times over and may possibly be used to manufacture a wide range of products. For instance, many old cotton mills are now being used for light engineering. If the best use is to be made of factory buildings they must be designed for flexibility, which is assisted by the following factors:

1. *Unobstructed Floor Area.* A large floor area unobstructed by pillars will provide maximum planning freedom. Spans of 60 ft are quite common in the United States and are being called for in the United Kingdom; the stronger roof trusses required for wide spans do, however, add considerably to the cost. Optimum economical spans in single-storey factories are about 30 ft, and about 20 ft in multi-storey buildings.

2. *Adequate Roof Height.* Unless 18 ft clearance is allowed below the lowest part of the roof truss mezzanine floors cannot be built to facilitate future expansion and change. More than 18 ft will be necessary if overhead conveyors are also required and clear heights of up to 36 ft are being provided in some factories.

3. *Electrical Connexions.* The use of individual motor drives for machines has greatly added to the flexibility of their siting. This flexibility can be increased if power and lighting supplies are near to hand throughout the whole production area. By using an overhead grid it is possible conveniently to take off electrical supplies near to the equipment and leave the floor unencumbered by electrical distribution points and conduit.

4. *Movable Machines.* It is desirable that production equipment can be moved easily when layout changes are required. Floor loadings should be sufficient to take the equipment likely to be moved into the area. The bolting of machines to the floor with its attendant lack of mobility can be overcome in many cases by positioning machines on rubber friction mats. The weight of the machine and the coefficient of friction of the rubber prevents the machine from "walking".

5. *Materials Handling.* Ceiling heights below 12 ft to 14 ft do not allow sufficient clearance if overhead conveyors are to be fitted. Roof trusses must be strong enough to take the additional load of any overhead conveyors attached to them. High capacity lifts in multistorey buildings will be required if fork-lift trucks are to operate on upper floors. The floor loadings of the upper storeys will also have to be designed to take the additional weight of these vehicles. For normal stacking of palletized loads a roof height of 18 ft will be required.

ENCLOSURE OF THE FACTORY

The ideal roof and walls with which to enclose a factory will admit light but exclude bright sunshine, will minimize heat lost in winter yet keep the building cool during summer. They must also be sound-absorbing, relatively inexpensive, durable and attractive in appearance. It will be seen that some of these conditions conflict with each other; glass is required to admit light but is a source of considerable heat loss. The excessive use of glass results in high heating costs and may involve the provision of sunblinds or some other means of reducing heat and glare. Heat loss through glass can be reduced by double glazing but only at additional cost. The admission of bright sunlight can be avoided by north light construction. In this type of roof the "saw tooth" ridges run from east to west, and the roof sections facing north have glass panels let into them, thus minimizing direct sunlight entering the building through the roof. In countries where there are extremes of temperature, factories without roof lights or windows are being constructed. A completely enclosed building enables an accurate control to be maintained over lighting, heating and ventilation. Lighting has at all times to be provided artificially but this additional cost can be off-set against reduced fuel bills resulting from lower heat losses.

Noise can be minimized by using acoustic tiles over conventional walling, although composite walling material, which is lined with sound-absorbing material is available. Particularly noisy operations can be isolated from the rest of the factory, for instance heavy blanking presses can have sound-proof enclosures built round them. Apart from keeping the noise level down in the factory too much noise should not be allowed to escape. This is particularly important where there is a night-shift working and the factory is in a residential area.

FIRE PROTECTION

Fire risk can be reduced if the building is constructed from fire-proof materials. A fire-resisting construction will not, however, prevent serious fire damage if combustible material is stored. Any large stocks of inflammable material should be isolated from the rest of the factory by fire-proof partitions; this partitioning of areas of greatest fire risk makes factory layout less flexible. A particularly serious fire hazard exists when paints and varnishes are held in elevated tanks through which dipping conveyors pass. The provision of automatic sprinkler systems, fire alarms and hydrants can do much to minimize fire damage. The relevant parts of the Factories Acts will have to be complied with, although these regulations are aimed chiefly at ensuring the safety of workers by providing them with adequate means of escape.

LIGHTING REQUIREMENTS

Good lighting is essential in factories as it reduces accidents, increases output, improves quality and creates better morale. The Factories Acts and Regulations do prescribe minimum standards of illumination for certain parts of the factory, but these are considerably lower than are provided in good current practice. The unit which is used to measure the intensity of illumination is the lumen, 1 lumen/ft^2 being equal to 1 foot candle. The intensity of illumination from a single lamp decreases according to the inverse square law. The table below indicates recommended standards of illumination:

Type of Work	Illumination
Rough	15 lumen/ft^2
Normal	30 lumen/ft^2
Fine	70 lumen/ft^2

Very fine   100 lumen/ft^2

Minute   200 lumen/ft^2

It is desirable that higher levels of illumination are provided for older operators or those with defective vision; rapidly moving parts also require higher illumination. Illumination is measured by a light-meter which is a direct-reading instrument placed at the working surface with the operator in position. By taking the reading in this way it is possible to take into account any shadows cast by the operator.

NATURAL LIGHTING

The intensity of natural lighting varies with the time of day, time of year and weather conditions. It also varies with the size and position of windows; with low sills the intensity of illumination falls off rapidly as the distance from the windows increases; shallow windows

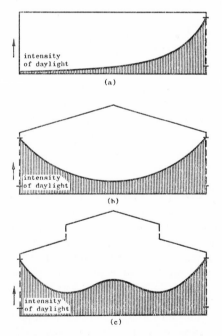

FIG. 3.2 *Variation in Natural Illumination with Window Position.*
(*a*) *room with window at one side,* (*b*) *windows at each side of building,* (*c*) *monitor construction* (*windows at each side and in roof.*)

with high sills although admitting less light provide a more uniform distribution of light as well as minimizing the loss of artificial light.

It will be seen in fig. 3.2 that the intensity of natural light varies considerably with the type of building. In *A* and *B*, where there is no admission of light through the roof, the level of illumination decreases sharply in areas remote from the windows. With monitor construction, as in *C*, the level of illumination does not fall so seriously at the centre of the building due to the supplementary light supplied through the roof. If a north light construction is used, the amount of illumination from natural light is almost uniform throughout the factory.

DESIGN OF LIGHTING SYSTEMS

Once the general levels of illumination have been decided upon for the various parts of the factory, a satisfactory system of artificial lighting to meet these standards will have to be devised. It is important that the artificial lighting system should be designed to supplement natural light. For instance, if parts of the factory are receiving daylight from a side window only, the artificial lighting should be wired so that the switches control groups of lamps parallel to the window. This permits lights which only serve areas away from the window to be switched on during the day.

Where processes are similar and no high visual demands are made, a general overhead system will be satisfactory, the fittings being spaced symmetrically near to the roof and giving a uniform illumination in the working area. A variant of this system is where the fittings are placed so that, although arranged reasonably symmetrically, they provide light to the workplace in the best direction. An example of this type of lighting is in a Drawing Office, where the fittings are placed to the left front of each board position, thus minimizing the effect of shadows cast by the draughtsmen. If a high level of illumination is needed, this can be economically provided by localizing the lighting fittings a few feet above the working area and having symmetrically arranged fittings near to the roof to provide background illumination. Local lighting over a very small area can be supplied by a single fitting used close to the work; this type of lighting is often supplied on machine tools. If local lighting is to be used safely and without strain, the background lighting should provide at least 6 lumens/ft^2 or the square root of the local illumination, whichever is the greater.

LIGHT SOURCES

1. *Tubular Fluorescent.* These are in common use in factories and

offices. Due to their low surface brightness they can be viewed directly, although as far as possible this should be avoided. A wide range of colours is available; some of them give accurate colour rendering and are valuable in supplementing natural light. They have a high efficiency, the current consumption being about one-third of that of tungsten filament bulbs of the same light output. The stroboscopic effect, which sometimes occurs when looking at rotating machinery, can be avoided by having two or three tubes mounted together but fed with supplies out of phase with each other. The low surface brightness of fluorescent lamps makes them suitable for applications where polished surfaces are being viewed, as highlights are avoided.

2. *Mercury Vapour.* These lamps have a high brightness, giving a greenish blue light and providing an economical method of lighting. They are often found in large buildings such as hangars and heavy machine shops, as well as in exterior factory lighting. Due to their high brightness they should be mounted high above the working surface.

3. *Tungsten Filament.* This source has been partly replaced by fluorescent lamps. Tungsten filament lamps are, however, inexpensive to purchase and install and are obtainable in a wider range of wattages than other types of lamp. Due to their warm yellow light, tungsten filament lamps are useful for blending with mercury lamps to give a warmer appearance. They are also used for local lighting, where they must be shielded to eliminate glare.

REFLECTORS

A very large variety of reflectors is available. They produce lighting broadly classified as direct, diffuse or indirect. Direct lighting systems are those normally used in factories because they concentrate a high percentage of the light on to the working area. If direct reflectors are mounted just above the working area, there should be either sufficient spillage of light from them to illuminate the upper walls and ceiling or a supplementary general overhead lighting system to avoid producing a tunnel-like effect resulting from the upper part of the factory being darkened. If fluorescent lamps are mounted near to the working surface in direct-type reflectors, shadow can be reduced if alternate reflectors are arranged with their axes at right angles. With diffuse lighting the reflectors do not control the light directionally and a large proportion of the light reaches the working area after having been reflected from walls and ceiling. It is a pleasant but less efficient method of lighting that gives softer shadows and is often found in offices and showrooms. In indirect lighting almost all the light reaches the working area by reflection, and it is little used industrially.

Apart from being satisfactory from an illumination standpoint lighting fittings should be robust and easily cleaned. If reflectors are not regularly cleaned, particularly in dusty or dirty locations, there will be appreciable reductions in illumination.

USE OF COLOUR AND CONTRAST

Appropriate colours, both of light source and for interior decoration, should be chosen to suit the processes and materials worked on; by producing satisfying and pleasing working conditions they help to improve morale and reduce fatigue. Light sources which emit a large amount of blue light are unsuitable when red materials are worked on, as under this light they appear black. For cool situations warm colours should be used for wall and ceiling decoration but if the process is one where heat is generated cool colours are more suitable. Walls should reflect not less than 60 per cent of the light reaching them; ceilings, particularly when they are low, should have a higher reflective factor. The once popular white-washed walls reflect light too readily and bright sunlight falling on them produces glare and eye-strain.

The use of contrast can greatly assist definition. An object viewed against a background of contrasting brightness can be more easily seen, and artificial light-coloured backgrounds are sometimes created in inspection departments so that parts can be viewed in silhouette. If work is carried out against a light background, as in Drawing Offices, the level of illumination must be adjusted to a lower value, about 30 lumens/ft², to avoid glare. Although bright highlights are undesirable when viewing polished surfaces, they can be an advantage when objects have to be distinguished by their form. For instance, the brighter highlights and deeper shadows produced by a bright light source are of great assistance in distinguishing between pieces of printing type and in examining fabrics.

LIGHT SOURCE CALCULATIONS

The following example shows how the number of light sources required for a specified level of illumination can be calculated. In addition to knowing the average light output of the lamps, the co-efficient of utilization, the maintenance factor and possibly the absorption factor will have to be known. The coefficient of utilization is the proportion of the light produced from new lamps and fittings which reaches the working surface. Initial illumination will be reduced after a time by dust and dirt which affects the reflecting power of walls and reflectors; this is taken into account by the maintenance factor. The reduction in light output of the lamps due to ageing is not allowed for in this factor as the average light output of the lamps is used. Where there is smoke and steam in the atmosphere, as in foundries and steel works, the light from overhead fittings will be partly absorbed before reaching the working level. In some instances, with high mounted fittings, the absorption factor can be as great as 0·5.

Example. A section of a factory measuring 30 ft by 15 ft requires 25 lumens/ft² at working height from 80-watt tubular fluorescent lamps giving an average light output of 3,200 lumens each. Coefficient of utilization is 0·5 and maintenance factor 0·8.

$$\text{Total lumens required} \quad \frac{25 \times (30 \times 15)}{0\cdot5 \times 0\cdot8} = 28,125 \text{ lumens.}$$

$$\text{No. of lamps required} = \frac{28,125}{3,200} = 8\cdot8 \text{ (say 9).}$$

The lamps must be arranged symmetrically to cover the required area. An arrangement which will be satisfactory is to have three rows of tubes placed longitudinally with three tubes in each row.

HEATING REQUIREMENTS

Increased attention is being paid to factory heating and the day of the slow combustion stoves, when those working nearest to the stoves almost roasted and those farthest away shivered, is almost over. The Factories Acts require that in every workroom where a substantial amount of the work is done sitting and does not involve serious physical effort, a temperature of at least 60°F must be maintained after the first hour. There is a great variety of heating systems but basically they consist of three components, the heat source, the distribution system and the heat disseminator.

HEAT SOURCES

The main fuels used in the United Kingdom are coal, oil, gas and electricity. It is difficult to provide cost comparisons which are likely to be valid for more than a short while due to variations in the production costs of the fuels and to the variable rate of discriminatory tax imposed on oil. However, assuming coal at £7 per ton, oil at 15*d* per gallon, gas at 20*d* per therm and electricity at 1½*d* per kilowatt hour and the usual heat conversion efficiencies, oil is about 20 per cent more expensive than coal as a source of heat, gas is twice as expensive and electricity costs over four times as much. Apart from the fuel cost per Btu of heat produced the convenience and flexibility of the heat source has to be taken into account. Although electricity is the most adaptable fuel its high cost rules it out as a major source of factory heating. Efforts are, however, being made to improve methods of heat storage and so increase the use of cheap rate "off peak" electricity for industrial heating. Due to its relatively low cost, easy handling and economy of boiler-house labour, oil has become the principal industrial fuel; it is, however, likely to be displaced by natural gas when supplies become available from the North Sea fields.

DISTRIBUTIVE SYSTEMS

Usually with coal and oil, and to a smaller extent with gas and electricity, the fuel is burnt centrally and the heat obtained transmitted to the various parts of the factory. The method of transmission is usually by pipes containing hot water, steam or heated air, and the main systems are reviewed below.

1. *High-Pressure Hot Water.* This is a flexible system which has a high thermal efficiency. The water pressures used are up to 200 lbf/in^2 and at this pressure the boiling point of water is increased to 388°F. The hot water is pumped through closed pipe circuits to the space heaters. Traps, strainers and condensate returns are not needed and the levels of the mains are not so critical as with steam. The system is flexible, being able to satisfy quickly changes in heating demand. Fuel economies of up to 20 per cent can be obtained with high-pressure hot water as compared with similar steam installations.

2. *Low-Pressure Hot Water.* This system is widely used in offices and canteens where there is a relatively high occupancy and the rooms are smaller. The temperatures are up to 190°F and the circulation is by convection or pump.

3. *Steam.* This method of heating is often used where steam is also required for the factory processes, these processes determining the steam pressure used.

4. *Plenum Heating.* This provides a combination of heating and ventilation which is particularly suitable for multi-storey buildings. The heated air, 20° to 60°F above room temperature is circulated by means of a fan through large roof-mounted ducts which have outlets for the warm air throughout the building. In multi-storey offices, when space is at a high premium, duct sizes can be reduced by transmitting air at speeds of up to 6,000 ft/min.

HEAT DISSEMINATORS

1. *Unit Heaters.* These are a very adaptable method of heat dissemination and can be used to warm either fresh or recirculated air. The heaters are compact and normally mounted at least 8 ft from ground level. Behind the radiator is usually an electrically operated fan which directs the heated air into the working area.

2. *Radiators.* These are usually used with low-pressure hot-water systems and, due to the lower temperatures at which they operate, can be mounted at floor level. Most of the heat given out by a radiator is by convection and only about 20 per cent is emitted by radiation. Valves fitted on each radiator enable its heat output to be adjusted.

3. *Radiant Heaters.* There are two main types of radiant heating. In one, panels and strips are mounted in or near to the walls and ceiling, and in the other, pipes or heating elements are embedded in the walls, ceiling or floor. The first type is of greater industrial use and provides comfortable heat without a high air temperature. Radiant heating is an effective method of heating small working areas in large unheated spaces such as stores. The heat is radiated from metal panels which have either pipes or heating elements running through them; when radiation is required from one side only, the other side of the panel is lagged to minimize heat loss.

Floors can be heated by low-pressure hot-water pipes or electric heating elements embedded in them. Although floor heating is useful in certain situations such as aircraft hangars, where doors are frequently open, it is difficult to put enough heat into floors for adequate comfort in cold weather without foot fatigue.

LAGGING OF BUILDINGS

Heat losses take place through walls, roof and ceiling as well as by ventilation. Unlined corrugated asbestos or iron may have been cheap materials to use in building factories but they are notoriously bad heat insulators. The cost of lagging them, however, can usually be recovered in a few years by reduced fuel bills.

The following list indicates typical coefficients of heat transfer of some of the commonly-used factory construction materials, and, in certain cases, the effect of lagging. The coefficient indicates the quantity of heat lost per square foot per hour for each degree of temperature difference.

	Btu/ft²h deg F
Corrugated iron roofing	1·50
3 in. flat Concrete roof (plastered)	0·65

3 in. flat Concrete roof (insulated 1 in. cork and plastered)   0·20
Glass window   1·00
Double glazing   0·45
3 in. plain brick wall   0·45
9 in. plain brick wall (insulated 1 in. cork and plastered)   0·15

HEAT INPUT TO MAINTAIN TEMPERATURE

The following simplified example shows how heat input to a building to maintain a constant temperature can be determined.

Example. How many Btu are required each hour to maintain the temperature at 60°F when the outside temperature is 30°F? There are three changes of air per hour. Specific heat of air is taken as 0·019 Btu/ft³.

The building details are as follows:
Length, 120 ft; Width, 60 ft; Ceiling height, 10 ft; Window area, 1,600 ft².

Coefficients of heat transfer, Btu/ft²h deg F

Walls	0·55
Floor	0·40
Ceiling	0·30
Glass	1·0

Total wall area = $(2 \times 60 \times 10) + (2 \times 120 \times 10) =$ 3,600 ft²
Wall area (less windows) = $3,600 - 1,600$ = 2,000 ft²
Ceiling and floor areas = 120×60 = 7,200 ft²
Volume of building = $120 \times 60 \times 10$ = 72,000 ft³
Temperature difference = $60 - 30 = 30°F$
Heat loss to walls (less windows) = $2,000 \times 0.55 \times 30 = 33,000$ Btu/h
Heat loss to windows = $1,600 \times 1.0 \times 30$ = 48,000 Btu/h

Heat loss to floor = $7,200 \times 0.40 \times \dfrac{30}{2}$ = 43,200 Btu/h

Heat loss to ceiling = $7,200 \times 0.30 \times 30$ = 64,800 Btu/h
Heat loss by ventilation = $72,000 \times 3 \times 30 \times 0.019$ = 123,120 Btu/h
                                                               ─────────
Total heat loss per hour   = 312,120 Btu/h

It will be seen that, with the exception of the floor, the heat loss was calculated by multiplying the area involved by its coefficient of heat transmission and by the difference between inside and outside temperature. In the case of the floor, which is sheltered from the outside air, a temperature drop of only half that between inside and outside atmosphere was assumed.

AUTOMATIC CONTROL OF HEATING

Factory heating systems in the United Kingdom are usually designed to deal with a minimum temperature of 30°F. The average winter temperature is, however, some 10° to 15°F more than this minimum. The system therefore is not required to operate at full load except for short periods. The most economical use of fuel will be achieved if only sufficient is burnt to maintain the temperature of the factory at 60°F. The best way to achieve this result is by the use of automatic control.

VENTILATION

The Factories Acts prescribe that at least 400 ft³ of space shall be provided for each worker in the work room, with space above 14 feet from floor level not taken into account. If air is not changed it will become tainted with smells, and the concentration of carbon dioxide, the humidity and the temperature will rise. Ventilation must provide an adequate replenishment of fresh air. The number of air changes per hour for factories, other than those producing harmful dust or fumes, is usually between one to four. When dust and impurities injurious to the health are present in the air the workers must be protected. Often this is achieved by providing a powerful exhaust near to the source of the contamination.

An important function of heating and ventilation is to control and balance the loss of heat from the body; in summer the rate of heat loss should be increased, in winter it should be slowed down. By increasing the speed of air movement and reducing its temperature, heat loss by convection and evaporation can be increased. Low humidity also helps to increase heat loss by evaporation. Inadequate ventilation results in discomfort and fatigue, too much ventilation adds considerably to heating costs.

METHODS OF VENTILATION

There are two methods of ventilation, natural and mechanical. Natural ventilation relies on wind forces and the difference between indoor and outdoor temperatures. Although natural ventilation requires only windows or roof ventilators, it is difficult to control accurately and works best in winter when the difference between inside and outside temperature is greatest. Natural ventilation is often a source of draughts and excessive heat loss. Mechanical ventilation employs fans to change the air. One type uses extraction fans, fresh air finding its way into the building by means of doors and windows. Another method of ventilation is to draw fresh air into the factory by fans, allowing the stale air to escape naturally. A third method uses fans both to supply and extract air. To avoid draughts in winter the fresh air supplied to the factory should be tempered by some form of heating. It is interesting to note that temperature has a considerable effect on whether or not air movement is felt; at 54°F currents of air moving at 30 ft/min can be noticed, whereas at 86°F air movements of 120 ft/min are not noticeable. Apart from taking the chill off cold air, ventilation systems can be adapted to filter the air if required. There are two main types of filter, the renewable sort made of cotton-wool or glass-silk elements and the cleanable type. A particularly efficient system of air cleaning is electrostatic precipitation; here the air is passed through an intense electrostatic field and the dust particles in the air are attracted to earthed plates from which they are subsequently removed. Due to the high cost of the apparatus required electrostatic precipitation is used only where a high standard of air cleaning is necessary. In some systems the incoming air is passed through a chamber where it is subjected to a fine spray of water. Although these air washers do not clean the air as well as most filters they are effective humidifiers.

AIR CONDITIONING

Air conditioning is the control of air purity, humidity and temperature to within pre-determined limits. The control of air temperature in summer involves the use of refrigeration, and the considerable cost of this equipment rules out air conditioning for all but a few factories. Users of air-conditioning plant include branches of the chemical and pharmaceutical industries where close control of air conditions are essential to the processes used. Air conditioning is also used in standards rooms; here close control of temperature to 68°F is important if precision measurement errors due to expansion are to be avoided.

Plant Selection, Layout and Maintenance

PLANT SELECTION AND REPLACEMENT

This section deals with general considerations of equipment selection and replacement. The responsibility for recommending the purchase of equipment is normally that of the production engineering department, although management approval of capital expenditure is usually required. There are three sets of circumstances which may require equipment comparisons.

1. Selection of the most economic plant when the factory is planned.
2. Replacement of equipment when new processes or improved machine designs have made the existing machines prematurely obsolescent.
3. Replacement of worn-out plant with the most suitable new equipment.

Several factors influence the choice of equipment; some of them are intangible and many of them overlap. In this chapter they have been divided into technical factors and cost factors.

TECHNICAL FACTORS IN PLANT SELECTION

1. *Competitive Advantage.* Will the company, by purchase of the equipment, obtain an advantage over competitors or redress an advantage already enjoyed by its competitors?

2. *Demand for Product.* Often the ideal equipment is of a special-purpose type. Should the demand in the foreseeable future seem likely to be constant and at a high level, then the ideal equipment can be specified; however, if demand is likely to change appreciably, then general-purpose equipment, which provides greater flexibility, will usually prove more suitable.

3. *Risk of Obsolescence.* Equipment quickly becomes obsolescent if new processes are developed or major advances in machine design are introduced. This is always a risk, but if some major change is on the horizon, it is obviously unwise to invest in equipment which will soon become outdated.

4. *Quality of Work Produced.* An important factor is whether the quality of work produced will be adequate. While it is obviously undesirable for the quality of work produced to be too low, too high a quality may be uneconomic. New equipment, however, should have something in hand so far as quality is concerned, because the quality standard of its output will probably deteriorate with age. Quality improvements from new equipment may enable subsequent operations to be eliminated, often with considerable cost savings.

5. *Maintenance Costs and Reliability.* This factor may be difficult to assess, particularly with new designs on which there is little operating experience. Reliability is vital for line production, and if plant history cards, showing frequency of breakdown and cost of maintenance, are available for similar equipment, they will act as a valuable guide. The cost and availability of spares should also be considered at this stage.

COST FACTORS IN PLANT SELECTION

Unlike technical factors, which have to be estimated by experienced engineers, cost factors can be assessed more accurately and are used as the basis of cost comparisons, examples of which are shown later. The more important of these factors are discussed below.

1. *Cost of Direct Labour.* This term is used for the wages of the workers engaged directly on production. With increased mechanization the tendency is to reduce this cost, first by reducing the amount of direct labour and then by enabling less-skilled workers to be employed.

2. *Cost of Direct Materials.* Direct material cost is the issued value of material actually used in the finished product; it does not include process materials such as polishing compound, cutting and lubricating oils and consumable tools. In factories where direct labour costs have been reduced to a small proportion of the total cost, material economies can provide a major source of cost reduction. Any processes which use either less materials or cheaper materials should be carefully examined. For example, less material is used in heading or rolling than in turning, as the shape is produced by deforming rather than by cutting away metal. If plating is replaced by a vacuum-deposited metallic coating, material economy can sometimes be obtained by using a cheaper material for the part being processed. An example was the replacement of brass headlamp reflectors, which were silver-plated, by reflectors made from lacquered steel, which had the aluminium reflecting surface vacuum deposited.

3. *Other Operating Costs.* These charges are grouped together although they have very little relationship with each other. They include maintenance costs, setting, power consumption, process materials and the cost of floor area occupied by the equipment. Depreciation is another indirect cost, which will be discussed below.

4. *Interest on Capital Invested.* This charge takes into account interest which would have to be paid if money were borrowed to purchase the equipment, or, if money were available for the purchase, then that money could be made to earn interest elsewhere. It is usually calculated by taking the average capital value of the investment and multiplying by an appropriate percentage. The average capital value is found by adding the installed cost of the equipment to its estimated value at the end of its expected life, and dividing by two.

AVAILABILITY OF FUNDS

Small and medium-sized companies often find difficulty in obtaining the cash to purchase new equipment. During recessions in business liquid assets may have to be conserved; at other times banks may not be willing to lend money, or it may be inexpedient to raise additional capital. Equipment can be obtained by hire-purchase and this is a useful method of acquisition when other means fail. Although the rates of interest charged are high when calculated on a balance of debt outstanding, it may be a minor consideration to the saving that would be lost if the equipment was not obtained.

DEPRECIATION

Depreciation is often one of the largest items in the cost of production and, therefore, has a considerable influence on replacement policy. It is a prepaid expense for the recovery of the capital invested in the equipment. There are many ways in which the original value of the equipment can be recovered by the end of its expected life. The simplest is the straight-line method by which an equal amount of money is put aside each year over the life of the equipment. The annual depreciation is calculated from the formula

$$D = \frac{I-R}{N}$$

where D is the annual depreciation,

     I is the cost of equipment as installed,

     R is realizable value of equipment at the end of its useful life,
and N is the estimated useful life of the plant.

Depreciation is intended to provide funds for the purchase of new equipment when the old is worn out, but systems such as the straight-

D

line ones often fall seriously short of this in times of inflation. A method of depreciation which takes replacement cost into account makes a yearly estimate of the current replacement cost, and depreciation for that year is charged accordingly. A company can make whatever charges for depreciation it thinks prudent provided these are shown in the accounts. For taxation purposes, however, the depreciation charges made by the company are ignored and a standard annual allowance is granted. These allowances are based on original, not replacement values, and on the estimated life of the equipment. In times of inflation the Inland Revenue tax allowances are inadequate to cover the real cost of equipment replacement. Additional tax-saving allowances are provided, from time to time, when the government wishes to encourage capital investment.

COST COMPARISONS BETWEEN EQUIPMENT

The total cost of production can normally be divided into two parts, the fixed and the variable costs. The fixed charges are made up of such items as depreciation and interest on invested capital. The variable charges, although not individually directly proportional to output, do collectively approximate to a directly proportional relationship. Variable charges include cost of material and cost of direct labour. Most charges are semi-variable, that is, they have some fixed and some variable content. Examples of this type of charge are maintenance, supervision, power and process materials.

By resolving the semi-variable costs into their fixed and variable contents, it is possible to express the total production cost as $F+NV$ where F is fixed cost per year, N is quantity produced and V is variable cost per piece. This relationship is shown graphically in fig. 4.1.

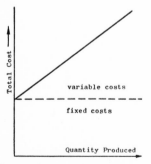

FIG. 4.1 *Cost Comparison: Total Production Cost.*

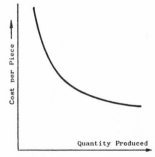

FIG. 4.2 *Cost Comparison: Cost per Piece.*

If we consider the cost per piece we find that it is obtained by dividing the total production cost by the quantity produced, and is $\frac{F}{N}+V$. It will be seen from fig. 4.2 that cost per piece is high when output is low.

When comparisons are made between different machines and between hand and machine-production, it will be found that the quantity required is often the deciding factor between one method and another. To generalize, small quantities are best produced by

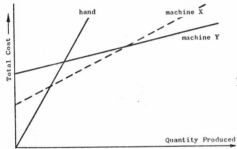

FIG. 4.3 *Cost Comparison: Total Cost by Hand and Machine Methods.*

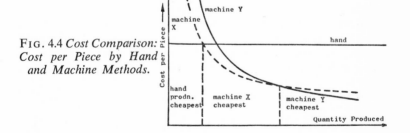

FIG. 4.4 *Cost Comparison: Cost per Piece by Hand and Machine Methods.*

hand and very large quantities by high-output equipment which, despite heavy fixed charges, reduces production cost per piece if fully utilized. These conditions are shown in figs. 4.3 and 4.4, where hand production is contrasted with two machines X and Y, machine Y having the heavier fixed charges but the lower cost per piece for large quantities.

CALCULATION OF OPERATING COST AND COST PER PIECE

Example 1. Determine the annual operating cost and cost per piece if production is 20,000 parts per year. Details of the plant are as follows:

Purchasing Cost	£3,000
Installation Cost	£100
Estimated life	10 Years
Realizable value after 10 years	£600
Interest on Capital	8%
Direct labour cost per piece	6d.
Direct material cost per piece	1s. 0d.
Indirect labour cost per year	£100
Power charge per year	£50
Other charges per year	£150
(maintenance, floor area, etc.)	

$$Annual\ depreciation = \frac{\text{installed cost} - \text{realizable value}}{\text{estimated life}}$$

$$= \frac{(3,000+100)-600}{10} = £250$$

Interest on Capital

This is taken as 8 per cent of the average value of the investment during its estimated life.

$$= \frac{(3,100+600)}{2} \times \frac{8}{100} = £148$$

Annual Operating Cost	£
Depreciation	250
Interest on capital	148
Indirect labour cost	100
Power	50
Other charges	150
Direct labour cost (20,000 × 6d.)	500
	1,198

Cost per piece (including material)

$$= \frac{\text{annual operating cost}}{\text{annual production}} + \text{direct material cost per piece}$$

$$= \frac{1,198}{20,000} \times 20 + 1 = 2{\cdot}198s.$$

$$= 2s.\ 2d.\ \text{approx.}$$

REPLACEMENT OF EXISTING EQUIPMENT

Frequently comparisons are required between equipment at present in use and new machines or processes that are available. When considering replacement it is necessary to determine how soon the new equipment must pay for itself. The shorter the repayment time the better, but what is an acceptable period will vary considerably. For special-purpose equipment, only a short period, geared to the expected life of the model, can be accepted; with general-purpose equipment, however, ten years or more may be reasonable. Three years is a figure accepted by many companies as the repayment period.

In the simplified treatment used in the example below, the time for the proposed machine to pay for itself has not been calculated, nor has the rate of return on the additional investment. Account has, however, been taken of these factors since the depreciation rate chosen forces the new machine to pay for itself in the required period, and both old and new machines have been charged with a return on capital which makes the investment an attractive one.

Example 2. A high production machine is being considered to replace two machines of the same total capacity. The installed cost of the proposed machine is £1,800 and it will be expected to return its investment in 3 years and earn 15 per cent on the average investment. The present market value of two existing machines is £300 each, although their book value is £550; their estimated life was 10 years and they are 5 years old. The other annual operating costs are shown below:

	Two existing machines £	Proposed machine £
Direct labour cost per year	1,000	500
Indirect labour cost per year	150	100
Power charges per year	100	70
Maintenance charges per year	80	60
Floor area cost per year	50	30
Other charges per year	50	40

Depreciation

$$2 \text{ Existing machines } 2 \times \frac{300-0}{5} = \text{£120}$$

$$\text{Proposed machine } \frac{1,800-0}{3} = \text{£600}$$

It will be seen that the existing and proposed machines are assumed to have a realizable value of nil at the end of their life. The proposed equipment has been depreciated over 3 years, the period in which it will be expected to return its investment. The depreciation charges for the existing machines, although spread over 5 years, have been calculated on their present market value and not book value.

Interest on Capital

$$\text{2 Existing machines } 2 \times \frac{300}{2} \times \frac{15}{100} = £45$$

$$\text{Proposed machine } \quad \frac{1,800}{2} \times \frac{15}{100} = £135$$

These calculations have been made on the average value of the investment. For the existing machines the present market value and not the book value has been used.

Annual Operating Cost

	Two existing machines £	Proposed machine £
Depreciation	120	600
Interest on capital (at 15%)	45	135
Direct Labour	1,000	500
Indirect Labour	150	100
Power charges	100	70
Maintenance charges	80	60
Floor Area charges	50	30
Other charges	50	40
	1,595	1,535

It will be seen from the annual operating cost that the proposed machine will repay the investment within 3 years and earn 15 per cent on the average investment. In addition, there will be, during this 3-year period, a further annual saving of £60 (£1,595 – £1,535). If the life of the proposed machine is greater than 3 years, as is likely, an additional saving of more than £60 per year will be obtained.

If the equipment is used to manufacture a number of different parts, a similar comparison to the one in the above example can be made, although it will probably be more difficult to obtain the estimated annual costs. In making a decision on plant replacement many companies are reluctant to replace old equipment unless it is almost fully depreciated, even though the depreciation period originally chosen may have been unrealistically long. They are usually even more reluctant to purchase new equipment if they find that the market value of the old equipment is considerably less than its book value.

In replacement studies, only the present and future costs should be taken into account and any loss of book value ignored and regarded as a write-off.

Although cost comparisons provide an estimate of operating costs, the relevant technical factors must be given due weight before making a decision on equipment purchase. Human factors must also be considered. Even if the proposed equipment passes muster on both cost and technical grounds, but is likely to embitter labour relations, its purchase must be carefully considered, for if it cannot be "sold" to the operators it is best forgotten.

TYPES OF PRODUCTION

It is found convenient to classify types of production for easy reference; the usual divisions are "jobbing", "batch" and "flow" production.

1. *Jobbing Production.* This is the sort of production where only small numbers of articles are ordered, without the likelihood of repeat orders for the same article. Examples of this type of production organization are to be found in shipbuilding, civil engineering construction and toolmaking.

2. *Batch Production.* With this method of production, batches of similar articles are produced to meet a continuing sales demand. Although batch sizes vary widely the quantities produced will be in excess of those immediately required, so the surplus has to be stored until needed. Batch production is the most widely used type of production in the manufacturing industries.

3. *Flow Production.* Where quantities required are large, flow production is sometimes possible. The processes are arranged so that the manufacture of the part or assembly proceeds as a balanced flow from one operation to the next. The materials or components are fed at the planned rate of output that will normally correspond to the sales requirement. Examples of flow production are to be found in the assembly of cars and in the machining of some of their major components such as crankcases and cylinder blocks. Flow production is sometimes called mass or continuous production.

It is not unusual for examples of all three types of production to occur within the same factory. For instance, in the motor industry tools and prototypes will be made by jobbing methods, most of the components will be produced in batches, and assembly will take place on flow production lines.

PLANT LAYOUT

The best positioning of plant is vital to the overall efficiency of the factory. A well-designed plant layout assists the reduction of manufacturing costs in the following ways:

1. Increasing operator output and reducing fatigue.
2. Reducing materials handling.
3. Simplifying control of production.
4. Assisting supervision.
5. Ensuring the best use of capital equipment.
6. Minimizing floor space required.

It is suggested that the following procedure will be a suitable one for laying out equipment in a new factory or in an existing factory undergoing a major reorganization.

1. Analyse manufacturing requirements.
2. Calculate amount of equipment required.
3. Choose between product and process layout.
4. Establish general direction of work flow.
5. Plan stores and service areas.
6. Prepare detailed factory layout.

ANALYSIS OF MANUFACTURING REQUIREMENTS

A complete list of parts to be manufactured and assembled will be required, together with drawings and, if possible, samples. Information on the operation sequence and method of manufacture for each part will also be needed. This information will be supplied either in the form of a manufacturing layout as shown in fig. 5.1, or as a preliminary listing prepared by a process planning engineer. In addition, estimated process times will be required.

To help visualize manufacturing and assembly operations, charts should be prepared. Either assembly charts or outline process charts will probably be the most suitable; the latter chart is sometimes known as an operation process chart. Both use the symbols standardized by the American Society of Mechanical Engineers, now adopted as a British Standard, ○ signifying an operation and □ an inspection. Examples of these charts are shown in fig. 4.5. At this

stage a more detailed analysis of work flow is not desirable, otherwise
the general picture will be difficult to see.

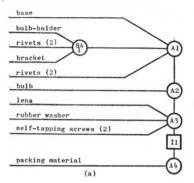

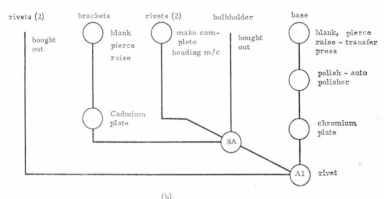

(b)

FIG. 4.5
(a) *assembly chart*, (b) *outline process chart* (*same
assembly as* (a), *up to A*1).

CALCULATION OF EQUIPMENT REQUIRED

The number of machines required for each operation can be calculated from estimates of manufacturing quantities, time per piece,
scrap and working hours. The following calculation shows how this
is done.

Output per year   120,000 parts
Expected scrap   3%

Output for 120,000 good parts $=120,000 \times \dfrac{103}{100} = 123,600$ parts

Working hours per year $=2,000$

Parts required per hour $= \dfrac{123{,}600}{2{,}000} = 61 \cdot 8$

Estimated time per piece $= 75$ sec

Output from 1 machine per hour at 80 per cent efficiency

$$= \frac{3{,}600}{75} \times \frac{80}{100} = 38 \cdot 4 \text{ parts}$$

Machines required $= \dfrac{\text{parts required per hour}}{\text{output per machine per hour}}$

$$= \frac{61 \cdot 8}{38 \cdot 4} = 1 \cdot 62$$

If other work is to be manufactured on this equipment the total load would be calculated by summing the machine requirements for each part planned to be made on the machine. If however, the equipment is to be used exclusively for the part considered, two machines would be required. The calculation of machine requirements is dealt with more fully in Chapter 16.

CHOICE OF PRODUCT OR PROCESS LAYOUT

The next step is to decide whether to use a product or process layout or to use a combination of the two. In a product layout the manufacturing equipment is arranged in the same sequence as the operations performed on the product. Each operation of a product layout should be capable of processing work at the rate required for assembly and so far as possible the output from each operation should be balanced so that all the parts march in step to final

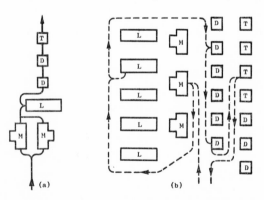

Fig. 4.6
(*a*) *product layout*, (*b*) *process layout.*

assembly. If a process layout is used the equipment will be grouped together so that all machines of a similar type are in the same section of the factory. Process layouts are associated with batch and jobbing production. Simple product and process layouts are shown in fig. 4.6. The actual path of work in the process layout is shown dotted as it will depend on which machine in the group happens to be available when the batch is being processed.

The advantages of a product layout are:

(*a*) *Lower Stocks.* Raw material, work-in-progress, finished parts and warehouse stocks are reduced. This all-round reduction in stocks is due to the balanced flow maintained through manufacture and assembly. Only a few days' stock of material and bought-out parts needs to be held, as one day's requirement of each is fed into the factory each day. The work-in-progress is kept low as the work does not wait between operations. Provided sales have not been over-estimated, finished products should be sold from the warehouse at the same rate as they are being put there from the assembly line.

(*b*) *Reduced Handling.* Materials handling is reduced as work is moved only short distances to the next operation. This avoids re-handling, reduces scrap and keeps work off the floor.

(*c*) *Work Simplified.* Due to increased mechanization and the possibility of breaking work down into simple tasks, less-skilled workers and a greater proportion of women can be employed. This results in lower labour costs and less difficulty in obtaining and training labour.

(*d*) *Easier Production Control.* Ordering of material and parts is simplified due to the constant rate of usage, and machine loading is reduced to feeding materials and parts at the correct rate into the factory. Production delays are quickly apparent due to the pile-up at any station which is at fault.

(*e*) *Reduced Manufacturing Area.* For a given output, provided machine utilization is good, less floor area should be required. This saving can be obtained by a more compact arrangement of equipment, the possibility of improved machine utilization and greatly reduced stores area.

The advantages of process layouts are:

(*a*) *Better Utilization of High-production Equipment.* Much production equipment has short cycle times so that parts can usually be produced faster than they are required on the assembly line. Unless very large quantities indeed are needed from short-cycle-time machines they have to be left standing idle for long periods if used exclusively to produce one part. For instance, high-speed presses can produce 300 components per minute, which in a 40-hour week with an 80 per cent efficiency means an output of 576,000 parts per week. Very few companies require half a million of the same component each week, therefore this type of machine is normally best used in producing a range of different parts, which is done by changing the tooling. In this way high-production machines can be kept in use for a large part of the working week with a correspondingly good machine utilization. The grouping together of like machines in the same department, as is done in process layouts, facilitates their use on a wide range of different parts.

(*b*) *Greater Flexibility.* Process layouts enable changes in quantity or type of component produced to be accommodated at minimum cost. The equipment chosen is of a general-purpose type capable of taking a wide variety of tooling. This is in contrast to the equipment employed in product layouts, which is normally used to produce one part only and is often of a special-purpose design. The inflexibility of product layouts is further increased as they are designed for a particular sequence of operations and rate of production. The greater flexibility of process layouts enables sub-contract work to be undertaken, whereas the one-product nature of product layouts make this almost impossible.

(*c*) *Greater Margin of Safety for Breakdowns.* In the event of equipment breakdown, or absenteeism, the effect on output need not be serious due to the cushioning effect of stocks and the interchangeability of equipment. With a product layout, however, buffer stocks are small and production cannot normally be switched from one machine to another; this means an almost inevitable loss of finished product output.

(*d*) *Greater Specialization.* Due to the grouping of similar machines into one section of the factory, the supervision and setters become specialized in a particular process and consequently can become more proficient in their work.

(*e*) *Higher Effective Labour Utilization.* Production lines used with product layouts are designed so that the work is, so far as possible, divided equally between the workers. This means that better than average workers cannot work to their full potential. In practice it may also be difficult to allocate equal work to everyone and there is often unrecorded waiting time due to unbalanced work stations or slow operators holding up the rest of the line.

ESTABLISHMENT OF GENERAL DIRECTION OF FLOW

The smooth flow of work into, through and out of the factory depends, to a large extent, on the success of the layout chosen. In flow production the work movement will be pre-determined, with the equipment arranged in operation sequence and the components and sub-assemblies flowing into the main assembly line at the correct position. With process layouts, used for batch or jobbing production, it is possible to establish only a general direction of work movement, due to the difference in operation sequence between one part and another. It may be possible to draw a work movement diagram by superimposing the path of movement of each part on a floor plan of the factory. However, after the routes of a few parts have been entered on this diagram, the picture produced is so confusing that it is difficult to decide on the general flow of work. Travel charts can be used to present the frequency of movement between departments in concise form. By analysis of travel charts it is possible to improve on the first tentative positioning of departments and achieve a better arrangement. An example of a travel chart is shown in fig. 4.7. In most cases, however, it is possible by knowledge of the type of work done to arrange departments so that the general direction of work

FROM / TO	Goods in	Parts stores	Matls. stores	Press shop	Auto shop	2nd op. m/c shop	Plating shop	Total
Goods in		-	-	-	-	-	-	0
Parts stores	120		-	35	40	44	172	411
Matl. stores	60	-		-	-	-	-	60
Press shop	-	5	102		-	-	-	107
Auto shop	-	-	90	-		-	-	90
2nd op. m/c shop	-	23	-	35	27		-	85
Plating shop	-	31	-	37	23	41		132
Total	180	59	192	107	90	85	172	885

FIG. 4.7 *Travel Chart.*

flow is correct. Considering a batch-production, light engineering factory the work flow is likely to be as shown below.

1. Receiving Bay
⇓
2. Raw Material Stores
⇓
3. First Operation Shops
Presses
Automatic Lathes
Capstan Lathes
⇓
4. Second Operation Shops
Milling
Drilling
Grinding
⇓
5. Finishing Shops
Polishing
Plating
Painting
⇓
6. Finished Parts Stores
⇓
7. Assembly and Test
⇓
8. Despatch

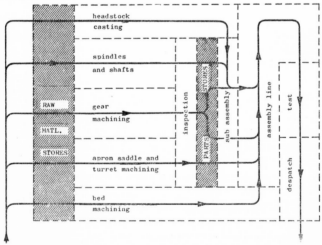

FIG. 4.8 *General Direction of Flow in Machine Tool Factory.*

If the various sections of the factory are located in this order, something approaching the best layout will result. Some doubling back will be inevitable; for instance, capstan lathes can be used for second operation work and milling machines for first. Figure 4.8 shows a factory layout where the departments have been arranged to give a good general direction of work flow.

PLANNING STORES AND SERVICE AREAS

The size and position of the various stores areas will have to be determined. Normally, raw material stores are sited at one end of the building and the finished product warehouse at the other, with a component store between the manufacturing and assembly areas. The size of raw material and finished product stores will depend on the type of production; with flow production often a few days' stock only is required, whereas with batch production, the stores may have to be large enough to hold an average stock of several weeks' or even months' usage. Tool and process material stores will have to be planned, and in larger factories these are often sub-divided so that they can be situated adjacent to the production areas they serve.

The position and size of the various offices directly concerned with the factory will also have to be determined. These include factory supervision, work study, wages booking and production control. Their sizes should be worked out with the departmental managers concerned and they should be sited as near as possible to the factory activity they are intended to control. For instance if a planned allocation of work to machines is contemplated, this will probably be far more successful if the machine loaders are situated adjacent to their respective sections of the factory instead of being centralized in one office remote from the shop floor. Commercial offices and the personnel department should be situated near to the factory entrance so that the general public can be kept out of the factory.

PREPARATION OF DETAILED FACTORY LAYOUT

By now the general picture of the layout should have emerged, but the individual items of equipment have yet to be located and the work stations planned. The actual arrangement will depend on a host of factors, and only a few generally applicable points can be mentioned here. Apart from allowing adequate space for operators, gangways and machines, space must also be provided for feeding work to the machines. This means that conveyor stations, work racks and pallet stands must have floor space allocated to them.

Over-generous spacing of equipment not only wastes floor area but provides an opportunity for the floor to become littered with work tins, setters' cupboards and other impedimenta. An example of a space-saving arrangement frequently used for bar-type capstans and automatic lathes is shown in fig. 4.9. When a worker is tending

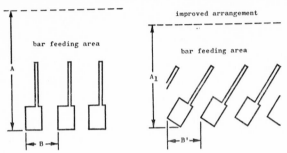

FIG. 4.9 *Space-saving Arrangement of Machinery. The reduction in dimension A more than compensates for the increase in B.*

more than one piece of equipment, as in automatic and semi-automatic machines, the equipment should be positioned to minimize operator movement. Examples of suitable and unsuitable machine arrangements are shown in fig. 4.10.

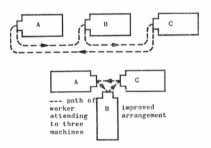

FIG. 4.10 *Machine Arrangement to Minimize Operator Movement.*

At this stage two other charts may be of assistance in planning the position of individual machines; they are the flow process chart and flow diagram. The flow process chart gives more information than the outline process chart previously discussed. It shows transporta-tions, permanent storages and delays in addition to operations and inspections. A floor plan of the manufacturing area is used for the flow diagram with lines showing paths of work movement and flow process chart symbols indicating what is being done to the part or assembly. Examples of each of these charts are shown in fig. 4.11.

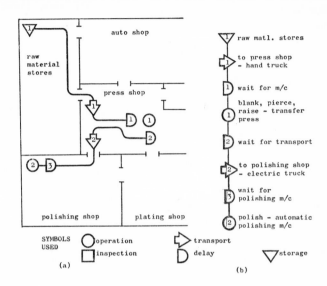

FIG. 4.11
(a) *flow diagram*, (b) *flow process chart*.

Templates showing the floor space occupied by individual pieces of equipment are useful when planning a layout. These templates are placed over a floor plan and then arranged and rearranged until the most satisfactory layout has been obtained. The templates must be made to the correct scale with due allowance for maximum table travel and projections such as control handles and bar-feed mechanisms. The usual way of securing the templates to the floor plan is by means of mapping pins; the floor plan itself being mounted on a board. It may be worth while using scale models instead of templates on large projects. Apart from creating a more realistic impression they are useful for checking vertical clearances, particularly where overhead conveyors are involved. When the position of each item of equipment has been finally decided, a layout drawing is made and copies of it issued for action.

RESPONSIBILITIES OF PLANT MAINTENANCE DEPARTMENT

Maintenance is the task of keeping the buildings and equipment in a

E

satisfactory condition according to standards set by management. The work is under the control of the works, plant or maintenance engineer, who normally reports to the works manager. The main functions of the department are listed below:

1. Mechanical maintenance and plant installation.
2. Electrical installation and maintenance.
3. Building additions and maintenance.
4. Plant overhaul.
5. Equipment spares storekeeping.
6. Plant records.
7. Factory cleaning.

In addition there may be a section responsible for the manufacture and, possibly, the design of special-purpose equipment.

EFFECT OF PLANT BREAKDOWN ON PRODUCTION

Equipment breakdown leads to an inevitable loss of production, the extent of the loss depends largely on the type of layout used. If any piece of equipment in a flow production factory is out of action for an hour, there is likely to be one hour's loss of finished product output. In some car assembly factories the prevention of one minute of assembly line stoppage each day more than pays the wages for that day of the maintenance workers concerned. With the increased use of flow production there has been a trend towards the pre-planning of maintenance so that, so far as possible, equipment is prevented from breaking down. How this is done will be discussed in the section dealing with preventive maintenance. Breakdowns will also reduce output in batch production factories, but usually alternative machines and component stocks are available to cushion the effects of breakdowns on finished product output. A less rigorous standard of maintenance is therefore usual for batch production equipment.

PLANT AND MAINTENANCE RECORDS

One of the duties of the maintenance department is to keep a record of all equipment owned by the company. A simplified plant record card is shown in fig. 4.12. The maintenance expenditure is often accumulated on a separate record and the totals transferred periodically to the plant record card. It is usual to give each new item of equipment a plant number to identify it. A small plate showing this number is fixed to the equipment. Electric motors are often given separate numbers as the same motors do not necessarily remain with the equipment throughout its life.

EQUIPMENT HISTORY CARD		Plant No.	
Description	Manufacturer Supplier Cost	Installed Building Floor	
Length Width Height Weight	Elec. motor nos. hp	Dept. Date	
Preventive Maintenance Routines		Spare Parts to Stock	
inspection or replacement	frequency	Mfgr's no.	name	qty.

Repair and Maintenance History			Plant No.			
Date	Description	Part no. used	Time out of prod.	Cost		
				labour	matl.	total

Reverse side of Equipment History Card

Fɪɢ. 4.12 *Equipment History Card.*

PREVENTIVE MAINTENANCE

The success of a system of preventive maintenance depends largely on an appropriate inspection and replacement routine. This is based largely on operating experience of similar equipment, although advice can often be obtained from the manufacturers. Although it may be possible, by periodic inspection, to guard against deterioration due to most forms of gradual wear, sudden mechanical or electrical failure, often due to inadequate design or incorrect operation, cannot be prevented by maintenance routines. If it is found, however, that certain parts fail regularly and their failure cannot be prevented, then a new part can be fitted just before the old one is due to fail.

Apart from routine inspections and replacements, regular oiling is necessary for most equipment. In some cases charts on the equipment are used to indicate oiling points, type of lubricant and frequency of attention needed; another method is to use a colour code adjacent to the oiling points themselves. The lubrication routines should include the replacement of oil in gear boxes and hydraulic systems and the cleaning of sumps and filters. Some systems make use of lubrication record cards. These are completed by the oilers to show when the equipment was lubricated or checked for oil level.

ORGANIZATION OF PREVENTIVE MAINTENANCE

After preventive maintenance schedules have been determined for each piece of equipment the routine inspection and examination tasks have to be allocated. This can be done effectively with the help of a tickler file, which is made up of cards giving a brief description of the maintenance task, a note of the equipment to which it is to be applied, and the time interval between performance of the tasks. These cards are then filed in a tray so that the earliest jobs to be done are in front, with month and day dividers placed between the cards. After completion of each job the card is re-filed so that it will come to the front of the file again after the appropriate time interval has elapsed; for instance, if a 3-monthly examination was carried out on 1 January,

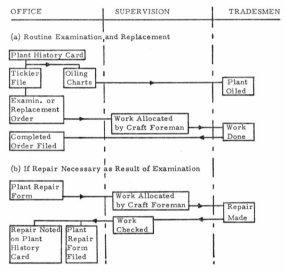

FIG. 4.13 *Preventive Maintenance Organisation.*

the card would be re-filed under 1 April. The chart in fig. 4.13 outlines a suitable clerical procedure for issuing preventive maintenance work.

MAINTENANCE OF FACTORY BUILDINGS AND
NON-PRODUCTIVE EQUIPMENT

The maintenance department is not only responsible for production equipment, but has also to look after the factory buildings, the power, lighting, heating and ventilating systems and the factory grounds. Space does not permit a detailed consideration of their upkeep, although a system based on planned inspection and attention is likely to be the most satisfactory.

The maintenance department can do much to assist good housekeeping in the factory by ensuring cleanliness and a high standard of interior and exterior painting and decoration. Management and supervision, however, have the main responsibility in seeing that there is a place for everything and insisting that everything is in its place. There are real advantages to be obtained from good housekeeping and these should far outweigh the cost involved. The more important of these advantages are summarized below:

1. Morale is improved, resulting in increased output and less labour turnover.

2. Better control can be kept of work-in-progress.

3. There is less chance of "losing" reject work which must be cleared to rectification or to the scrap yard.

4. Accidents and fire risks are reduced, there being less material about to cause accidents or to catch fire.

5. A good impression of the factory is given to visitors.

6. Cleanliness, particularly in canteens and toilets, helps to protect the health of the workers.

The appointment of good-housekeeping committees containing management and workers' representatives can do much to promote interest in good housekeeping; this interest can be kept up by poster campaigns and by competitions.

Where there is surplus land round the factory it is being increasingly used for lawns and flower beds. Apart from making the factory grounds more attractive, they give pleasure to the workers and convey the impression that management is interested in more than harder work and higher profits. The mowing, weeding and planting can be done by the maintenance department or sub-contracted by them to specialists.

Selection and Planning
of Manufacturing Processes

SELECTION OF MANUFACTURING PROCESSES

Selection of the most economic process demands a different approach in different types of industry. If the industry makes a single end product or a single range of products, as in extractive industries such as oil refining, the whole process must be considered whenever an alteration is suggested. Here it is likely that any alteration to the process will involve considerable expenditure, and large savings or losses can be expected. Most of the process improvements in these industries have been due to the work of chemists rather than production engineers. This points to the need for an integrated process research and development programme, so that the results of basic research can be efficiently converted to practical applications. Generally speaking, these alterations to process are unlikely to be affected by changes in demand since the process, once installed, will determine the layout of plant and will allow of no alternative method of manufacture.

In industries where a large variety of component parts is made, as in most light engineering companies, changes to the manufacturing processes of the components will not as a rule affect other components and the savings, although collectively considerable, are likely to be individually small. In most cases the changes in method are developed by engineers who are particularly experienced in the processes of the industry.

If the maximum benefit is to be derived from improved manufacturing methods all products should be under constant review in the light of changes in demand and of the development of new processes, tool materials and machine tools. Frequently it has been found that sales of certain products have gradually changed until they have rendered the original methods of production uneconomical.

Although cost-consciousness plays an important part in production engineering it must not be allowed to become an obsession to which all other standards are subordinated. If this happens, quality usually suffers and working conditions may deteriorate. Even if the quality of the finished product is not seriously affected by a decline in component quality, assembly difficulties may more than outweigh the savings in component cost.

A first attempt to reduce the cost of manufacture of established components may often be guided by an analysis showing how the total cost is split between material, labour and overheads. Subsequent approaches to the same problem will require a less superficial consideration as the most obvious savings will have already been made. The production engineer must ensure that a saving in one direction is not outweighed by a loss in another direction. It is sometimes necessary, for instance, to blank metal components from strip material in an uneconomic manner from the material utilization standpoint so that the metal grain shall be in the best direction for subsequent bending operations.

In many companies Works Suggestions Schemes make monetary awards to employees whose suggestions on process changes are adopted. The large amounts paid out are an indication of the tremendous savings which can be made by applying a little thought to the question of manufacture.

In Chapter 2 the specification of the correct materials was stressed as a requirement of good design. Sometimes the material specified by the designer may be suitable for one type of process but a poor choice for another process. This shortcoming should be apparent to the production engineer who would request the designer to change to a more generally suitable material. This may occur in press-work where the choice of a material with better drawing properties may avoid the need for an intermediate annealing operation.

The best process from the point of view of material economy is the one which converts the maximum percentage of raw material into the final product. Since material cost is almost invariably a large part of the value of a component, it is essential that maximum utilization of material shall be obtained. Utilization is reduced not only by the necessity to cut away unwanted material during the shaping processes, but also by the amount of scrap produced. In some engineering factories the swarf lorry takes out as much as 30 per cent of the weight of the raw materials purchased. This is one reason for the great interest shown in recent years in cold extrusion techniques and other chipless methods of manufacture of metal parts.

The economic factors relating to the selection of plant have been dealt with in Chapter 4, and the production engineer must compare these factors when making a choice, but to do this he must have a sound knowledge or means of quick reference to the latest developments in machine-tool design, since obviously he can select only from machines of whose existence he knows, or whose development he can visualize.

LABOUR GRADING

Labour is an expensive cost factor and it is essential that the labour grade specified for the job should be commensurate with the task to be performed. Some jobs require a high degree of manual dexterity, for which female labour is particularly suited; some require a long period of instruction or training and demand a greater financial reward; while others may involve uncongenial working conditions. The choice of the correct labour grade is not only necessary for efficient and economic manufacture, but it is of great importance if harmonious relations are to be maintained in the factory. Although the decision concerning grade of labour must depend on the process, labour supply may often, to a large extent, determine the method of manufacture. For instance, if the supply of skilled labour is short it may be necessary to employ lower grades of labour and train them as setter-operators instead of employing trained setters and operators. In many factories, the decision on which labour grade to use is frequently left to the shop supervision and work-study engineers, but the decision is properly the responsibility of the production engineer who determines the process.

ORGANIZATION OF PRODUCTION ENGINEERING DEPARTMENT

The complete specification of the most suitable manufacturing process is, then, the main function and concern of a production engineering department. We will now consider how the department should be organized to achieve the best results. In a large company, using a variety of processes, the production engineering department will probably employ product engineers, process engineers, planning engineers, methods engineers and tool draughtsmen. The functions of product and process engineers were described in Chapter 2. Planning engineers should be men of wide and varied experience who can be relied upon to compile a manufacturing layout in common use for most parts. Often these men have limited specialist knowledge, in fact such knowledge may be unnecessary in larger companies since most specialist information required can be obtained from process engineers. Methods engineers have a departmental location, their work usually being associated with improvement of production methods in that department. These men are frequently drawn from the supervisory staffs of the departments to which they are assigned or, where tooling is an important factor, they are sometimes ex-tool draughtsmen. Tool draughtsmen are responsible for the design of jigs, tools and fixtures and sometimes of special-purpose machine tools or attachments to existing machine tools. Preferably these men should have served a tool-room apprenticeship, so that their designs shall be functionally suitable and simple to make.

The productivity achieved on specific products may be improved by the use of management teams, as mentioned in Chapter 2. A typical team consists of the production manager, product engineer, methods engineer, quality control engineer, and the designer associated with the product.

One advantage of a senior team of this sort is that action can be taken with a minimum of delay, and everyone responsible for taking action must report back at the next meeting. Although co-ordinating committees are to be discouraged generally, there are in larger companies great advantages to be obtained from decentralizing some aspects of the management of products to these teams. Higher management is thus able to watch the progress of teams towards targets of higher productivity without becoming involved in unnecessary details.

PROCESS PLANNING

An essential requirement when planning a manufacturing process is a knowledge of the accuracy and consistency of the plant in use. Some types of equipment such as packaging machines will either perform their job in a satisfactory manner or, alternatively, will be an obvious failure, but most machines used in the engineering industries are required to produce large quantities of components within defined limits of accuracy in order to satisfy the design specification. The ability of a machine to perform consistently within these limits determines its technical suitability for the job in mind. Where the design limits are fairly wide compared with the known consistency of a machine there is no problem, but some applications require close limits where the suitability of the machine is in some doubt. Under these circumstances a system of statistical quality control as described in Chapter 10, where already in use, will often provide the information required.

The process planning staff perform three main functions: they plan new jobs; with the methods engineers they investigate production troubles and suggestions concerning running jobs; they handle the tooling aspects of design changes. Their success is frequently affected by their ability to enlist co-operation, since they are in a pivotal position between the component design, tool design, production, plant layout, work study and production control functions.

When new products are designed the expected sales at a given price, both as a long-term forecast and as a short-period requirement, must be established before tooling is put in hand. A long-selling product having a low monthly sale will require less specialized high production plant than a medium-selling product having a high monthly sale. Based on the expected sales a tool budget can be assessed, and the process planner must work with this figure in mind. Although a certain elasticity must be allowed, tool budgets must not be regularly exceeded if economic control is to be enforced.

The process planning engineer, after examining the component and assembly drawings, drafts out an operation sequence for each

MANUFACTURING LAYOUT				Part No. 6584321		
alt. note date init. 6421 7/6/62 CdF		alt. note date init.		Material MS hex 0·82 A/F Description connecting union sheet 1 of 1		
op. no.	dept.	description	machine	tools and gauges	T P W performance	
					no/hr	hr/100
10	70	turn, drill, bore, form, tap, part off	Herbert 4S	½" drill, 1264 QR boring tool, 6328 HF form tool, ⅝ UNF tap, Gauges: 1468 GA 1672 GF 2664 GN	35	2·857
20	30	inspect 10%				
30	70	face, countersink, turn, die ¾ UNF	Herbert 4S	1" coventry die-head, ¾" UNF chasers, ¾" UNF Wickman Gauge	50	2·000
40	30	inspect 10%				
50	66	mill, slot, deburr	No. 1 H'mill	2642 VR mill fixt., 2462 MH saw, Gauge: 6384 GH	72	1·389
60	30	inspect 10%				
70	52	wire up, cadmium plate	tanks		40	2·500
80	30	inspect				
		Deliver to stores				
					form 864	

FIG. 5.1 *Manufacturing Layout for Engineering Component.*

component. He then considers for each operation which machine is best-suited to the job, what dimensions must be measured, how the work is to be held and what cutting or forming tools are required. Probably tool and gauge numbers will also be allocated at this stage, although this could be done later by the Tool Drawing Office.

A manufacturing layout is then drawn up for each component and sub-assembly, showing the sequence of operations, departments performing these operations, and specifying the tools, fixtures and gauges to be used. It is possible that the layout will also include a column for the labour grade used and the piecework value. These values can be added only after time studies have been made on the shop floor, but an estimated time may sometimes be inserted provisionally by the process planner. A typical form of manufacturing layout is shown in fig. 5.1.

During the life of a component a large number of copies of each layout will be required, and it is a laborious process if these copies are individually typed. A widely-used method is to type the original layouts on duplicating masters. This method provides a difficult storage problem if masters are to be kept without deteriorating for long periods, and is inconvenient when alterations become necessary, as often occurs. Another method, although more expensive, is to type the layout information on pre-printed tracing cloth and produce copies by photo-copying. The recent introduction of desk-type "black heat" copying machines may provide a more convenient form of reproduction for this type of work direct from typed sheets, although the tendency to discolour when subjected to strong light is a disadvantage.

CONSIDERATIONS OF PRODUCTION TOOLING

Production tooling is a general expression used frequently by production engineers to include all the jigs, tools, fixtures and gauges necessary for quantity production from machine tools. Some industries built around a basic process, such as the chemical industry, employ plant which performs the operation required without the need for special tooling. However, since most manufacturing industries are concerned with cutting or forming materials this section is devoted to the consideration of tooling requirements in these industries.

The term "tool" as used here is not meant to imply a machine tool but a cutting or forming tool, which may be defined as a device fitted to a machine tool designed for shaping or removing material from a workpiece under controlled conditions. Jigs and fixtures are devices for holding and supporting the workpiece during manufacturing or assembly operations, a jig performing the additional function of guiding the tools. Gauges are used in quantity manufacture for ease of inspection, and they show whether or not a component is within the prescribed limits of size or form.

Correct production tooling ensures the interchangeability of manufactured parts and permits the use of lower grade labour, while at the same time speeding up the manufacturing process. Interchangeability is of particular importance in eliminating selective assembly and in guaranteed replacement of worn or defective parts. The possibility of using unskilled labour and the increase in productivity obtained by the use of production tooling will obviously reduce the labour cost per piece, but this saving will outweigh the increase in tool cost only if quantities are sufficiently large. Economic consideration of tool costs is a specialist study, but the principles involved are fundamentally similar to those governing selection of plant, and any choice made should be based on expected sales.

ECONOMICS OF TOOL DESIGN

Cutting tool selection and design should be determined by the need to produce components in the quantities required at the minimum cost per piece and to a satisfactory standard of quality. Factors to be taken into account will vary with each process; an important factor in most processes is cutting speed, which is itself affected by a number of considerations such as depth of cut, rate of feed, tool and work materials, coolant, tool life expected and surface finish required.

Total cycle time of the process is made up of cutting time and idle time, idle time being due to unloading, loading and non-cutting cycle time. It is obvious that the greater the percentage of cutting time to total time, the greater is the productive efficiency of the operation. This percentage may be improved by good jig and fixture design but it is unlikely that cutting-tool design will greatly affect it. Idle time therefore represents a constant cost per piece irrespective of the cutting speed. The cutting time is inversely proportional to the cutting speed, other things being equal, so this part of the cost can be reduced by increasing the speed. Unfortunately, higher speeds for a given tool result in a greater amount of time lost due to tool regrinding and an increase in tool cost. It will be seen from fig. 5.2 that a point exists at which the total cost per piece is a minimum, lower or higher cutting speeds resulting in increased costs.

The use of tool materials which retain their hardness at high tem-

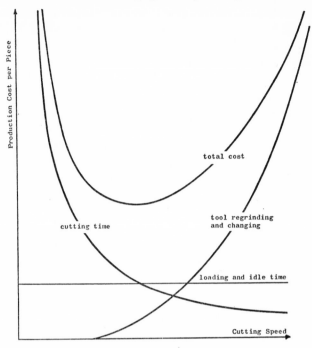

F IG. 5.2 *Production Cost Related to Cutting Speed.*

peratures enables the speed to be increased, but these materials are generally more expensive and may sometimes be too brittle for the operation in mind. Also, many machine tools are not designed for high material removal rates and lack the speed range, power and rigidity to utilize economically the high duty cutting materials. In engineering a number of new tool materials have emerged during the past thirty years with the result that high-speed steel has now given way to tungsten carbide in many instances and tungsten carbide, in turn, is beginning to give way to ceramic tools which, given suitable conditions, enable even higher material removal rates to be achieved. However, for ceramic tools to be economic it is necessary that esti- mated quantities should justify the high initial cost of new plant capable of fully exploiting them.

Press tools have also been influenced by improved punch and die materials such as tungsten carbide. In this case the saving is unlikely to be one of time, but rather one of tool life and, possibly, ease of tool manufacture.

PRINCIPLES OF JIG AND FIXTURE DESIGN

Four main factors should be taken into account when designing jigs and fixtures; they are the reduction of non-productive time, quality of the finished component, cost of tools and safety of operation.

Reduction of Non-productive Time. The proportion of non-productive time to total cycle time can be reduced by ensuring that the fixture is easily accessible when mounted on the machine and that the lead-in for the component is large enough to prevent jamming or unnecessary manipulation. Awkward lifting of heavy components can be very tiring and is likely to lead to a fall in production after a long period of operation. Fixtures should be designed for ease of cleaning in order both to save time and maintain quality. Wherever possible, spanner-tightened nuts should be eliminated when designing clamps, but where this cannot be avoided, nuts should be confined to one size so that a single spanner only is necessary. At the completion of the operation, time can be saved if some form of ejection of components is embodied in the design. Sometimes a saving can be made by changing the component design, either to simplify clamping or to allow simpler machining.

Quality of the Component. Selection of the best location surfaces is important if components are to be accurately machined. Generally speaking the principal location surface on the component should have three location points suitably spaced to prevent the component tipping. On the second location surface, as near perpendicular to the first as possible, there should be two location points suitably spaced, and on a third surface, mutually perpendicular to the first two, will be a single-point location. Such ideal locations are seldom met in practice, but the aim should be to approach them as nearly as possible. In order to ensure uniformity, it may sometimes be necessary to stipulate a closer limit in a previous operation so as to provide a better datum face for subsequent location purposes.

Adequate clearance must be allowed for chips, irregularities and burrs which may be on the component from previous operations. It may sound obvious to state that the component must be capable of being put into the fixture, but in fact fixtures have been designed which have not allowed for the large tolerances occurring on such components as sand castings and drop forgings.

Clamps should hold the component firmly against the locations and should be placed directly above the location points to prevent the possibility of warping or distortion due to bending. For reasons of accuracy and safety, machining forces should always be directed against solid parts of the fixture and never against clamps. The fixture and clamps should be rigid and sufficiently massive to prevent the possibility of movement or vibration.

Where coolant is used, the fixture should be designed to allow the coolant to reach the cutting edge. This requirement is very difficult to achieve in practice, and many fixtures seem to be designed in com-complete ignorance of it.

Cost Considerations. The cost of fixtures can be reduced by the use, where possible, of standard parts such as drill bushes, clamps, screws and dowels. These also enable worn parts to be easily replaced. Some tool materials are expensive, and the most suitable materials from the aspects of machine-ability, performance, fabrication and cost should be specified for all parts.

Another aspect of cost is the amount of scrap produced. This can often be avoided by fool-proofing the fixture by a design which prevents the component being inserted or clamped in any but the correct position.

Safety Considerations. No tools or fixtures should be designed if they are dangerous when used properly. Many factors contribute to safety, most of which also affect quality and unproductive time. Points which deserve special mention in this sense are the adequacy of clamping both component and fixture, the fitting of guards where required, and the elimination of loose parts which are likely to get in the way of tools.

Temporary Jigs and Fixtures. For short-quantity orders, where production tooling is not economic and jobbing methods of production are prohibitively expensive, it is now possible to buy sets of standard jig parts, including bases which are machine with T-slots, and assemble these fixtures or jigs to suit the particular application. Although the initial outlay is high, it should soon be repaid if there is a large volume of short-run work. Temporary fixtures are also a valuable means of ensuring continuity of production if the production fixtures fail in service, or they may be used to supplement the production fixtures in the event of an overload.

The use of temporary fixtures should be discontinued as soon as output justifies production tooling. This avoids using them for long periods when they would be more usefully employed elsewhere.

PRODUCTION GAUGES

In large quantity engineering production, gauges are used as a rapid means of checking if a component lies within the prescribed limits of dimensional accuracy. They also allow the employment of lower-grade labour for inspection purposes. Most gauges simply accept or reject a component according to whether or not it is within the limits of size or form. Comparator type mechanisms may be used to measure several features simultaneously, the actual sizes being shown relative to their limits; the instrument is set with a standard-sized test-piece.

Many limit gauges can be bought as standard designs and adjusted to the particular sizes required, but others must be made to suit the requirements of the job. The question of gauge design does not appear to receive anything like the attention given to jig and fixture design and as a result a disproportionate amount of time is often devoted to inspection. This book is no place to discuss gauge design, but it is important to realize that it is of little use showing economy in production time if inspection time is deliberately wasted due to poor gauge design.

6

Materials Handling

UNTIL the beginning of the present century handling assistance was provided only when loads were too great to be moved by human effort. This philosophy still applies in some factories, but there is now a much greater awareness of the advantages to be obtained from good methods of materials handling. Although there is considerable variation between industries, the average materials handling cost amounts to one-fifth of the total production cost and the average weight of materials handled in manufacturing a product is fifty times the weight of the finished product itself. The materials handling techniques adopted must result from the needs of the manufacturing processes used; progressive managements are, however, becoming increasingly conscious of the need to integrate handling with the manufacturing processes, instead of superimposing handling as an afterthought. With flow production, the handling methods have to be considered almost as soon as the manufacturing equipment, in fact with transfer machines inter-operational handling is built into the machine tool itself.

BASIC RULES FOR MATERIALS HANDLING

When planning handling methods in a new factory, or re-planning those in an existing one, certain basic rules should be kept in mind.

They are summarized below:

1. *Minimize Handling and Handling Effort.* So far as possible avoid handling; this can be done by eliminating and combining handling operations and considering the possibility of moving the workers instead of the material. If gravity can assist in handling, it should be used, if not, mechanical assistance should be provided.

2. *Plan Handling.* Handling should be considered as a continuity from the supplier, through the factory and out to the customer, and not just planned within the confines of the factory. Equipment should be positioned so that distances between operations are kept short and doubling back avoided. Handling should be planned to fit the production methods used. Low-cost handling should be avoided in one

F

place if it results in disproportionately high handling costs elsewhere.

3. *Select Correct Equipment.* So far as possible simple standard equipment should be chosen, special-purpose equipment being ordered only when its use is essential. A full consideration of all equipment available must be made and that selected should provide the highest overall savings. Before buying new equipment a check should be made that the existing equipment is being effectively used.

4. *Make the Most Effective Use of Handling Equipment.* Material should be handled in the largest loads practicable. Work containers should be designed so that they can be easily handled and the transfer of work from one container to another avoided. When material is stored it should be stacked so that maximum use is made of space to ceiling height. Workers using handling equipment should be instructed in its safe use. Preventive maintenance routines should be designed so that foreseeable causes of equipment breakdown are eliminated.

METHODS OF ANALYSIS

The collecton of information on which to base handling decisions is a somewhat similar task to that of collecting information for plant layout. Similar recording charts are used, the two most useful probably being the flow process chart and the flow diagram, examples of which were shown in fig. 4.11. Flow diagrams used for materials handling sometimes have additional symbols to provide further information, for instance ◿ is used to indicate a ramp up and ∨ a lift going down. These additions are by no means essential and the standard operation, inspection, delay storage and transport symbols are adequate. Once the existing method, or in a new factory the proposed method, has been presented on a chart it can be subjected to critical examination with the object of improving it. The critical examination techniques are designed to provide a systematic rather than a haphazard method of checking. Where a team of workers is engaged in handling, the most suitable method of recording is to use a ciné camera, the results being entered on a multiple operation chart. If the handling time is very short, then a two-handed process chart or a simo chart may prove to be the best way of making the analysis. A discussion of the construction and use of the various charts and their examination appears in Chapter 8.

After examination, improvements to the handling method can be developed and shown on a re-drawn chart or diagram. Models or templates, similar to those described under plant layout in Chapter 4 may also be used. The paths of movement of the work can be indicated by coloured lines or strips of self-adhesive plastic material. In models, the work flow can be indicated on a transparent plastic ceiling over them, while overhead conveyors can be shown by wire on the models.

SELECTION OF HANDLING EQUIPMENT

There is a wide variety of handling equipment, much of which is of a special-purpose nature. Before the more important equipment available is reviewed, we will consider some of the general factors which influence equipment selection.

1. *Material to be Handled.* Apart from the size and weight of the material itself, its liability to damage in handling and the possibility of deterioration in storage must be considered.

2. *Types of Production.* With fixed operational sequences and large-volume production, fixed route equipment, such as conveyors, will be the most suitable. Equipment utilization will probably be high, and initial cost of less importance than with low-volume production. Flexible equipment such as powered trucks and portable conveyors are likely to be required for batch or jobbing production.

3. *Factory Buildings.* These considerations will apply chiefly to older buildings which often seriously limit the type of equipment that can be used. Frequently encountered difficulties are low permissible floor loadings, insufficient ceiling height for stacking palletized material, or lifts which cannot take fork-lift trucks and their loads. Differences in floor levels may restrict the use of wheeled vehicles, although ramps can often solve this difficulty. If overhead conveyors are contemplated there may be insufficient ceiling height or the roof may not be strong enough to take the weight of the loaded conveyors.

4. *Handling Costs.* The cost of handling is often difficult to isolate. For instance, it is almost impossible to estimate the savings from replacing non-standard work tins by standard ones. However, when costs are obtainable the proposed equipment can be made the object of a cost study similar to that described in Chapter 4.

HORIZONTAL FIXED ROUTE EQUIPMENT

This is equipment which takes work mainly in a horizontal direction, although often some vertical movement is involved. Being floor-mounted and having a fixed route it is a permanent feature of the factory layout and is used chiefly for flow production.

Chutes. Chutes are inclined sheet metal troughs down which work slides under the action of gravity. They are used to feed conveyors and move material between work stations. The horizontal distances are limited by the vertical gradient necessary to provide smooth movement under the effect of gravity.

Belt Conveyors. The belts used are of the endless type and are usually made from rubber-covered canvas, although steel or plain fabric can be employed. At each end of the belt is a roller, one being driven by an electric motor. In order to drive the belt satisfactorily it must be tensioned, and a third roller is usually fitted for this purpose. The load-carrying portion of the belt is supported by rollers, or for light loads, by sheet metal or hardwood. Woven wire or steel belts are used for high-temperature applications, although certain types of rubber belts are satisfactory up to 300°F. Where bulk materials, e.g. powder or granular substances, are carried, troughed belts should be used. Belt conveyors, although restricted to straight runs and small inclines, are able to carry a wide variety of materials and parts. Removal from the conveyors can be effected by a plough discharge, which is a strip mounted just above the conveyor at an angle to its direction of movement.

Slat Conveyors. These are similar to the flat-belt type of conveyor except that the carrying surface is made from wood or metal slats which connect two strands of chain conveyor. They can be used for heavy assemblies such as car engines.

Roller Conveyors. Roller conveyors can be of the powered or gravity type and can take any article that has a flat firm surface. Small articles should be put into work tins, and flexible items, like sack loads, on flat pallets. The gravity type must have sufficient fall to move the work, this will vary from $\frac{1}{4}$ to 2 in. per ft depending on the load to be moved. The length of horizontal movement can be increased by short sections of power belt conveyor which lifts the work to a higher level again. Gravity roller conveyors are widely used for inter-operational movement and provide live storage for limited quantities of work. This type of conveyor can be quickly set up and is suitable for temporary handling arrangements such as the loading of motor vehicles. Power rollers are less frequently used, they have either a chain and sprocket drive or a belt drive to the underside of the rollers. Roller conveyors can be used for curved paths and can, in a rather similar way to a railway system, be fitted with points, crossovers and turntables.

Drag Chain Conveyors. An endless chain moving along a fixed route can be used to move material. In some cases the chain drags trucks along tracks, the trucks enabling a large variety of units such as refrigerators, washing machines and cookers to be handled. In another type, a chain running at the bottom of a trough pushes material forward along the trough by means of specially adapted chain links. Reasonably robust objects such as crates and timber can be moved in this way. If the trough is replaced by guide rails movement round sharply curved paths, as is required in bottling operations, can be obtained.

An interesting method of handling, shown in fig. 6.1, coming within

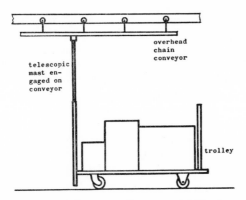

FIG. 6.1 *Tow-type Conveyor and Truck.*

this category is the tow-type conveyor where hand trucks with castered wheels are dragged round a circuit by means of an overhead or a trench-mounted chain. The trucks can be disconnected easily from the chain and they then become non-fixed path equipment. This type of conveyor is suitable for use in large warehouses. The trucks can be pushed round the aisles collecting goods and then attached to the chain, which takes them to the despatch department.

Exposed drag chains can be exceedingly dangerous and the safety aspect of any such installation must receive special consideration.

Vibrating Conveyor. The parts on this type of conveyor are advanced by vibrating action along metal troughs. It is an ideal method of moving hot or abrasive materials, such as hot sand castings, which would be difficult to move by other types of conveyor. It is also possible, by means of a vibrating conveyor, to move parts up inclines and is a useful method of moving parts between machines and feeding small parts for automatic assembly.

OVERHEAD MOVEMENT

There are considerable advantages in handling material overhead rather than at floor level. More floor space is available for production work and greater flexibility of factory layout is possible. Overhead movement is also independent of variation in floor levels and can be used to move work between floors in multi-storey buildings.

Monorail. This type of conveyor consists of an I-section beam which is attached to the ceiling, and from which is suspended a mobile hoist. The material to be handled is lifted by the hoist and then moved horizontally to another position under the path of the beam. The vertical and horizontal movements can be controlled electrically or manually from the ground, although many larger monorail hoists have an overhead travelling cab. Some installations have extensive coverage with systems of points to take the hoist on the selected track. There is a very wide variety of applications, chiefly for intermittent handling in machine shops and stores.

Chain Conveyors. Although mechanical details vary, these conveyors are basically an overhead-mounted endless chain which takes a fixed path round the factory and from which the material being moved is suspended. The conveyor descends to a suitable height for loading and unloading and, on some designs, extremely sharp bends are possible. Apart from transporting material, this type of conveyor can carry work through processes such as bonderizing, painting and plating, and can also serve as limited storage for work in progress. Automatic unloading of the conveyor at selected points and the transfer of work from one conveyor system to another is possible by means of pre-selector switches. The disadvantage of having to wait until the conveyor brings the correct part to a particular work station can be overcome, on some designs of overhead conveyor, by stops which allow a small bank of work to be built up at each operation.

Cranes. Cranes provide overhead movement in the whole rectangular or circular area served by them and not just along a track, as in the case of a conveyor. One of the most common factory cranes is the travelling bridge crane which spans parallel overhead tracks carried on the columns of the building or on piers. Across the bridge runs a trolley and on the trolley is a winch which raises and lowers the material. The hoisting and horizontal movement of the crane is usually electrically controlled either from the ground or from a cab mounted on the bridge. Where travelling bridge cranes cannot be accommodated, or where lifting is needed in a few locations only, jib cranes are often used. The hoist unit is mounted on a horizontal I-section jib which is supported on a column. In some, the jib pivots on bearings attached to a stanchion at the side of the building, the area of movement, however, being reduced to a semicircle. Small hand-operated wheeled cranes are used to assist operators and setters in moving heavy tools and attachments to and from machines. Cranes and hoists fitted with electromagnetic lifting devices can be used for handling ferrous sheet and scrap material. Cranes are not used directly for flow production but are widely employed in heavy engineering and used for intermittent movement in jobbing and batch production.

VERTICAL MOVEMENT

Lifts. Vertical movement over fixed paths is required in multi-storey factories. Intermittent vertical movement is obtained by lifts; they provide a fast and flexible means of movement between floors. Where continuous vertical movement is required, it can be provided by a suspended tray type lift. The work is loaded on a series of trays mounted between two endless chains which are taken over sprockets at the top and bottom of the lift shaft. Small parts can be loaded into work tins which are then placed on the trays. This type of lift would be suitable for connecting a parts stores with the other floors of a multi-storey building. Loading and unloading of the trays can be effected automatically.

Bucket Elevators. Granular or powdery material can be lifted vertically by using a bucket elevator in which small buckets are attached to vertically-moving belts or chains.

Spiral Chutes. These provide vertically downward movement and can be of the smooth or roller base type. Care must be taken to protect the material on its journey against damage and spillage. Although gravity drops do not require power, the cost of protecting the material may make this method of vertical movement an expensive one.

COMBINED VERTICAL AND HORIZONTAL MOVEMENT

Most of the equipment already described is capable of moving material both horizontally and vertically, although movement in the second direction is usually strictly limited; for instance, flat-belt conveyors can only move work up or down slight inclines.

Flight Conveyors. Flight or scraper conveyors are an effective way of moving materials up inclines too steep for belt conveyors. The flights are plates attached to a single or double strand of chain which push the material along a steel trough. A variant of the flight conveyor is the "en masse" type, where free flowing powdery or granular material is moved along a totally enclosed dust-proof housing by skeleton-type links or flights, which become buried in the material being moved.

Portable drag flight conveyors are valuable for stacking piling

Management of Production

and moving components between operations. They can be used, as shown in fig. 6.2, in a press shop when there is a series of operations

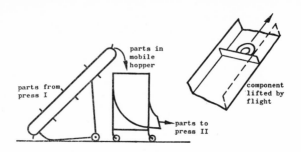

parts in
mobile
hopper

parts from
press I

component
lifted by
flight

parts to
press II

FIG. 6.2 *Portable Drag Flight Conveyor.*

set up on adjacent presses. The parts ejected from the first operation tools fall on the drag flight conveyor and are transported to the top of a portable hopper from which they are available for the next operation.

Pneumatic Conveyors. Air flow is used to move material along pipes in pneumatic conveyors. One type employs a carrier into which the material to be moved is placed. The carrier is sucked at high speed along the tube and is used to convey articles such as documents, cash or small tools. A second type of pneumatic conveyor is used to handle bulk materials. Suction is used for granular substances like wheat or salt; fine powders such as starch are mixed with air as they enter the conveyor and become sufficiently fluid to be forced through the pipes by mechanical pressure.

HORIZONTAL NON-FIXED PATH EQUIPMENT

Non-fixed path equipment has greater flexibility, and manually propelled trucks are a traditional method of moving work round factories. Old prints show that wheelbarrows were the main means of materials handling in the sixteenth century, and in one well-known Midland factory they were being used until a few years ago to transport parts from the stores to the assembly line.

Hand Trucks. There is a wide variety of one, two, three and four-wheeled trucks which provide an inexpensive method for intermittent short-distance movements. Hand trucks should not be used as the main method of materials handling but can usefully supplement powered equipment.

An interesting system of handling is the use of live skids, fig. 6.3. These skids consist of a small platform with wheels at one end and

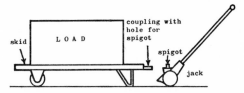

FIG. 6.3 *Live Skid with Two Wheeled Jack.*

legs and a coupling at the other. When a two-wheeled jack is placed under the coupling it lifts the legs of the skid, enabling the material to be moved as if on a four-wheeled truck.

Palletized Handling. A major development in handling has been the movement of material in unit loads, which are obtained by collecting the material to be moved into suitably large loads instead of moving it piecemeal in small lots. Time and effort are saved by moving in unit rather than smaller loads, as anyone who has used a tray to clear a table will appreciate. Powered handling devices have enabled larger unit loads to be moved and stacked, and pallets have provided the means of building up unit loads.

The type of palletization chosen will depend on the material to be handled. Some articles such as goods packed in cartons can be built into rectangular shapes and are often sufficiently strong to resist crushing when stacked. These items can be made up into unit loads on

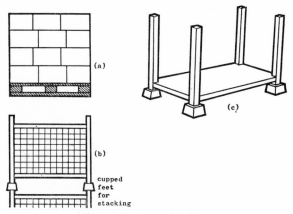

FIG. 6.4 *Types of Pallet.*
(a) *flat wooden pallet with load,* (b) *box pallet with wire mesh sides,* (c) *post pallet.*

flat pallets, thin steel bands often being used to strap the loads to the pallets. Pallets with uprights at the corners, called post pallets, are used for crushable or awkwardly shaped material, and box pallets are employed for smaller parts. There is a number of variants of each main type of pallet, for instance, box pallets can be fitted with drop bottoms, so that parts can be discharged into hoppers. Three types of pallet are illustrated in fig. 6.4.

Fork-lift Trucks. These trucks have been specially developed to handle pallets; they are usually battery-driven for internal work, although petrol or diesel-driven models are available. At the front of the truck are two tapered prongs which are run under the palletized load; these forks can be raised to lift the load from the floor and tilted backwards to keep the load on the forks while in transit. The trucks will lift the pallets so that they can be stacked one on top of the other, the forks being raised by telescopic masts for high stacking, fig. 6.5. A large

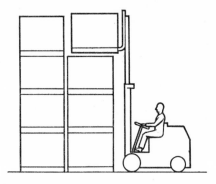

Fig. 6.5 *Fork Lift Truck Stacking Pallets Four High.*

variety of attachments can be fitted to fork-lift trucks, in place of the forks, for specialized handling; these include cranes, booms, rotating heads and squeeze clamps.

With most types of fork-lift truck the operator sits on the vehicle; where trucks are being used almost exclusively for stacking in stores, pedestrian controlled stacking trucks are often preferable to conventional fork-lift trucks, due to the narrower aisles in which they can operate. Some designs of stacker truck can stack in aisle widths of 6 ft, whereas conventional fork-lift trucks of similar capacity require aisles almost twice as wide. The calculation of aisle widths is dealt with later in this chapter.

Hand Pallet Trucks. These hand-propelled trucks have forks which lift pallets manually or hydraulically just clear of the floor, enabling them to be wheeled away. When power-operated equipment is available, hand pallet trucks should not be used for long journeys and 75 ft should be the normal operating range. The use of this type of truck or of a powered pallet truck of similar design can reduce the number of more expensive fork-lift trucks required.

Tractor Trains. These consist of a tractor pulling a number of four-wheeled trolleys on which material is loaded. Most types of trolley can take a palletized load, and tractor trains may be profitably used for long-distance moves sometimes necessary in large factories. Tractor trains are extensively used at larger railway stations to move luggage along platforms.

Platform Trucks. The material is loaded on a platform, which is usually electrically propelled, with the operator sitting either on the truck and driving it, or walking and guiding it. A wide variety of loads can be handled by this type of vehicle.

Straddle Trucks. The straddle truck, fig. 6.6 is a self-loading device

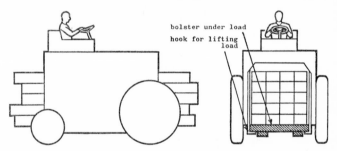

bolster under load
hook for lifting load

FIG. 6.6 *Straddle Truck with Timber Load.*

which is used for long loads such as timber, pipes and structural steel. It is designed so that it straddles the load, grips it, lifts it and takes it to a new position. The load is then lowered to the ground and the truck driven away.

STORAGE

Palletized Loads. This system of storage does not require bins, racks or shelves: all that is required is a clear floor space, adequate ceiling height and a suitable fork-lift or stacker truck. Pallets are often stacked in blocks 4 or 5 high, thus utilizing space better than in most other types of stores. When pallets are used to store different parts, care must be taken to allow aisles between the blocks so that any pallet can be removed without having first to move too many other pallets. The aisles will have to be from 10 to 12 ft wide for a conventional fork-lift truck to manoeuvre, and the pallets should be arranged in rows two deep for easy accessibility.

The minimum aisle width for right-angle stacking can be calculated. In fig. 6.7

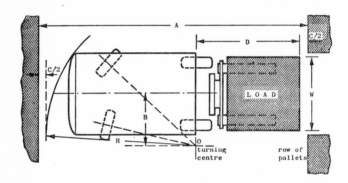

FIG. 6.7 *Clearance for Right-angle Stacking.*

A = aisle width,
D = distance from centre-line of front axle to front end of load,
R = minimum turning radius of truck,
O = turning centre for minimum radius,
B = distance from O to centre-line of truck,
C = minimum total clearance,
W = width of load.

It will be seen for loads of width less than $2B$

$$A = R + C + D$$

If the width of load is greater than $2B$

$$A = R + C + \sqrt{\left\{ D^2 + \left(\frac{W}{2} - B \right)^2 \right\}}.$$

A disadvantage of the floor stacking of pallets, particularly where a variety of parts is being stored, is that unless the part required happens to be at the top of a stack the pallets above it have first to be removed. This difficulty can be overcome if pallet racks are used; these are so designed that pallets can be inserted or withdrawn independently of any pallets located above them.

Where a travelling bridge crane is available it can be used instead of a fork-lift truck for stacking. As the handling is done from overhead floor space can be better utilized because pallets can be removed from the centre of the block. Typical arrangements of pallets for fork-lift truck and bridge crane handling are shown in fig. 6.8.

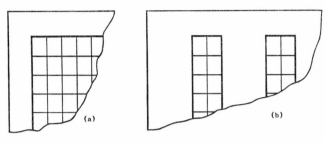

FIG. 6.8

Work Tins. In light engineering many of the parts are not produced in sufficient quantity to be stored directly in pallets, some other type of container therefore being required both in the factory and in the stores. For this purpose work tins or tote boxes are employed. Sizes frequently used in this country are 2 ft × 1 ft × 6 in. deep, and a smaller tin measuring 1 ft × 1 ft × 6 in. deep. The tins are usually constructed from galvanized sheet steel, have handles at each end and a slot for an identification ticket. Different parts can be stored in the same work tin by using sub-divisions, or smaller containers which fit into the tin.

Although work tins are often temporarily stored on the factory floor while containing work-in-progress, stacking racks built from angle iron and holding a dozen or more tins can be used to make up unit loads. While palletized handling of work tins is suitable when a large volume of parts is being manufactured, hand and platform trucks are widely used for moving work tins between sections. For dragging the tins short distances, a bent piece of ¼ in. diameter rod about 3 ft long, an industrial shepherd's crook, is a most useful device. When work tins are being used to work from, or into, they should be placed on stillages alongside the process so that stooping is avoided and reaching minimized.

Racks and Shelves. Racks and shelves can be used for the storage of work tins. Racks have definite locations for the work tins and in some types the tins are tilted forward so that their contents can be more easily seen. Shelves are not so restrictive as racks to particular sizes of work tin or to the shapes of material stored on them. Although racks and shelves are found chiefly in stores, they can also be used to store work-in-progress in machine shops and assembly sections. Their use reduces floor space occupied by work-in-progress, yet provides easy accessibility. Lifting into racks or on to shelves should offer no difficulty as the loads put into the tins should not exceed normal lifting capacity.

Bins. Bins used in stores are of wooden or steel construction, having compartments into which parts are stacked or tipped. They suffer from the disadvantage that components have to be removed from their original containers for binning and then put into another container for despatch. Apart from the additional cost of double handling, there is an increased risk of damage to the parts. Bins do, however, provide a suitable method of storing small low-stock items such as consumable tools. Although bins, racks and shelves are usually arranged in back-to-back rows, improved floor space utilization can be obtained by mounting them on rollers. The rollers engage in parallel tracks which allow the units in the front rows to be pushed aside to reach parts stored in the back rows which are fixed. The use of this arrangement considerably reduces the total aisle space required for a given size of stores.

ORGANIZATION OF MATERIALS HANDLING

The planning and specification of materials handling equipment should be the responsibility of a handling engineer who is normally responsible to the chief production engineer. In small companies the chief production engineer may handle this work himself; in large organizations the materials handling engineer may have a sizeable department working for him. Another arrangement which can work very satisfactorily is to combine the responsibility for materials handling and plant layout in one section.

A planned maintenance routine on handling equipment should be drawn up and operated by the maintenance department. Probably it will also be their responsibility to attend to the daily charging of battery-driven handling equipment.

It would be quite unsuitable in most factories if the day-to-day operation of materials handling was the responsibility of the handling engineer. Perhaps the most satisfactory arrangement is to give operating responsibility to the production controller, particularly if he is also responsible for stores. Various methods of arranging for despatch and collection of work within the factory by non-fixed path equipment are possible. They fall into two categories, the regular journey and the centralized system; often both are used in the same factory. The first method employs a pick-up and delivery service at fixed time intervals; although this is satisfactory for moving most items, it will not move urgent work quickly or rapidly clear an unexpectedly large volume of work. A centralized system employs a control point which receives requests for material to be moved and issues instructions to truck drivers. An effective method of operating such a system in a large factory is to have radio communication between the control point and the trucks, so that they can be called up wherever they happen to be working.

Centralized control can be applied to fixed route equipment such as conveyors; this aspect of materials handling is likely to be of growing importance with increased automation. Manually operated control stations may be employed, although in some systems input information is fed to the control apparatus in the form of punched card or tape. Work can be automatically loaded on and discharged from conveyors, marshalled on storage conveyors and then fed in correct sequence to the factory. Photoelectric devices can be used for a wide variety of control tasks. They can discriminate between sizes of packages on conveyors; they can also operate mechanisms to divert work to other conveyors and operate loading and unloading devices.

7

Value Analysis and Standardization

VALUE ANALYSIS

Value analysis, which is sometimes called value engineering, was originated in the U.S.A. in the late 1940s. It is a method by which the value of a product can be maximised by consideration of both cost and function. Value analysis is not simply directed at reducing cost, frequently improvements in value and reliability are achieved while the cost is left unaltered.

PROCEDURE

One of the most important aspects of value analysis is the team approach, in which the members of a team drawn from different departments work in co-operation with the common purpose of improving value. A typical team might consist of the value engineer as chairman with representatives from sales, purchasing, costs, manufacturing and production engineering. In some larger companies teams may be constituted on a full-time basis but a more usual arrangement is a full-time value engineer co-ordinating the work of a part-time team. A procedure often followed in a value analysis project is:

1. Collection of information on the cost and function of the existing design.
2. Speculation on ways of increasing value.
3. Investigation of proposals.
4. Recommendations on methods of increasing value.
5. Implementation of improvements.

A factor contributing to the success of value analysis is the free and constructive exchange of ideas which are encouraged at team meetings. No idea, however revolutionary, is rejected out of hand at the speculation stage but it is noted, sifted and where appropriate, tried out.

Initially it will be necessary to specify areas of activity and allocate work priorities. As with method study the priorities should be dictated by senior management; obvious candidates for attention are products which represent a large proportion of the company sales and those which are making an unsatisfactory contribution to profits or customer satisfaction. Apart from designs which are already in production, value analysis can be effectively employed on new products once they have reached the prototype stage. In this way the product goes into production with maximum value and expensive modifications due to subsequent changes in design and production methods are avoided.

A useful device when planning value analysis work is to find where the bulk of the cost lies. In most engineering assemblies it is found that individual parts vary considerably in cost with a high proportion of the cost concentrated in a small proportion of the parts, either because of their high intrinsic value or because of their multiple use in the finished assembly. A distribution such as that shown in fig 7:1 helps the team to concentrate their main effort on a

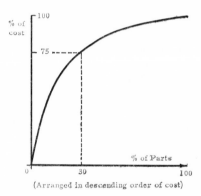

(Arranged in descending order of cost)

FIG. 7.1 *Distribution of Parts Value.*

comparatively small number of expensive parts where large savings are most likely to be obtained. In Chapter 13 it will be seen that use is made of a similar cost distribution, fig 13:6, to determine appropriate levels of production control. Unequal distributions of this type are found in other fields, for instance the causes of parts being rejected by inspection and the sales value of a range of products (fig. 7:2 shows individual sales values plotted by product). These uneven distributions are associated with the economist Pareto, who used them in his studies of the distribution of wealth.

G

GAINING ACCEPTANCE

It is frequently difficult to gain acceptance for value analysis due to a natural reluctance to make changes and a fear that shortcomings will be uncovered. However, if full endorsement is given by senior management acceptance lower down the organisation will be relatively easier. Good management is always seeking to improve profitability and is likely to see in value analysis a replacement for piecemeal and unorganised attempts at design improvement and cost reduction. Often it is possible to convince doubting management of the benefit to be obtained from value analysis by demonstrating what can be achieved by analysing a product which is being undersold by a competitor or which is unprofitable. It is of interest to note that the U.S. Department of Defence not only applies value analysis to their own purchasing operations, but often employs it indirectly by requiring its use in vendors' factories.

STANDARDIZATION

One of the methods of increasing the value of a range of products is by simplifying it; this and other aspects of standardization are discussed in the rest of the chapter.

THE NEED FOR REDUCING VARIETY

The growth of uneconomic variety is likely to occur in most manufacturing companies. In a desire to sell more, sales managers often persuade managements to introduce new models for which there is little demand. Designers in their quest for perfection frequently design parts and specify materials only slightly different from those already being used. Even if designers wish to minimize variety, it is often an almost impossible task to sort out what is available from the tens of thousands of different parts and materials used by a large company. Production engineers are likely to specify different types of manufacturing equipment without due regard to the capabilities of that already installed. To reduce this haphazard growth of variety it is necessary for management to adopt a policy of standardization and simplification and for the departments concerned to understand fully and implement this policy.

Before the subject is considered in greater detail the terms standardization and simplification should be examined. Standardization refers to the preparation of specifications such as the composition of materials or of criteria relating to the size and quality of products. Examples of national standards are to be found in the wide range of specifications issued by the British Standards Institution. Simplification means the deliberate reduction of unnecessary variety; the availability of suitable standards will assist in simplification.

Let us now consider four important applications of standardization and simplification:

(*a*) finished products,
(*b*) components,
(*c*) materials,
(*d*) production equipment.

FINISHED PRODUCT STANDARDIZATION

A useful starting point in considering whether to reduce the number of models of a certain product in order that the remainder may be standardized is to review the volume of sales achieved by each model. It will probably be found that comparatively few models account for the majority of the sales income; a quarter of the models accounting for three quarters of the total sales is not unusual. Before a decision is made to eliminate any of the less popular lines it is important that the profit or loss made by each should be examined. The amount of profit or loss contributed by each model may be difficult to determine, particularly where several models are manufactured in the same factory. An analysis by model of sales and profit is shown graphically in fig. 7.2. The reason for profit being considered is to

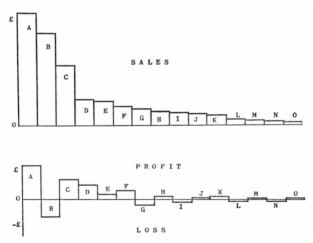

FIG. 7.2 *Analysis of Model Sales and Profits.*

avoid standardizing on unprofitable models, in fact the popularity of certain models may be due to their uneconomically low selling prices.

In many surveys of this type, however, it is found that the models with the largest sales are subsidizing the losses made by those with a low demand. In some companies, such as those supplying the motor and aircraft industries, a manufacturer cannot arbitrarily reduce his range of products. If persuasion cannot induce the customer to accept something from the standard range, then a fully economic price should be charged for the non-standard model; by doing this the customer will be made to realize the advantage of purchasing a standard design.

The advantages of standardizing finished products result largely from lower production costs, which can be passed on to the customer as lower selling prices. Assuming that the total volume of sales remains constant, then larger production runs of the standardized designs will be possible. These longer production runs offer the following advantages:

1. Greater mechanization is possible as the larger quantities of parts and assemblies warrant higher expenditure on manufacturing and handling equipment.

2. Less direct labour is required due to the larger proportion of work performed by machines.

3. Lower grade labour can be employed as tasks will be simplified. Unskilled and semi-skilled labour is cheaper and more easily obtained than highly skilled workers.

4. Fewer changeovers of production equipment are required. This means that fewer setters are needed and higher machine utilization is possible.

5. Lower stocks of raw material, work-in-progress and finished parts are required due to the more continuous type of production.

6. Simpler production control is possible as the result of reduced product variety.

The disadvantages of standardizing finished products chiefly affect sales and design; they are summarized below:

1. Business may be lost if customers cannot purchase the model they require.

2. New models and major design modifications are more difficult to introduce due to less flexible production facilities and to the high cost of specialized production equipment. Major model changes in the British car industry now occur about each 5 years with periodic "face lifts" to bridge the time gap.

3. Changes in public taste may affect a company with a standardized product range more seriously than one with a diverse range of products. The "eggs" are in fewer "baskets".

COMPONENT STANDARDIZATION

Although finished products may vary widely in appearance and performance, the components and sub-assemblies used in them can to a large extent be common. Also, within a product itself it may be possible to reduce the variety of components by designing a single part to take the place of two or more parts in the non-simplified design.

Component standardization reduces production costs, because these lower costs result from longer production runs and are similar to those stated as advantages of finished product standardization. In addition, the customer can be offered a wide range of finished models made largely from standardized parts. For instance, a basic range of a few models can be enlarged to several hundred by comparatively minor changes, usually in outside appearance. The variety thus offered is normally provided where it costs the least, and major items requiring expensive tooling remain standard to a wide range of models. This type of standardization can be found in the British Motor Industry.

Component standardization can greatly assist servicing. Not only is it important to produce a good product, but in most cases it must be backed by a national and, often, a world-wide service organization. The cost of setting up such an organization will depend to a large extent on the variety of components used in the company's products.

A disadvantage of component standardization is that in an attempt to reduce variety, a common component may be used which is either technically or aesthetically unsuitable. There is also the possibility that the designer will select too expensive a standard. It must be said that these disadvantages are not the result of component standardization but of bad design; there is, however, in most component standardization the need for some compromise between the part specified and the one which is ideally suited to the job.

MATERIAL STANDARDIZATION

Material standardization can be applied to both the direct material used in the product and to indirect materials such as oils and greases. There are two main processes involved when creating material standards. First, the variety of material sizes ordered can be simplified, and secondly the number of different types of materials specified can be reduced. If fewer material sizes are to be used a suitable range of standard sizes will have to be decided upon and any necessary tooling changes carried out.

The advantages of reducing material variety are lower total stocks of material, simplified purchasing, easier storekeeping and the possibility of negotiating better terms with the supplier. So far as the disadvantages are concerned, there is the possibility that an unsatisfactory standard will be chosen, specifying either too expensive a material or one which fails in service. Size standardization is likely to give a lower material utilization as more material will be wasted as swarf or off-cuts.

PRODUCTION EQUIPMENT STANDARDIZATION

Standardization of production equipment is often neglected although it can result in considerable advantages. Generally there is a wide variety of plant available and if each part were to be manufactured on the ideal machine there would be considerable diversification in the equipment used. In batch production factories where similar types of machines are grouped together and are able, with tooling changes, to process a large number of different components, difficulties arise when machines of the same general capacities have differences in detail design. These design differences often prevent batches of work being switched from one machine to another due to tooling not fitting or attachments not being transferable. This lack of flexibility is likely to result in low machine utilization as more machines would be required than would have been with standardized machine tools. Maintenance is also made more difficult, and for the same degree of protection in the case of breakdown a larger stock of spares will have to be carried.

There is a danger, of course, that unwise standards will be chosen: for instance, it would be foolish to install all high tonnage presses in a general press shop because they are capable of doing any of the work routed there. In these circumstances a standardized range of presses varying in tonnage would be required so that advantage could be taken of faster production rates and the lower cost of smaller presses.

CLASSIFICATION SYSTEMS

Classification Systems can be of great value in material and component standardization. Each item is allocated a meaningful part number which provides a basis for the systematic application of variety reduction. The numbers consist either of digits or a combination of digits and letters and are normally arranged so that the classification proceeds from the general to the particular.

An example of a code number used by E. G. Brisch and Partners, Ltd., is 1174–401 which indicates bright mild steel tube, round seamless 0·750 in O/D × 10 S.W.G.* The code is made up as shown:

Class	1 * * * _ * * *	Primary material
Sub Class	* 1 * * _ * * *	Iron and carbon steel
Group	* * 7 * _ * * *	Tube
Series	* * * 4 _ * * *	Mild Steel
	* * * * _ 4 * *	Round seamless specified lengths
	* * * * _ * 0 1	0·750 O/D × 10 S.W.G.

The allocation of classification numbers should bring together all similar items and at once reveal any duplication of parts or materials. It also provides a quick reference for designers to what already exists, and enables them to examine quickly the existing range of materials and components to see if any are suitable for incorporation in a new design.

Classification systems are difficult to design and although they may have features in common, systems should be compiled for their specific applications. One difficulty is in deciding which basis of similarity between the parts or materials to recognize in the classification. For instance, is the system to be based on the use of the part or on its form? The code is of necessity designed to meet existing needs and once designed its form is set. Account must, however, be taken of future changes in products and space left in the framework of the system for new parts and materials to be added. Unless adequate space has been allowed there will come a time when new items will have to be allocated numbers not properly related to the original system.

BRITISH STANDARDS INSTITUTION

This is the national standardizing body, founded in 1901, which deals with standards in all industries except agriculture and medicine. It is independent and non-profit making, deriving its support from industry, the government and from the sale of its publications. The objects of the Institution are set out in a Royal Charter issued in 1929. They include the co-ordination of producers and users for standardization and simplification of materials, production and distribution, the reduction of unnecessary variety and the setting up of standards for quality and dimensions.

Before starting a project the Institution must satisfy itself that there is a recognized need for the work. The standards issued are

---

* Maximum ex minimo, E. G. Brisch, *Journal I. Prod. E.,* Vol. 33, No. 6.

compiled by committees composed of representatives from organizations having an interest in the Standard. Before publication the draft standard is widely circulated for criticism and comment. The Standards are not compulsory although in certain products such as crash helmets and car safety belts there is a strong moral obligation on manufacturers to accept them. If products comply with a British Standard Specification, the maker can indicate this by marking them with the kite-mark emblem.

The British Standards Institution is not concerned with standardization policies adopted by individual companies although they and the British Productivity Council have done much to interest industry in the benefits of standardization and simplification.

INTERNATIONAL STANDARDIZATION

To an exporting nation such as the United Kingdom, international standards are of great importance. If importing countries insist that their various national standards are observed, designs have to be altered and a standard model becomes a "special". So that home standards line up with export requirements, British Standards are often compiled with international standards in mind; where there are no international standards, those of the major importing countries are taken into account.

The work of international standardization is carried out under the aegis of the International Organization for Standardization (ISO) with the electrical aspects covered by the International Electrotechnical Commission (IEC). Most industrialized countries are members of ISO, which was founded after World War II to take over the work of the International Federation of National Standardizing Associations. The ISO does not issue standards of independent validity, but makes recommendations which are included in the national standards of the collaborating countries.

Work Study and Ergonomics

WORK study consists of two techniques, method study and work measurement; it is frequently associated with incentives, job evaluation and merit rating. Any situation where work is being done is suitable for the application of work study, although when applied to office work it is usually referred to as organization and methods. The terminology used has been standardized by the British Standards Institution and can be found in B.S.3138:1959, "Glossary of Terms in Work Study".

DEVELOPMENT OF WORK STUDY

Almost all the ideas used in work study have come from the United States, the pioneer work being done by F. W. Taylor and F. B. Gilbreth at the end of the last century and at the beginning of the present one. At first the two main techniques developed separately. Taylor interested himself chiefly in time study, a method of work measurement, while Gilbreth shunned work measurement and studied ways of making human movement more effective. C. E. Bedaux, who is still a controversial figure, did much to introduce time study as we know it today and was one of the first people to bring it to this country in the 1920s. Since World War II the application of work study in the United Kingdom has greatly increased in the manufacturing industries and new applications have been developed in agriculture and in hospitals.

THE USE OF WORK STUDY TO INCREASE PRODUCTIVITY

There are many ways in which productivity or industrial efficiency can be increased. Let us briefly review the main methods.

1. Develop new basic processes or introduce major improvements to existing ones; a long-term and expensive method which can produce almost limitless increases in productivity.
2. Install new and more highly-mechanized equipment. This is again expensive and usually the result of re-equipment policies often requiring several years to carry out; it can bring very large productivity increases.

3. Improve product design. By redesign and by development the products can be made easier to manufacture; standardization and simplification will also assist in the rationalization of product design.

4. Reduce the work content and improve existing processes. This offers a quick return and is a comparatively inexpensive method of increasing productivity. The improvement achieved will, however, be limited by the existing product designs and the manufacturing equipment in use.

Method study can assist in all these ways of increasing productivity, particularly the last. Work measurement is chiefly used to improve the effectiveness of existing processes.

HUMAN FACTORS

Unless workers' feelings are considered the best results will not be obtained from work study and in extreme cases its use may have to be abandoned.

New ideas are more easily accepted when there is an atmosphere of mutual confidence between management and workers. This trust is built up only after years of fair dealing by management. If work study is introduced into an atmosphere already polluted by suspicion it is likely to be made the excuse for disputes.

Work study aims to raise productivity, hence to improve living standards for everyone. If, however, by the introduction of work study into a factory the lot of the average worker is worsened, it is likely to be vigorously opposed. Where workers have not been doing a fair day's work, work study is likely to be resisted as it threatens to terminate easily earned wages and pleasantly slack conditions.

Let us examine some of the other factors which will create resistance when a proposal to use work study is announced.

1. Reluctance to change methods of working, particularly among the skilled and the older workers.

2. Suspicion of the techniques to be used, particularly stop-watch timing.

3. Fear that as the output of each worker increases there will not be enough work to go round and some workers will be made redundant.

4. Fear, usually in the older or slower workers, that they may not be able to maintain the necessary pace and will be dismissed. They may also think that they will injure their health by working too hard.

These fears must be appreciated by management and steps taken to allay them. First, work study should be explained to supervisors and workers' representatives so that misconceptions can be removed. Undertakings must be given that older workers will be sympathetically treated and that there will be no redundancy. Redundancy can usually be avoided by not engaging new workers for a period and letting the natural labour wastage reduce the size of the working force. Some idea should also be given of the likely level of wages; if the workers' rate of working is going to increase, they will naturally want increased earnings. Higher wages can be provided because a suitable incentive scheme based on work measurement should produce more output per operator; often a one-third increase over non-incentive output can be obtained. Proportionally higher wages can therefore be afforded and should be paid.

METHOD STUDY

Method study is the critical examination of ways of doing work in order that they may be made more effective. It may be claimed that this can be done by anyone applying common sense, and a large proportion of methods improvements are obtained in this way. Method study, however, differs from ordinary common sense in the systematic way in which it is applied and particularly by the techniques used of examining the existing method. The usual procedure for conducting a method study is:

1. Select work to be studied.
2. Record existing method of working.
3. Critically examine existing method.
4. Develop improved method.
5. Install improved method.
6. Maintain new method.

SELECTING WORK TO BE STUDIED

The work selected for examination should offer a high return on the cost of the study. Although this is usually measured in terms of cost savings, improvements in unpleasant or fatiguing work can do much to create and maintain good labour relations. It is better for management to decide which work is to be method-studied, although if this lead is not forthcoming the selection will have to be made by the chief work-study officer. The types of work chosen are likely to include:
1. Work with high direct labour content.
2. Jobs with a large and continuing demand.
3. Processes which are production bottlenecks.

4. Jobs on which there have been low earnings or excessive overtime.
5. Fatiguing, unpleasant or dangerous work.

It is unwise to start method study in a section of the factory where bad labour relations exist. Work-study staff walking about with note books and asking questions may be the "last straw".

RECORDING EXISTING METHOD

There is a large number of charts which offer concise and standardized methods of recording the existing method of working. The temptation to sit comfortably in an office and construct a chart from operation layouts or similar documents should be resisted, as the charts ought to be based on actual observations of the method being used. Of the charts which could be used probably only one or two will be really suitable for each job. Normally the chart which gives the best "bird's eye view" of the process should be used first, with more detailed recording methods employed, if necessary, at a later stage. Charts can be divided into three main classes: process charts, charts with a time scale and those which show a path of movement.

Process charts are used to show the sequence of events and employ the following symbols:

   ◯   operation

   ◁   transport

   ▽   permanent storage

   D   temporary storage or delay

   ☐   inspection

There are three types of process charts. The first, the outline process chart, uses only operation and inspection symbols and gives

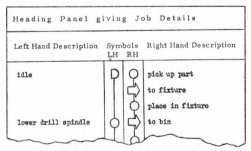

FIG. 8.1 *Two-handed Process Chart.*

an overall picture. The second is the flow process chart, which provides more detail and makes use of all five symbols. The two-handed process chart is the third type, and it shows the activity of the hands in relation to each other. Examples of an outline process chart and a flow process chart are shown respectively in fig. 4.5(*b*), and fig. 4.11 (*b*); a two-handed process chart is shown in fig. 8.1.

Another class of charts makes use of a time scale against which the activity is plotted. The more important is the multiple activity chart on which the activity of more than one subject, either worker or equipment, is shown against a common time scale. A simple multiple activity chart is shown in fig. 8.2. The other time scale chart, the simo

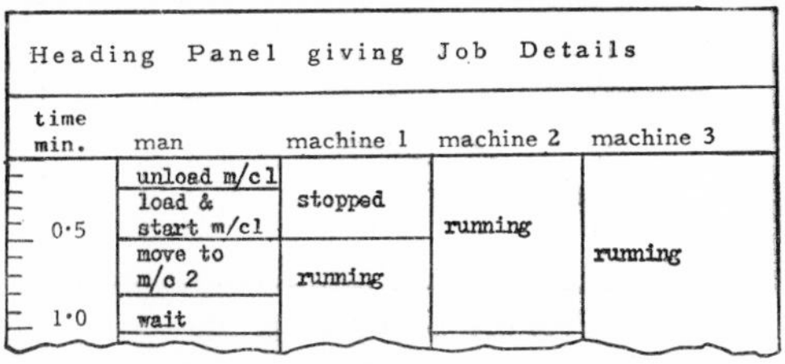

Heading Panel giving Job Details				
time min.	man	machine 1	machine 2	machine 3
0·5	unload m/cl load & start m/cl	stopped	running	running
	move to m/c 2	running		
1·0	wait			

FIG. 8.2 *Multiple Activity Chart.*

chart, is used to record simultaneously the detailed body movements or reasons for lack of movement. Therbligs (the word is an anagram of Gilbreth's name) are used to indicate the fundamental motions, and the time scale of the chart is divided into "winks", which are time intervals of $^1/_{2,000}$ minute. A film is taken of the operation which is

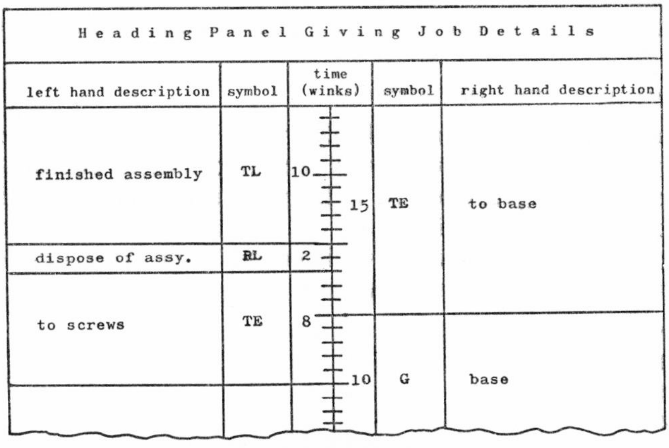

Heading Panel Giving Job Details					
left hand description	symbol	time (winks)	symbol	right hand description	
finished assembly	TL	10			
		15	TE	to base	
dispose of assy.	RL	2			
to screws	TE	8			
		10	G	base	

FIG. 8.3 *Simo Chart.*
Therblig symbols used: TL transport loaded, RL release load,
TE transport empty, G grasp.

then transferred to a simo chart, a fragment of which is shown in fig. 8.3.

The third class of chart indicates movement of workers, equipment or materials. In this group is the flow diagram which shows on a floor plan where specific activities are carried out. A string diagram is somewhat similar to a flow diagram, except that a piece of thread is used to trace and measure the pattern of movement during a specified sequence of operations. Figure 4.11(*a*) shows a flow diagram and fig. 8.4 a string diagram.

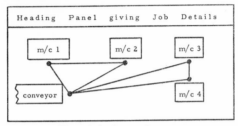

FIG. 8.4 *String Diagram.*

The use of a film has already been mentioned in connexion with the simo chart. A film taken by a ciné camera can also be used for the otherwise difficult task of recording the activities of several workers and machines working as a team, or to record long or irregular work cycles. The usual filming speed for this type of work is 1 frame per second, which provides a considerable saving in film as compared with normal filming speed of 16 frames per second. From the film, multiple operation or other suitable charts can be prepared.

EXAMINING EXISTING METHOD

The existing methods appropriately charted offer a suitable basis for examination. The most widely used method of analysis in this country is the questioning technique. This technique should be applied first to the key operations, and it consists of a series of questions designed to examine systematically what is being done. The following aspects of the existing method are examined:

purpose
method
sequence
place
person

Each of these aspects is examined by a series of four questions. The first establishes the existing facts, the second challenges these facts by asking why, the third question asks for alternatives to the existing method, and the last asks what action should be taken. An example of the type of form used for this technique of analysis is shown in fig. 8.5. It is important that all alternatives, however ridiculous they

PRESENT	FACTS	ALTERNATIVES	ACTION
what is done	why	what else	what should be done
how it is done.	why that way	how else	how it should be done
when it is done	why then	when else	when it should be done
where it is done	why there	where else	where it should be done
who does it	why that person	who else	who should do it

FIG. 8.5 *Critical Examination Sheet.*

may seem, are considered; some apparently impractical suggestions often lead to profitable new lines of thought.

An alternative to the questioning technique is the possibility guide and check list. The possibility guide proposes consideration of changes to—

raw material

product design

tools workplace and equipment

hand and body movements

The check list enables processes to be examined in greater detail. It consists of a large number of questions which, when answered, should enable a better method to be devised. A check list may be constructed for each type of chart. Part of a check list used to examine multiple operation charts is shown below:

1. Can any operation be eliminated?

(*a*) as unnecessary,

(*b*) by changing the order of work,

(*c*) by new or different equipment,

(*d*) by layout changes.

2. Can any delays be eliminated?
(*a*) by changing order of work,
(*b*) by changing the layout,
(*c*) by new or different equipment.

Whatever method of examination is used the problem should be considered first from the broad viewpoint, details of materials handling and operators' movements being considered only after the correct process has been determined. Every effort must be made to eliminate work; it may be satisfying to improve an operation but far better get rid of it altogether.

DEVELOPING NEW METHOD

Out of the critical examination of the old method should come ideas for its improvement. These ideas will have to be developed and discussed with the departments concerned. For instance, a suggested change in material will probably have to be discussed with the designer, the buyer and the production engineer. Some ideas will appear less attractive when talked over with the experts, but the work-study man must not allow himself to be unduly influenced by the person who tells him that all this has been tried before and did not work.

It will be necessary at this stage to estimate the time needed to make the proposed changes, the cost of the changes, and the savings that will result. In some companies a formal report may be required setting out the new method and presenting the case for its adoption. Shop supervision will have to be kept in the picture and the attitude of the workers to the proposed changes will have to be determined.

INSTALLATION OF NEW METHOD

After the new method has been fully developed and general acceptance obtained for it, installation can be planned. A minor change is usually handled by the work-study officer himself in co-operation with the departments concerned. A major change, however, will involve considerable detailed planning and is often best dealt with by holding regular meetings attended by representatives of the departments involved. The production engineering department will be responsible for specifying new plant and tooling, the maintenance department for the installation or re-positioning of plant, the personnel department for the procurement and training of workers, the production control department for building up stocks and with the issue of manufacturing orders, and shop supervision will be responsible for operating the new arrangements. If possible the installation should take place at a time that will cause the minimum loss of pro-tion, such as during the annual holiday or at a week-end. The work-study officer should be present during the changeover to encourage, assist and co-ordinate. He should not be panicked into making ill-considered changes to the new method resulting from teething troubles, which will probably occur during the "start-up" period. It will take a while before the new arrangements are running smoothly, and the work-study officer should consider the installation completed only when output has reached the predicted level.

MAINTAINING THE NEW METHOD

Once an improved method has been installed, it must be protected against unauthorized changes. This can be done by insisting that alterations to the manufacturing method can be made only if the proper authorization has first been obtained.

MOTION ECONOMY

Certain rules of human movement, work-place arrangement and tool design have been formulated to help devise economical methods of working. Some of the more important of these rules are noted below.

HUMAN MOVEMENTS

1. Both hands should not be idle unless during rest periods.
2. Arm motions should be simultaneous, symmetrical and opposite.
3. Minimum hand and other body motions should be used.
4. Continuous curved movements should be used and movements which produce sharp directional changes should be avoided.
5. The hands should be assisted by other parts of the body whenever possible.

WORKPLACE ARRANGEMENT

1. Work and tools should have fixed positions allocated to them so that habitual movements are encouraged.
2. Tools and material should be located as near to the operator as possible and within the most suitable working area. A diagram of these areas is shown in fig. 8.6.
3. Material and tools should be arranged so that they are in the best sequence for correct motions.

H

4. The operator should be comfortably seated with the bench at the correct height and the workplace well-lighted.

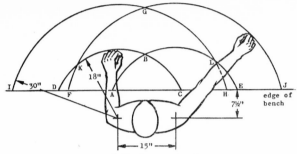

FIG. 8.6 *Normal Working Area for Average Man.*
Best working areas. *High visual requirements: Best A–B–C,*
Next K–G–L–B, Next F–G–H; low visual requirements: Best
D–B–E, Next I–G–J

TOOL DESIGN

1. The work should be clamped mechanically and not held by the hand.
2. Machine controls should be positioned so that they can be used with the minimum operator movement and so that adequate force can be applied to them.

WORK MEASUREMENT

Work measurement determines the time required to carry out a specific task at a defined standard of performance by a qualified operator.

Although work sometimes has to be measured when conducting a method study, work measurement is normally undertaken only after the method of working has been thoroughly examined and satisfactorily established.

The principal work-measurement techniques are listed below:

1. Time study.
2. Synthesis.
3. Predetermined motion times.
4. Analytical estimating.
5. Activity sampling.

Work measurement has a number of important uses, in fact without it the work of production planning and cost control would be

seriously impaired. Six uses of work measurement are shown below:
1. As a basis of comparison between different methods of working;
2. To distribute work equally between members of a team;
3. For planning and machine loading;
4. To set standards of machine and labour productivity;
5. As the basis of an incentive scheme;
6. For costing, particularly to establish standard costs.

TIME STUDY

This is the most important and widely used method of work measurement. It was originated by Taylor at the turn of the century and modified by Bedaux when he introduced the present-day concept of rating.

PROCEDURE FOR TAKING A TIME STUDY

1. Inform the foreman that a particular job is to be studied.
2. Get to know the operator concerned and put him at ease.
3. Decide whether or not the method of working is satisfactory and if the operator is proficient. Unsatisfactory methods and untrained workers should not be timed.
4. Note all the relevant details of the jobs so that at any future time the exact method and conditions of working can be determined.
5. Where appropriate split the work cycle into suitable elements for timing. An element is a distinct operation or group of operations within the work cycle, preferably having a clearly defined end point and for convenience of timing and rating lasting not less than 3 seconds. Any non-repetitive or occasional elements should be separately noted.
6. Estimate the rate of working and time with a stop-watch each of the elements into which the work cycle has been divided. Frequently at least thirty cycles are noted and timed, alternatively the number of cycles to be timed can be found statistically. The concept of rating and a method of calculating how many cycles to time are described subsequently.
7. Calculate the basic time for each element which has been rated and timed. Basic time (using British Standard scale) = observed

time $\times \dfrac{\text{estimated B.S. rating.}}{100}$ Average the basic times for each of the elements and add these average times to obtain the basic time for the study.

8. Add allowances to the basic time for the study. A relaxation allowance is always given, this should be added elementally and is usually a minimum of 10 per cent but can be in excess of 100 per cent of the basic time for highly fatiguing work. A variety of relaxation allowance tables are in use, examples of these can be found in textbooks on work measurement. Other allowances such as tool allowances or reject allowances are added if necessary. The resultant time is called the standard time and is the time value for the job issued to the factory. Arbitrary allowances are added by some managements solely to increase operators' earnings. These are referred to as policy allowances and when a policy allowance is added to a standard time it is known as an allowed time.

Calculation of the Number of Cycles to be Observed. If the time to perform the elements of work being observed were constant from cycle to cycle only one work cycle would need to be studied. In practice random variations occur due to differences in pace and movement pattern and to slight changes in the position of work and tools. The greater the variation in elemental times between cycles the larger the number of work cycles which need to be studied to obtain a reasonably representative sample of the work. If it is assumed that the difference in elemental times arises from random causes then the distribution of individual times follows a normal distribution. In normal distributions the spread of times about their mean value is measured in terms of the standard deviation σ where

$$\sigma = \sqrt{\left\{\frac{\Sigma(x - \overline{X})^2}{N}\right\}}$$

$x - \overline{X}$ is the deviation of individual times from their mean.

N is the number of cycles timed.

If groups of individual values are considered the variation of group means will also follow a normal distribution but with less dispersion due to the averaging effect of the means. The standard deviation of group means σ_g is obtained from the equation

$$\sigma_g = \frac{\sigma}{\sqrt{N_g}}$$

where σ is the standard deviation of individual values, (N_g is the group size).

It is a property of all normal distributions that approximately 95 per cent of the values lie within $\pm 2\sigma$ of their mean. If we now adopt the widely accepted criterion that the means of the group times should, 95 times out of 100, be within ± 5 per cent of the mean of the individual times, $\overline{X}$ $\left(\text{where } \overline{X} = \dfrac{\Sigma x}{N}\right)$

$$\text{Then } 2\sigma_g \leqslant \frac{5}{100}\,\overline{X}$$

$$\frac{2\sigma}{\sqrt{N_g}} \leqslant \frac{5}{100}\,\overline{X}$$

$$2\sqrt{\left\{\frac{\Sigma(x - \overline{X})^2}{N\,N_g}\right\}} \leqslant \frac{5}{100}\,\overline{X}$$

$$N_g \geqslant \frac{1600N}{(\Sigma x)^2}\left\{\Sigma(x - \overline{X})^2\right\}$$

Example. The elemental times in a particular study are 11, 16, 11, 13, 12, 14, 13, 14, 16, 11, 12, 13 and 13 (measured in 0.01 min). How many elements should be recorded so that the mean of the study is within ± 5 per cent of the mean elemental time?

Substituting into the above formula

$$N_g \geqslant \frac{1600 \times 13 \times 34}{(169)^2} \geqslant 25$$

Therefore to satisfy our condition a study of at least 25 cycles will be needed.

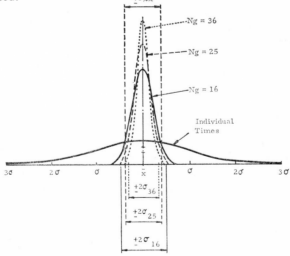

FIG. 8.7 *Distribution of individual and group mean times.*

The graphs in fig. 8.7 show the distribution of group means and individual values where elemental times are of similar variability to that in the example. It will be seen that the $\pm 2\sigma$ limits of group of 25 coincide with the 5 per cent limits on each side of the mean, therefore for this level of variability at least 25 cycles will need to be timed. Due to the mathematics involved this method of calculating the number of cycles to be timed is little used in practice.

Rating is a process of estimation used to convert observed times into times which would be taken by an average qualified operator working at a predetermined level of performance.

If a very large group of trained workers are set the same task, it is found that the time taken varies widely, due to different individual abilities, and that the fastest worker works at about twice the speed of the slowest. The rest of the times are likely to form a normal distribution between these two extremes. Motivation will affect the speed of working, in fact the distribution of performances from a well-motivated group is likely to be 33 per cent above that of a group without an incentive. Typical performance distributions are shown in fig. 8.8.

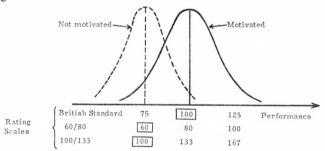

FIG. 8.8 *Distribution of Operator Performance.*

There are a number of rating scales in general use, the three most popular being the British Standard 0/100 scale and the American 60/80 and 100/133 scales. The 100 on the British Standard scale corresponds to the 80 and 133 on the other two scales. The major difference between the rating scales is the performance level at which observed times are converted in the calculation of standard times. The British Standard system uses a level of performance which qualified workers will naturally achieve without over-exertion as an average over the working day or shift, provided they know and adhere to the specified method and provided they are motivated to apply themselves to their work. The 60/80 and 100/133 scales convert at

60 and 100 respectively, which is $\frac{3}{4}$ of the British Standard conversion performance. The reason for the lower conversion levels can be traced back to Bedaux who considered an average worker paid by timework produced 60 'Work Units' per hour, whereas when motivated by an incentive he produced 80 'Work Units.' The table below indicates some of the main steps in the rating scales related to walking speed on level ground and card dealing.

Rating B.S.	Scales		Description of pace	Walking speed (m.p.h.)	Dealing 52 playing cards into 4 piles (seconds)
0/100	60/80	100/133			
50	40	67	slow	2	45
75	60*	100*	steady	3	30
100*	80	133	brisk	4	22½
125	100	167	fast	5	18
150	120	200	exceptionally fast	6	15

*conversion level

When rating the observer assesses the worker's rate of working relative to his concept of a standard performance by choosing a suitable number from the rating scale. Rating is a subjective process and since normally no bench-marks exist, as for walking or card dealing, it is extremely difficult, even after considerable experience, to visualise the pace of a standard performance. Changes in work pace of less than 5 per cent cannot be reliably detected by observation and it is therefore normal to rate in steps of 5. Each element is rated before its time is recorded; in this way the ratings are independent assessments unaffected by their elemental times. Surveys show that even with experienced observers rating accuracy is low; a reasonable standard might be that half of the ratings are within ±5 per cent and three quarters within ±10 per cent of the true rating. Inaccurate ratings produce 'tight' and 'loose' time values for jobs and lead to difficulties on the shop floor, particularly if a piecework scheme is in operation.

It is usually more difficult to accurately rate very fast or very slow workers and for this reason a person working near average pace should be studied. Rating can be made more accurate and drift avoided by holding regular rating practices at say 3 to 6 month intervals. Here films can be rated and the observer's rating checked against known true ratings. By plotting the observer's rating against the true rating, as shown in fig. 8.9, and drawing the best line through the points, any personal bias can be detected and an effort made to correct it.

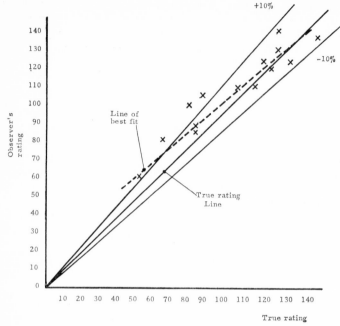

FIG. 8.9 *Typical results from rating exercise.*

SYNTHESIS

Many operations can be conveniently synthesised from element times for which time study values have already been collected. The allowed time can then be quickly and economically found by summing the appropriate element times.

Element times, which are variously called standard data, elemental data or synthetic times should be compiled for carefully chosen basic elements. The shorter their duration the greater the work of compiling the study times, but the wider the range of work which can be accommodated. All element times should be accompanied by an adequate description of the method and equipment used and the end points of each element should be clearly defined.

As element times are usually compiled from a number of time studies, they are likely to be more accurate than a single time study because rating errors will tend to cancel each other. Inaccuracies can, however, be introduced if elemental data is inadequate and a considerable amount of interpolation is necessary.

If a very wide range of production work is performed there are usually insufficient common elements to warrant the use of synthesis. It is, however, particularly useful for machine-shop work, for instance on capstan lathes, where the handling elements are often similar and some machining times can be calculated from consideration of feed and cutting speed.

PRE-DETERMINED MOTION TIME SYSTEMS

Like synthesis, pre-determined motion time systems use standard data to predict the time required to complete a task. The elements used are much shorter, many being similar to the therbligs used by Gilbreth. By using very small basic elements it is possible to compile, from a comparatively brief set of tabular data, a time value for almost any task.

There are a number of systems, the earliest, Motion Time Analysis, was introduced in the 1920s and the two most popular, Work Factor and Methods Time Measurement, followed some 20 years later.

Pre-determined motion time systems may appear to be ideal forms of work measurement as they eliminate both rating and timing. They lack accuracy however, due to the large number of factors affecting the performance times of the elements. It has been found that the time taken to complete a therblig is not just a function of distance moved or force to be overcome, but can be affected by:

1. Complexity of the task.
2. Direction of movement.
3. Amount of body used.
4. Eye—hand co-ordination needed.
5. Sensory requirements,
6. Position of the therblig in the motion pattern.
7. The number of therbligs making up the motion pattern and the number of times the pattern has been performed.

Although the various systems cleverly attempt to account for as many of the above factors as possible in their tables, the synthesised times are often not considered to be sufficiently accurate to set times for incentive schemes. Pre-determined motion times are of value in applications such as method comparison in the pre-production stage of a product, or the initial allocation of work between stations on a production line.

Simplified versions of both Methods Time Measurement (Simplified MTM), and Work Factor (Ready Work Factor) have been developed which enable times to be rapidly compiled from less elaborate tables. Use of a full pre-determined motion time system requires considerable training in order that the work being studied is accurately analysed and the tables are correctly interpreted.

ANALYTICAL ESTIMATING

This method is intended to replace old-fashioned rate fixing and is used for non-repetitive work such as that in tool rooms and maintenance departments. It is important to have as an estimator a man of integrity who is fully experienced in the work being done and trained in method study. The job is studied by the estimator and after the method has been decided upon it is broken down into elements. Where possible the times for these elements are determined by synthesis but where no synthetic data are available they are filled in from the estimator's experience.

Apart from providing the basis for an incentive scheme analytical estimating provides a control over the time taken by toolmakers and maintenance fitters, a type of labour whose effort is difficult to assess without some form of work measurement.

ACTIVITY SAMPLING

This is a major British contribution to work study, having been introduced in 1934 by L. H. C. Tippett for use in the cotton industry. It is used to find out the amount of time occupied by various activities associated either with workers or machines.

If an office manager notices what is being done by a particular typist each time he walks past her desk he will, after a while, have an idea of how she spends her working day. If out of ten snap observations, he finds that she was on

5 occasions typing

3 occasions talking

1 occasion answering the telephone

1 occasion away from her desk

it would appear that she spends 50 per cent of her time typing. However, it would be unwise to claim this with any certainty, although more observations would tend to confirm or refute this assumption. The result of the observations may be affected by the time of day that the activity was noticed, for instance, if observations were made just before finishing time they might indicate that she never did any typing at all.

Having decided on the activities which require study a preliminary survey is made to estimate the proportion of time occupied by each of the activities to be measured. This is necessary to find how many observations need to be made to obtain a result of the desired accuracy. A confidence limit of 95 per cent is usually used, which means that the accuracy will be within the desired limits 95 times out of 100. The formula used for this confidence limit is

$$N = \frac{4p\,(100-p)}{L^2}$$

where N = number of observations needed,

  p = percentage of the total time occupied by the activity,

  L = required limit of accuracy, expressed as a percentage.

The period during which the sampling is to take place must be representative. For instance, in a service depot, where there may be considerable variation in activity on different days of the week, the study must be planned to extend over a typical week. The times at which the observations are made must also be arranged so that they occur at random intervals; this can be done by lot or by using a table of random numbers. The actual frequency of the activity is noted by the observer, and when the correct number of observations has been obtained the percentage of the total time occupied by the activity under investigation can be calculated. The actual accuracy of the result can be found by transposing the original formula into

$$L = 2\sqrt{\left\{ \frac{p\,(100-p)}{N} \right\}}$$

Example. A preliminary survey showed that in a group of machines 40 per cent were working. How many observations are necessary to determine their utilization to an accuracy of ± 2 per cent? A 95 per cent confidence limit is acceptable

$$N = \frac{4p\,(100-p)}{L^2}$$

$$N = \frac{4 \times 40\,(100-40)}{2^2} = 2,400$$

If the 2,400 observations showed that the machines were working on 920 occasions find the actual limit of error.

Percentage utilization $= \dfrac{920}{2,400} \times 100 = 38\cdot33$ per cent.

Actual error $L = 2\sqrt{\left\{\dfrac{p\,(100-p)}{N}\right\}}$

$$L = 2\sqrt{\left\{\dfrac{38\cdot33\,(100-38\cdot33)}{2,400}\right\}} = 1\cdot98 \text{ per cent.}$$

Limits of error $= 38\cdot33\pm1\cdot98$ per cent, i.e. utilization is between 40·31 and 36·35 per cent.

FINANCIAL INCENTIVES

The use of piecework is not new, and was quite common in industry in the thirteenth century. F. W. Taylor, however, did much to establish incentives on a sound basis by determining the best method of working and measuring the work content of the job. Many of the self-styled efficiency experts who followed Taylor scrambled on to the scientific management bandwaggon. They did much to discredit work measurement and to embitter industrial relations by the incorrect and sometimes unscrupulous application of incentive schemes.

Requirements of a Sound Incentive Scheme. An incentive scheme must be carefully planned and selected if it is to be successful. A badly designed incentive plan becomes an immediate and continuous source of trouble between workers and management. The following points should be borne in mind.

1. The scheme should be simple and the wages easily calculated.
2. The reward should be directly proportional to the effort.
3. There should be sufficient difference between guaranteed base rate, when used, and the normal bonus earnings so that there is adequate incentive.
4. The allowed times should be based on sound methods of work measurement and definite quality requirements.
5. Allowed times once accepted should not be changed unless there is a change to the method of working.
6. Where failure to earn reasonable bonus is beyond the control of the worker, for instance due to bad material, the earnings should be fairly adjusted.
7. The incentive scheme should be clearly set out and rigidly maintained.

TYPES OF INCENTIVE SCHEMES

In this section some of the more widely used systems of wages payment are examined. Most incentive schemes have a minimum wage and, often, the operator performance below which the minimum wage operates is subject to trade union agreement. To provide a good incentive this point should not be high and a 75 B.S. performance (timework) is a suitable point to choose. Figure 8.10 shows the effect of a minimum wage on a pieceworker's earnings.

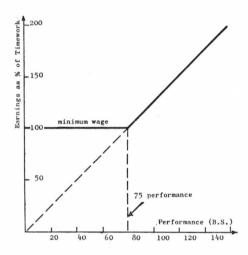

FIG. 8.10 *Piecework Earnings with Minimum Wage at 75 BS Performance.*

Piecework. By one of the oldest methods of wages payment a worker is paid a fixed amount of money for each piece produced. A similar system is the modified Bedaux, except that in this case the standard is expressed in terms of time, not money. The original Bedaux scheme paid the workers 75 per cent of the bonus they earned, the other 25 per cent being split between foremen and other indirect workers. The sharing of their reward with others, particularly the foreman, did little to endear this scheme to the worker.

Piecework and the modified Bedaux system go farther than most other systems in meeting the requirements of an ideal incentive scheme, although piecework undesirably links work measurement directly with money. The graph of earnings against operator performance is similar to that shown in fig. 8.10.

Halsey 50–50 Premium Bonus. This was the first incentive scheme to express standards in terms of time and not money and to provide a guaranteed wage. The worker is paid half the savings made on the allowed time for the job. The allowed time is usually set so that the normal bonus is earned for BS.100 performance. As compared with piecework, less bonus will be earned for greater than BS.100 performance, but the bonus earnings will be higher for sub-standard performances. The comparison of this system with piecework is shown in fig. 8.11. Some schemes vary the division of savings between manage-

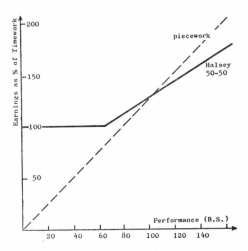

FIG. 8.11 *Halsey 50–50 Premium Bonus*
Arranged to Give 133 per cent of Time Rate at
100 BS Performance.

ment and workers, others give less than full bonus at BS.100 performance. The Halsey and other premium bonus schemes such as the Rowan are suitable where allowed times are estimated and may be particularly inaccurate.

Measured Day Work. Measured day work is an alternative to the more direct forms of incentive. It found some use in the United States in the early 1930s, when opposition to direct incentives was at its height, and is currently used by some large companies in the United Kingdom. The performance of each worker against measured standards is calculated and at the end of a fixed period, often one to three months, the average performance determined. It is this average performance, sometimes coupled with an assessment of factors such as quality of work and punctuality, which determines the wage rate to be paid to the operator over the next fixed period. Although measured daywork provides a useful control device for operator and departmental performances, it is not a good incentive as the performance does not have an immediate effect on the wages paid to the operator.

INCENTIVES FOR INDIRECT WORKERS

Incentive schemes for indirect workers can rarely be based on standards measured as accurately as those used for direct workers. When designing incentive schemes for indirect workers such as foremen and setters there is often difficulty in knowing what weighting to give the various aspects of their work. For these reasons many companies do not pay their indirects an incentive bonus but only a standard wage. Where a standard wage only is paid, there is a feeling, however, particularly with those who are closely associated with production, that their efforts also deserve an incentive bonus.

Maintenance and Toolroom Work. As mentioned earlier in this chapter maintenance and toolmaking tasks can be measured and allowed times set by analytical estimating. Due to the probable inaccuracy of the allowed times, premium bonus schemes such as the Halsey 50–50 rather than incentive systems in which earnings are directly proportional to effort should be used.

Supervisors. Unless supervisors' bonuses are carefully devised they can often produce undesirable results. By weighting some factors too heavily or by omitting others, the supervisor is made to pay excessive attention to certain aspects of his work to the neglect of other important ones. For instance a scheme which pays undue attention to operator utilization can produce a good bonus for the supervisor who understaffs his department and argues his way out of the consequent failure to achieve production targets. To obtain a reasonably balanced bonus scheme the following factors should be taken into account:

1. Output against planned programme. It is most important that only output against the planned programme is taken into account, otherwise the supervisor may be tempted to avoid difficult or unpopular work and bring forward simple work to make up the required numerical output.

2. Quality. As with direct bonus schemes quality should be included; this can be measured by comparing actual results with scrap and rectification targets.

3. Operator performance and utilization. This can be taken into account by calculating waiting time and average operator performance against measured standards and comparing them with targets previously set.

Clerical Workers. Clerical work is not a field in which incentives are frequently used, although successful allowed times based on time study have been calculated for routine tasks such as copy typing and punched-card work. Another approach is to determine a labour cost budget for each section and to award a bonus which depends on the wages actually paid as compared with the section budget.

GROUP INCENTIVES

These are usually found more satisfactory than individual incentives where the rate of working is controlled by previous operations such as is the case with conveyor belts or where it is impossible or impracticable to measure individual effectiveness.

Where group incentives are applicable they have the following advantages over individual incentives.

1. Less clerical work is required.

2. A spirit of co-operation between members of the group is encouraged.

3. Supervision is made easier as good groups often solve many minor difficulties themselves. These difficulties would otherwise be brought to the supervisor for settlement.

The disadvantages can be summarized as follows:

1. Production limits may be set by the group, which they are reluctant to exceed. Good leadership and an adequate incentive scheme can do much to overcome this difficulty.

2. Good workers do not have the opportunity of showing their full ability; this is partly compensated by the slower workers in the group being forced to work faster.

3. Schemes lose their incentive value if groups are large.

ERGONOMICS

Ergonomics is a study of the relationship of people and their working environment; an alternative description used in the U.S.A. is human engineering. Data on body size is provided by anthropometry and information on body structure and functioning is provided by anatomy and physiology respectively. From psychology comes a knowledge of the nervous system and a guide to human behavior.

Much of the work done in ergonomics can be of direct value to industry in the design of optimum working methods, the results being of particular value to the product designer and the work study engineer.

MAN-MACHINE SYSTEMS

When a man uses a machine, he and the machine form a control loop; the man receiving information, processing it and taking the necessary action with the machine controls until the required result has been achieved, fig. 8.12. The efficiency with which the system

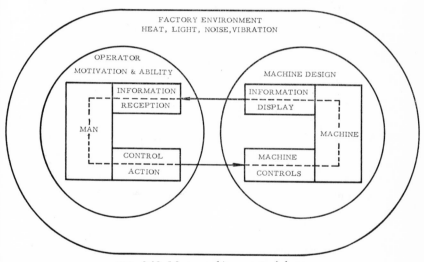

FIG. 8.12 *Man-machine control loop.*

functions is affected by the machine design, the ability and motivation of the operator and by the physical environment of the factory. The machine design aspect of the system falls into two broad categories, the display of information and the design of controls. The factory environment consists of the physical aspects such as heating, lighting, noise and vibration, and the psychological environment. Environmental factors and machine design considerations have a considerable effect on the rate of output and quality of the work produced.

I

ENVIRONMENTAL FACTORS

Heating. Extremes of heat or cold are undesirable as they reduce the ability to work and increase the possibility of accident. In manufacturing industry very cold working conditions are unusual but it can be uncomfortably hot in many industries, particularly those associated with casting and hot forming of metal. Much of the heat from furnaces and from the metal is radiated and cannot be effectively dissipated by cooling or reducing the humidity of the air. Some success, has, however, been achieved by the use of reflecting screens between the worker and the heat source or by dressing the worker in a permeable suit connected to a cool air supply. In recent years considerable progress has been made in mechanising very hot and cold jobs and this trend will no doubt continue. The general aspects of factory heating and ventilation are discussed in chapter 3.

Lighting. Investigators in this field are not agreed on the amount of illumination required for specific tasks and the recommendations of the American Illuminating Engineering Society are considerably higher than those of the Illuminating Engineering Society, London. For instance, in medium machine work the British recommendation is 30 lumens/ft^2 whereas the American is 100 lumens/ft^2. The human eye is, however, a remarkably versatile organ and in terms of output and quality of work there is a decreasing return from expenditure on additional lighting, particularly at the levels suggested by the American Illuminating Engineering Society.

Normally the provision of adequate factory lighting is the concern of an illuminating engineer, but the ergonomist must satisfy himself on the adequacy of the lighting design when considered in combination with other aspects of the work place design. Factory lighting is considered in chapter 3.

Noise. Many manufacturing operations are noisy, for example riveting, power press blanking and weaving. In very noisy industrial situations conversation is impossible, other than by lip-reading, and several generations of mill owners have seen their weaving shed operators made permanently deaf without compensation and without providing them any protection for their ears. Although individuals vary in their susceptibility to noise, permanent loss of hearing will depend on the intensity of noise, its frequency and the length of exposure. The graph, fig. 8.13, indicates the level of noise which is dangerous to a person subjected to it for 40 hours each week throughout his working life. The greater the intensity of noise above the safe level, the more rapid the onset of permanent deafness.

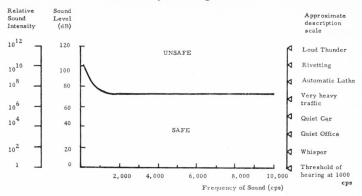

FIG. 8.13 *Sound Levels Likely to Cause Deafness.*

Although workers dislike noise they rapidly become accustomed to working in noisy situations. There is little evidence that continuous noise has an adverse effect on rate of output, although noise levels >90 dB are likely to reduce the accuracy of work and increase the liability to accidents. Unexpected noises should be avoided as they cause stress and may interfere with production. Continuous music played in the factory appears to be generally liked but its use is unlikely to directly increase output. The authors have found that music is normally preferred by female operatives but frequently disliked by craftsmen such as toolmakers.

Often noise can be minimised at source by appropriate tool or machine design, for instance the noise from metal blanking can be reduced by grinding the punch base at a slight angle so that the complete periphery of the blank is not ruptured at a single instant. If noise from the process cannot be kept to a reasonably low level it may be possible to isolate it from the rest of the factory by building a structure made from sound-proof material around the offending process. If a large floor area is occupied by noisy equipment the sound level can be reduced by using sound-absorbing tiles on the ceiling and walls. Finally, if the noise intensity is still above danger level, protection in the form of ear plugs or ear muffs should be provided for the workers. It should be noted that ear protection will only reduce noise levels by about 30 dB at frequencies around 1000 c/s. If protection is needed it is advisable to test hearing at six-monthly intervals.

Vibration. Although vibration is not a serious problem in most factories, it occasionally warrants attention, particularly when portable tools, such as riveters, are used. Apart from the obvious difficulty of doing fine work under conditions of vibration there is evidence that prolonged exposure to vibration will produce fatigue. Equipment should be designed so that vibration is kept to an acceptable level, although operators differ considerably in the amount of vibration they are prepared to tolerate.

Psychological Environment can easily override physical environment and greater productivity is obtainable from a happy group of workers working under deplorable conditions than could be obtained from an unhappy group working in near perfect conditions. Factors affecting the psychological environment are discussed in chapter 9.

DESIGN OF DISPLAYS

A large amount of work has been done on the design of visual displays so that they can convey information unambiguously and in such a way that it can be easily converted into decisions and actions. In factories the mis-reading of instrument dials and graduated scales often results in spoilt work, damaged equipment and accidents.

Visual displays are needed for a variety of reasons, those usually found in industry fall into three categories:

1. Quantitative—a measurement in numerical terms (e.g. 1360 rev./min.)
2. Checking—a broad indication of the state of affairs (e.g. coolant pump on).
3. Setting—adjusting controls to a predetermined setting (e.g. adjusting the cross slide of a centre lathe to 0.012 in.).

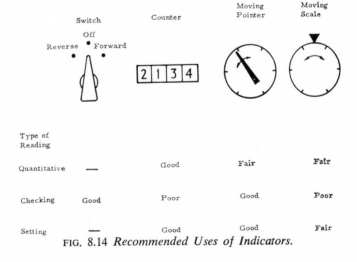

Type of Reading	Switch	Counter	Moving Pointer	Moving Scale
Quantitative	—	Good	Fair	Fair
Checking	Good	Poor	Good	Poor
Setting	—	Good	Good	Fair

FIG. 8.14 *Recommended Uses of Indicators.*

The main types of indicator are shown in fig. 8.14 with recommended uses.

The detailed design of dials and pointers are of importance and some of the salient points are listed below:

Use a suitable numerical progression (e.g. 0—10—20—30, not 0—15—30.)

Use the minimum number of sub-divisions between numbered divisions (never > 9).

Use the appropriate size of number or letter

$$\left(\text{height} = \frac{\text{reading distance}}{200} \right).$$

Use clear and unembellished numbers, suitable recommendations appear in B.S. 3693 : 1964.

Use vertical figures on stationary dials and radially oriented figures on rotating dials.

Arrange the scale so that it is not hidden by the pointer.

Use a bold pointer which just falls short of the scale divisions.

Use an appropriate pointer if accurate readings are required (knife-shaped ends with mirrors set in the dial minimise parallax errors).

DESIGN OF CONTROLS

Controls are used to operate machines and consist of levers, cranks, handwheels, knobs, switches, push buttons and pedals in almost infinite variety. Most are hand-operated although the foot and occasionally other parts of the body are used.

When designing controls the operating conditions must first be defined. Some of the questions which might be asked are:

1. Does the control have to be accurately set?
2. How fast does the control have to be operated?
3. Is the control operated only by touch?
4. Does the control have to be picked out from others around it?
5. In what way will the operator know that the control has been set?
6. Will the operator's clothing or the environmental conditions impose limitations on the operation of the control?

As a guide to the type of control to be selected a table based on Morgan, Cook, Champanis and Lund—*Human Engineering Guide to Equipment Design* is shown overleaf:

Small Forces

2 discrete settings	Hand or foot push buttons, toggle switch.
3 ,, ,,	Finger push button, toggle switch, rotary selector switch.
4—24 ,, ,,	Bank of finger push buttons, rotary selector switch, detented thumb wheel.
> 25 ,, ,,	Bank of finger push buttons.
Small range of continuous settings	Knob, lever, thumb wheel.
Large ,, ,, ,, ,,	Crank

Large Forces

2 discrete settings	Detent lever, hand or foot push button.
3—24 ,, ,,	Detent lever.
Small range of continuous settings	Hand wheel, rotary pedal or lever.
Large ,, ,, ,, ,,	Large crank.

The control movement should produce a compatible result, i.e. one which would be naturally expected to occur.

Control	Movement	Compatible result
Knob or hand wheel	Clockwise	On, forward, increase, up, to the right,
Lever or toggle switch	Up or to right	move away

Where there are a number of controls they should be coded for easy recognition. This can be done either by changes in shape, size, labelling or colour, or by a combination of these methods. Shape and size variation are suitable for operation by touch only.

Where dangerous equipment is to be operated the 'on' switch should be recessed so that it cannot be accidentally operated. The 'off' switch should however, be easily operated; such a design is a mushroom-headed push button.

Controls should be easily accessible and logically positioned. Similar types of equipment should have standardized controls to minimise the risk of error when operators are transferred.

FATIGUE

When a person is fatigued his ability to continue work is reduced and this is shown by a reduction in the working pace.

When heavy work is being done energy reserves are depleted and if a rest pause is not taken, tiredness becomes progressive and collapse may eventually result. Energy reserves vary from person to person, so does the pace at which they are able to work without drawing on their reserves. As a very rough guide, if an average man uses energy in excess of 5K cal/minute his energy reserves have to be used, (a man of normal weight walking at 4 m.p.h. on level ground uses energy at the rate of 5·2 K cal/minute). On average a man has reserves of 25 K cal and if he is working at the rate of 7K cal/minute his energy reserves will be exhausted in $12\frac{1}{2}$ minutes $\left(\dfrac{25}{7—5}\right)$. If a rest of 7 minutes is then taken the energy reserve will be rebuilt to its former level.

For light physical work no rest allowance to overcome fatigue is necessary as the energy expended is less than 5K cal/minute. However, breaks in the work routine are helpful to relieve boredom and hence maintain quality and rate of output. Often breaks can be conveniently introduced into the work routine, for instance assemblers can fetch components when they have run out. Work requiring considerable concentration, such as some inspection tasks, can be efficiently performed for short periods only and working spells can be as short as 15 minutes where extreme concentration is needed.

STATIC WORK

Muscular work has been divided into two types—dynamic and static. Dynamic work occurs when there is alternate contraction and expansion of the muscles and is normally associated with useful industrial work. Static work is done when there is prolonged muscular contraction such as in standing, leaning, bending, exerting pressure or work with arms extended. Static work cannot be completely avoided, it is always needed to maintain the posture of the body and to control its movements. It should however be minimised as in most instances it causes fatigue without contributing any useful work. Much can be done to reduce static work by an appropriately designed work-place.

WORK-PLACE DESIGN

Work-places should be designed so that the worker is seated and only when this is impracticable, as with heavy manual tasks, should work be done standing. The chair used should be stable and compatible with the height of the work. The height of the seat should be adjustable and there should also be adjustments to the height and angle of the back rest, so that the chair can be altered to best suit the operator using it.

Although not widely found in industry, arm rests mounted on benches are valuable in supporting the forearm when it has to work unsupported away from the body. Also in some types of fine assembly work it can be helpful to support the outer edge of the hand to minimise the static work of keeping it in a fixed position. The hands should never be used to maintain a tool or the work in a fixed position; this should be done by a suitable fixture. Leaning can be avoided by arranging that the work is within the area reached by the arms without trunk movement, and bending may be prevented by presenting and disposing of work at a suitable height. Bending to get parts from the bottom of box pallets can be extremely fatiguing but this may be avoided by feeding work from drop-bottom pallets into hoppers which discharge at bench-top level or by mounting pallets on special tilting stands.

When using machine tools it is often impossible for the operator to be permanently seated, although some machines are either fitted with a fixed seat or one which can be swung out of the way when not in use. Portable seating is also used when operating some types of machines, for instance light presses, and should be generally available for occasional use in the machine shop.

Human Aspects of Production Management

PERFORMANCE AND MOTIVATION

A technically competent production manager will fail to achieve his objective if he neglects the selection, training and motivation of those responsible to him.

Over the past forty years a vast amount of information has been accumulated by behavioural scientists in an attempt to discover a pattern of industrial behaviour and use it to predict the reactions of workers to work situations. Industrial psychologists have studied individuals and their response to changes in working conditions, and social psychologists and industrial sociologists have examined working groups and their attitudes and behaviour in relation to their organizational and physical environment. It is difficult to distinguish between the work of social psychologists and industrial sociologists, although the former have tended to take an assumed organizational structure and study group behaviour in relation to it, whereas the latter have tended to probe the structure to find out how it works and how management decisions are implemented. It is well-known that as well as the formal organization structure dictated by management there exists in firms an informal structure, which is created by the environment of the firm and which in turn affects the environment by creating its own norms and standards of behaviour.

Most of the early work by the behavioural scientists in industry was of a simple cause—effect kind, intended to establish a correlation between working conditions and productivity. Although it is preferable to provide conditions which minimise physical effort and fatigue it was found that physical conditions did not usually affect output and quality to the extent expected. In fact, many factories which boast of their excellent working conditions have poor records of productivity which are frequently a reflection of poor group motivation. Such firms frequently surround their employees with fringe benefits and paternalistic attitudes which make workers loath to leave their employment although they suffer from a lack of job satisfaction. The result may well be a low rate of labour turnover but a high rate of lateness and absenteeism coupled with poor effort.

The work of Elton Mayo in the U.S.A. during the late nineteen twenties and early nineteen thirties demonstrated the incompleteness of the industrial psychology approach and emphasized the importance of the collective response of the working groups. The formation of informal work groups increases the feeling of security of their members, as the group frequently assumes a protective role, creating its own standards of performance and conduct. During recent years sociologists have been attempting to test whether these standards are predictable and what effect the organizational environment has on them.

It has been found that production methods are an important factor in determining both the formal structure and the formation of working groups. As examples of the way in which the manufacturing methods affect the formation of groups let us consider two types of assembly work, a car assembly line and the batch assembly of electrical switchgear by a group of operators who have some latitude in deciding their method of approach. The car assembly line is automatically paced, so that an average operator is working near his maximum capacity. An assembly line operator can normally talk only to the operators immediately adjacent to him, and under these circumstances it is unlikely that a coherent working group will be formed as each operator has a different set of acquaintances. The work on an assembly line is uninteresting and highly repetitive, and the fixed pace demanded creates nervous strain. The uncongenial conditions are doubtless one of the main reasons why the motor industry has such a poor history of labour relations with recurrent strikes and demands for higher pay.

Batch type assembly naturally encourages the formation of working groups and there is a greater variety of work calling for a higher grade of skill. Although a reasonable output of work is expected the working pace is not inexorably controlled by the speed of an assembly line and the layout of the workplace normally allows more conversation between operators.

Viewed by pre-war standards, when workers were nearer the subsistence level, it might be assumed that financial rewards are now relatively less important as a form of motivation but changes in the concept of social necessities (cars, washing machines, continental holidays, etc.) have tended to preserve the importance of the pay packet. The improved standards of living demanded and the growth of hire-purchase commitments frequently require overtime to supplement the basic pay.

Non-financial incentives such as shorter working hours and longer holidays have also assumed a greater importance if many of the new 'necessities' of life are to be enjoyed. Hence, alongside the financial demands of recent years have been demands for shorter working hours (frequently to allow more overtime at higher wage rates to be worked) and longer paid holidays.

Twenty-five years of comparatively full employment has taught managements that labour wastage is an expensive item which cannot always be made good by employing new recruits. Even comparatively unskilled jobs require some training and the cost of engaging and training labour, and the disruption to production caused by people leaving, justifies considerable efforts to reduce the labour turnover rate. Labour turnover among skilled personnel is far more serious if, as generally happens, replacements cannot be readily obtained. Shortage of skilled labour is largely the result of erosion of wage differentials since the war, caused by the disproportionate increase in the wage rates of unskilled workers and by higher direct taxation. To reduce labour turnover and to improve the image of the company in the eyes of long-service employees, many firms provide inducements for long service in the form of merit bonuses and longer holidays. Other fringe benefits in the form of social amenities, profit sharing and superannuation schemes are frequently provided. These benefits usually accrue with length of service so there is an added incentive for long-service employees to stay with the company.

It has been argued that fringe benefits of this sort are so compulsive as to be immoral, acting as a soporific which prevents the expressions of discontent which may otherwise be caused by the physical or organizational conditions in the factory. Be this as it may, fringe benefits have grown rapidly in recent years, both in the United Kingdom and on the continent.

EMPLOYEE PARTICIPATION

The trade unions, most of which have long-since lost their craft character, provide a basis for negotiation at national level with employers' federations on wage rates and conditions in industry. At company level they not only provide a basis for the settlement of differences, but also an important vehicle for communication between management and workers which could not easily be provided by any other means.

In manufacturing industry many of the larger companies have continued to run Joint Production Advisory Committees, originally created during the war. These are composed of representatives of management and workers, and provide a means of encouraging suggestions and discussion of grievances which would otherwise be stifled by the complexities of the organisation. As a result of these committee meetings communication between workers and management can be improved and an atmosphere of confidence and understanding established.

Suggestion schemes are another worthwhile method of securing worker participation. Rewards are paid for suggestions which are of use and interest is stimulated by suitable publicity.

In the Federal German Republic, the constitution ensures the right of worker participation by requiring the formation of works councils in all private firms employing more than five persons. The councils have the right to express the views of their members on social and personal matters as well as on the economic affairs of the firms. German workers also have one-third of the seats on the boards of directors of joint stock companies. So far, British industry has not encouraged participation on this scale but it is conceivable that the increasing requirement for a stable working force brought about by automation may stimulate thought in this direction.

PERSONNEL POLICY

A sound personnel policy is necessary to ensure that a sense of unity is created among the employees, and to develop a feeling that the personnel department will deal fairly and sympathetically with all matters concerning employment. The policy should also ensure a continued supply of trained workers ready to accept positions of greater responsibility. The essential principles of a good personnel policy may be summarized as follows:

1. Employees are guaranteed confidential access to the personnel manager, or a senior member of his department, to express grievances or discuss troubles arising from their employment.

2. Competent employees are guaranteed, so far as possible, continuous and permanent employment.

3. All employees shall be given adequate training to make them competent in their work, and those showing promise shall be trained for promotion.

4. A suitable system of personnel selection shall be devised to decide the suitability of applicants, with provision for a subsequent review of new employees to find their degree of proficiency.

5. Promotions should be made from within the organization where possible.

6. Employees shall be guaranteed against unfair treatment or unfair dismissal.
7. Fair wages agreements and nationally or locally agreed rates of pay shall be observed.
8. Good working conditions shall be maintained, including adequate canteen, medical and safety facilities.
9. Effective consultation machinery between management and workers shall be maintained.
10. Full freedom of association shall be allowed and there shall be no racial, religious or political discrimination.
11. Social facilities shall be organized and encouraged.

SELECTION AND TRAINING

SELECTION PROCEDURES

The degree of sophistication in selection procedures usually depends on the importance of the job to be filled. A post in management is likely to require knowledge and ability of a high order, and the appointment of the wrong person to fill such a post could prove disastrous to the company. These appointments therefore require careful selection, based on a well-drafted job specification and in some cases on the social requirements of the company. In conditions of full employment it is often difficult to find sufficient labour to fill less pleasant manual jobs and unsuitable candidates are frequently engaged on the basis that a poor worker is better than nothing.

Much has been written about the use of aptitude and intelligence tests to measure the suitability of applicants, but these are not in general use in the United Kingdom although some companies find aptitude tests valuable when looking for special skills such as the ability to assemble very small components.

Usually, applicants are first required to complete a standard application form which provides the basis for a subsequent interview. The questions on the form should be phrased to discover qualifications and experience without including topics which encourage the applicant to give untrue answers. For instance, it is desirable to know how long the applicant has spent in previous employment to give some idea of how stable an employee he is likely to be. It is, however, unwise to ask for the reason for leaving the previous job unless this information is volunteered at the interview.

Employment interviews take many forms, but it is usually agreed that if more than one interviewer is necessary the interviews should be separately conducted so the applicant is not put at the disadvantage of being outnumbered. For senior appointments the candidate is often interviewed by a panel at one sitting. It is claimed that this method is less time-consuming, and shows how the candidate behaves in a situation demanding the simultaneous consideration of a number of isolated factors, a typical management situation. Many good candidates, however, do not show up to advantage in such an interview unless the interviewers adopt a carefully-prepared plan of questioning and the seating is arranged so that the candidate is not submerged by the interviewing board.

For junior staff appointments it is desirable that the interview should be conducted by the person in charge of the department. Sometimes a preliminary interview with a member of the personnel department is considered desirable, but this should act purely as a filter to eliminate obviously unsuitable applicants.

Many companies advise their interviewers to obtain information by applying the 7-point plan devised by the National Institute of Industrial Psychology. The seven points about which the candidate is questioned are:

1. Physical condition, which may be supplemented by a medical examination.
2. Attainments, including academic achievements and past industrial experience, giving time spent in each situation.
3. Intelligence, an assessment of which can be made from the way questions of a general nature, which do not require specialist knowledge, are answered.
4. Special aptitudes, which may be discovered and tested in some cases by aptitude tests.
5. Interests, hobbies and other forms of relaxation.
6. Disposition, attitude toward authority and toward other workers.
7. Circumstances under which the applicant is living, whether married or single, how many children, willingness and ability to work on a shift basis.

Information given to the applicant should include probable earnings or salary and conditions of service. This can be supplemented by a visit to the workplace with an explanation of the main points of the process on which the new employee will work and a general idea of how the process helps in the making of the finished product. From the results of the interview the supervisor should be able to make a general assessment of the candidate's ability to perform the job in mind.

INDUCTION TRAINING

Induction training of operators may be performed either among the working group or in a separate training school, often within the factory. The use of training schools enables specialist training skills to be applied, thereby reducing the time required to attain proficiency and preventing undesirable methods from being developed. This method of training is particularly suitable for learning basic workshop skills. In fact, under the Industrial Training Act, 1964, centres are being set up to provide training for employees in certain industries. These centres will no doubt help to fill a pressing need for the training of apprentices and the re-training of older workers.

It is possible that operators from training schools will not be readily acceptable to established work groups when they arrive in the factory. Where group harmony is important, as in batch assembly groups, training is often done within the group and to do this effectively it is important that group leaders are well-trained in instructional procedures. If the group is paid by an incentive scheme, the rates will require adjustment to allow for the low performance of the new member and the time taken to instruct. Preferably, the rates should be adjusted on a time basis, so that the training allowance is progressively reduced until the new operator attains proficiency and the allowance is finally withdrawn. If the time allowed for training is realistic the group will not lose earnings and will make every effort to train in the most effective manner.

The performance of an operator under training will depend on the complexity of the task, the operator's ability, the efficiency of the instruction and the work-place layout. Fig. 9.1 shows a typical learning curve; the improvement will not as a rule be uniform, but consists of a series of steps and plateaus. Effective training will help to reduce the duration of the plateaus and thereby reduce training time. It is found that most of the improvement is due to the elimination of fumbles during the work cycle rather than to an improvement in the effective motions. This emphasises the need for a fixed work-place arrangement which enables a repetitive pattern to be developed.

The need for training a large additional labour force in a short time during the war prompted the Ministry of Labour and National Service to introduce the Training Within Industry for Supervision (T.W.I.) scheme. Instruction is given by the group conference method, with workers attending on a part-time basis, generally for periods of about two hours at a time. There are three training courses, one to improve instruction, one to improve production methods and one to improve labour relations on the shop floor. They are pitched at chargehand and foreman levels and are intended to give supervisors a systematic and common-sense approach to training, production and labour problems. The success of T.W.I. has led to its continuation in various forms.

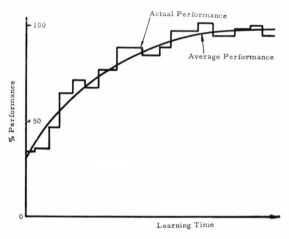

FIG. 9.1 *Typical Learning Curve.*

The T.W.I. Job Instruction course stresses the need for correct work-place arrangement and encourages supervisors to break tasks down into basic elements for instructional purposes, with particular emphasis on key points relating to quality and safety. The trainee watches the job being demonstrated and then attempts it himself under close supervision, having mistakes corrected as he makes them. As proficiency improves the closeness of supervision is gradually relaxed.

To increase flexibility of the labour force it is desirable that operators should be able to perform a variety of tasks and it is helpful to supervision if a visual record is kept showing the amount of versatility achieved by each operator. In some factories operators who achieve proficiency in a specified range of jobs are given a versatility award.

JOB EVALUATION

Job evaluation determines the value of an individual job within an organization in relation to other jobs in that organization. Job evaluation is not concerned with appraising the workers themselves but just the jobs they are doing. The main objectives of job evaluation are stated below:

1. To develop a policy of equal pay for equal work value.
2. To pay a wage which is directly related to the responsibilities and difficulties of specific jobs.
3. To fix wage rates so that they are in reasonable relationship with those paid locally and nationally.
4. To clarify the function, authority and responsibility of each job, so assisting in the selection and promotion of employees and helping to show where each job fits into the overall structure.

METHODS OF JOB EVALUATION

The following systems are the most widely used. The first two described are non-quantitative, that is they do not show how much more important one job is than another.

1. *Ranking Method.* This is a simple method which is suitable when there is a small number of jobs to be evaluated. Each job is examined and ranked in order of importance to the company. The result is a list of jobs with the most important at the top and the least important at the bottom.

2. *Classification Method.* A number of levels of responsibility and skill are determined for the jobs to be evaluated. For instance clerical work could be divided into five grades varying from Grade 1, which is simple routine work carried out under close supervision, to Grade 5, which represents the highest level of non-supervisory clerical work. Once these grades have been defined the various clerical jobs are allocated to one of the five grades, each of which carries an appropriate salary scale.

3. *Weighted Points Method.* In this method each job is divided into a number of factors common to the rest of the jobs being evaluated. Each factor is weighted by awarding a number of points depending on its relative importance. The factors are then sub-divided into grades which are defined and allocated a certain number of points. The jobs to be evaluated are considered against the grade definitions and the points attributable to each grade are totalled into a score. The score obtained by each job indicates its relative value.

The weighted points method is the most widely used system of job evaluation. It is somewhat complicated and may be regarded with suspicion by workers who do not understand it. A more detailed description of its application is given below.

K

4. *Factor Comparison Method.* A range of key jobs generally considered to be fairly paid are selected. The money paid for each job is allocated between about five factors in proportion to their estimated importance. This provides a money rating scale for each factor. The rest of the jobs have their factors fitted to these scales, and by totalling the money awarded to each job factor a new money value for the job can be obtained.

Due to its complication the factor comparison method is not easy to explain to workers. It is the second most popular system of job evaluation.

JOB EVALUATION USING WEIGHTED POINTS

To show how a system of job evaluation is used the steps in applying the weighted points method are considered. The evaluation is usually made by a small management committee with preparatory and routine work being done by the personnel department or by consultants.

1. *Job Analysis.* Each job is defined by means of a job description. This is usually prepared from information obtained from a questionnaire or by interview. The job description is written up in a standard fashion and indicates the minimum needs of skill, responsibility and knowledge, as well as giving a brief account of the duties and working conditions.

2. *Selection of Key Jobs.* To simplify the work of evaluation a number of key jobs, often fifteen, are selected to act as bench marks. The key jobs should be stable, clearly defined and representative of the range of jobs to be evaluated.

3. *Selection and Definition of Job Factors.* It has been found that almost all jobs can be divided into the following main factors:
skill
effort
responsibility
working conditions

Each of these factors can be split into a number of sub-factors for, instance skill can be divided into:
education
mental requirements
physical skill
experience
judgement and initiative

It is desirable that each of these factors and sub-factors should be briefly defined. For example, the definition of education might be, "The level of formal education demanded by the job; this level of knowledge need not have been acquired at school but could have been obtained subsequently".

4. *Division of Factors into Grades.* Each sub-factor is now graded into steps so that assessment can be made easier. Education may be divided into say, eight levels from Grade 1, Ability to read simple English, no writing or counting required, to Grade 8, Technical training up to appropriate professional level.

5. *Weighting of Factors by Allocation of Points.* The factors are awarded points depending on their relative importance. These points are then divided between the sub-factors and the points awarded to each of the sub-factors are allocated to the grades. This process can be seen in the following example:

Factors:			Grades of education:		
skill	300	points	Grade 1	10	points
effort	100	,,	,, 2	20	,,
responsibility	80	,,	,, 3	30	,,
working conditions	60	,,	,, 4	40	,,
Sub-factors of skill:			,, 5	50	,,
education	80	points	,, 6	60	,,
mental requirements	40	,,	,, 7	70	,,
physical skill	50	,,	,, 8	80	,,
experience	100	,,			
judgement and initiative	30	,,			
	300	,,			

6. *Evaluation of Key Jobs.* The committee evaluate the key jobs and allocate points to each sub-factor using the previously determined

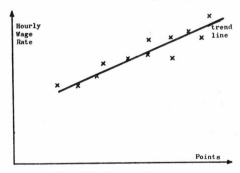

FIG. 9.2 *Scatter Diagram.*

grade scale. After the key jobs have been evaluated and the points scores totalled, each is plotted on a scatter diagram as shown in fig. 9.2. From these points a trend line is drawn. This is a straight line which best fits the points on the scatter diagram, and is referred to as a conversion line as it can be used to convert points into wages.

7. *Conversion of Points into Money.* Information on key-job earnings is collected from industry both locally and nationally. If applicable, any limitations likely to be imposed by wage agreements should be noted.

The following courses of action are possible:

(*a*) Fix wages on the existing slope, thereby eliminating anomalies.

(*b*) Raise or lower wages by a constant amount by drawing a new conversion line parallel to the existing trend line. (Line *A*, fig. 9.3).

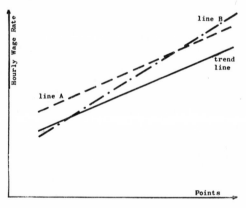

FIG. 9.3   *Points-to-Money Conversion Graph.*

(*c*) Draw a new conversion line with a different slope so that the differential between jobs of different points level is raised or lowered. (Line *B*, fig. 9.3).

In practice, stepped conversion lines are often used to avoid too many wage rates. It is frequently necessary to establish maximum and minimum wage rates; this can be done by drawing limit lines above and below the trend line, as shown in fig. 9.4.

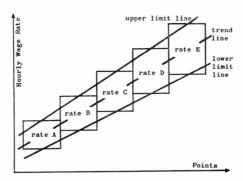

FIG. 9.4 *Stepped Points-to-Money Conversion Graph.*

MERIT RATING

Merit rating establishes standards by which the value of individual employees can be measured. Merit rating if correctly applied provides a fair basis for the selection of workers for promotion, the award of wage increases and for the dismissal of staff if production has to be cut back.

The method of rating can be by ranking or by comparison with predetermined standards. The factors which are assessed will vary between about twelve and six, the present trend being towards fewer factors.

Typical factors include:

intelligence
accuracy
output
leadership
integrity
personal appearance

The factors are entered on a rating form and if the rating is against predetermined standards these gradings will also have to be printed on the form.

Rating is usually done by the employee's immediate superior filling in a rating form for each member of his staff once a year. In some schemes the ratings are discussed with the workers, in others they remain confidential.

INDUSTRIAL HEALTH

The health and physical efficiency of workers receives considerable attention, particularly in larger companies because:

1. It is a legal and a social obligation to protect the health of workers from diseases caused by or aggravated by their work.
2. By safeguarding health, productive efficiency of workers can be improved and absenteeism reduced.
3. A study of the incidence of stress diseases and industrial fatigue may uncover shortcomings in the organization.

The Factories Acts demand certain first-aid facilities, but many factories far exceed these requirements, having their own sick bay and, frequently, the services of a resident physician. Routine functions of such departments include:

1. First-aid treatment of casualties and treatment for minor ailments.
2. Medical examination of applicants for employment.
3. Periodic examinations of employees working on processes involving a hazard to health.
4. Care of health of young persons employed by the company.
5. Assistance in the resettlement of workers after protracted periods of sickness.
6. Advice to management where employees have bad sickness records.
7. Investigation of stress diseases, which are usually particularly prevalent among supervisory and managerial staff.

Apart from giving workers the feeling that management cares about their health, a well-run medical department can reduce absence from work by minimizing the time workers have to spend in the often demoralizing surroundings of doctors' waiting rooms and hospital outpatient departments.

Control of Quality

SPECIFICATION OF QUALITY

Every production process suffers from an inherent variability in all its specified attributes, whether they relate to dimension, colour, chemical composition or physical properties. Since it is impossible to eliminate this variability we must learn how to live with it without allowing the variation adversely to affect the finished product. The maintenance of quality standards specified to contain this variability within defined limits is known as quality control.

For quality control to be effective it is necessary that the dimensions or other attributes to be controlled should be defined as clearly as possible. These parameters should be chosen to give the best guarantee of requisite quality, the requisite quality being that which is necessary to ensure customer satisfaction. There are, however, many quality considerations which do not affect the finished product but which must be observed in order to allow easy assembly.

Quality standards are dictated by the following requirements:

1. Functional efficiency of the completed product.

2. Cost and estimated life of the product.

3. Interchangeability and ease of assembly.

4. Appearance and "feel" of the product in use.

The first three requirements can usually be fairly easily assessed from previous experience, by endurance testing or by experiments which simulate normal service conditions. Additionally, they can sometimes be determined by reference to an appropriate British Standard.

The fourth requirement, appearance and "feel" of the product, is far less tangible, and in most cases is determined by the subjective decision of the inspector. This is where the old criticism, that inspection standards depend on the condition of the inspector's liver, is often only too well founded. To test their degree of consistency, two inspectors each checked a batch of electric machines for operating noise, and it was found that the acceptance standards varied considerably. Further investigations were carried out to find if individual inspectors were consistent in what they rejected. The same batch of machines was inspected by the same man twice on consecutive days and it was found that not only did the quantity of machines rejected vary considerably between the first and second day, but some which were passed on the first occasion were rejected on the second, and vice versa. These results did nothing to promote confidence in subjective inspection techniques, but since the rejection was based not only on the volume of noise but on the type of sound emitted, it would be difficult to devise any less subjective system of checking. These simple tests illustrate the great difficulty that may be encountered when setting some standards for quality.

When a product has been established for some time it may be necessary to alter standards as a result of customer complaints or to simplify production. Alterations should not be made until extensive tests have proved them to be a satisfactory remedy, because quality standards which are too easily modified are likely to be treated with scant respect.

The necessary quality standards decided upon are stated on the drawing in terms of dimensioned tolerances, or written into the test specification. The production staff must then work to these standards and the quality department must inspect to the same standards. Despite efforts to work to specified limits it is frequently necessary temporarily to amend standards in order to maintain production. Such concessions as may be required due to imperfections of workmanship or material must not be lightly given. Every concession granted weakens the position of the quality control department and leaves it open to criticism from the customer, due to inferior quality, and from the production departments for having previously demanded an unnecessarily high standard.

ORGANIZATION OF THE
QUALITY CONTROL DEPARTMENT

Since the chief quality engineer is responsible for ensuring that the functional quality of the product is maintained, it is unfair and undesirable that he should be responsible to any production executive, even the works manager; in fact, in some companies the chief quality engineer enjoys equal status to the works manager. Depending on the importance attributed to quality control he may be responsible either to the chief engineer or immediately to the board of directors.

To ensure that a complete check is kept on the quality of purchased parts, materials, equipment, and manufacturing accuracy at all stages in production, the quality department must be organized to perform the following functions:

1. Raw material inspection.
2. Inspection of bought-out parts and sub-contracted parts.
3. Checking of parts made in the factory.
4. Inspection and test of finished products.
5. Gauge or instrument inspection.
6. Tool inspection.

RAW MATERIAL INSPECTION

Procedures for incoming material inspection will vary considerably with the types of materials used and with the quality standards specified. If they are engineering materials, it is reasonable to suppose that there should be a dimensional check and a test of physical properties or chemical composition. The last-named test will probably demand the services of a metallurgist or possibly a complete metallurgical and chemical laboratory in a large company. Usually one sample only is inspected from each batch of material received, but if considerable variation has been found previously it may be necessary to check more than one sample.

INSPECTION OF BOUGHT-OUT AND SUB-CONTRACTED PARTS

These parts should be dimensionally checked, and occasionally samples are taken to have their physical properties examined. The dimensional inspection may sometimes be on all the parts received, but generally only a percentage of the batch will be checked. This sort of inspection lends itself particularly to the application of statistical control, of which more will be said later.

CHECKING OF PARTS MADE IN THE FACTORY

Controlling the quality of all parts manufactured in the factory usually represents the largest and most difficult function of a quality control department. It is affected considerably by the type of manufacture and by the quantities produced. Where batch production is practised there are three main methods of inspection. One is to view the first components off the new "set-up" and then sample periodically from the running job with or without reference to a statistical quality control chart; another is to sample from the completed batch, and the third is to view all the completed parts. The third method is very time-consuming and is not normally used unless the process is performed under conditions of marginal accuracy with the possibility of a high percentage of rejects.

Continuous production methods obviously demand a continuous form of inspection, and where line production is used it is usual to station inspectors at specified stages in the manufacturing process. It is important that inspection should be adequate, but it is equally important that unnecessary inspection operations should be eliminated as they increase the cost of production. In place of, or sometimes in addition to, the above procedure, a patrol viewer may be employed to sample components coming off each operation. This type of inspection is useful when new operators are being trained, as it allows added concentration on trouble-spots and often leads to a considerable reduction in scrap and work requiring rectification.

Increasing emphasis is being placed on operators checking their own work; it helps to relieve monotony, it creates a new pride in the work, it develops a feeling of quality-consciousness and leads to a reduction in the amount of scrap and work needing rectification. Since the value of work lost due to scrap in a light engineering factory is often about £2 per operator per week, it is easy to see that considerable savings can be made by enlisting the help of operators in improving quality. Incidentally, not only is the scrap bill reduced in this way, but labour utilization may be considerably increased due to the reduction of time spent on rectification. Operator inspection can often be performed during the automatic cycle time of the machine; if this cannot be arranged an appropriate increase in the allowed time for the job must be made. Although an overcheck by the inspection department is usual, if the operator is aware of his responsibility to produce good work and is provided with adequate means to check it, the percentage overchecked can be reduced.

The advent of automation has resulted in the wider use of automatic sizing and gauging equipment. Usually this sort of equipment works on a pneumatic principle and measurements of 0·0001 in. can be obtained on sizing equipment fitted to grinding machines. Automatic gauging fixtures can measure a large number of dimensions simultaneously and are often fitted as a stage in a transfer machine. It is feasible that these automatic measurements could be used to provide a certain amount of adjustment to tool settings, thereby further eliminating the need for a setter, except to replace or re-grind worn tools. Automatic control over manufacture is possible to an even greater degree in the process industries where variation from the prescribed standard can be fed back in the form of instructions to the input mechanism, thereby adjusting the process to give the desired output quality.

Sub-assemblies must conform to a dimensional standard but may also require a functional test as with voltage regulators and cut-outs. Such tests should be made on the entire batch because the result of a faulty sub-assembly of this type being fitted to a product could result in heavy rectification costs.

INSPECTION AND TEST OF FINISHED PRODUCTS

The quality check on finished products is of importance since it is the last chance of finding imperfections that may render the product unsuitable to the customer. This final inspection will generally take two forms which may be performed simultaneously. The first is a visual check to ascertain if the appearance is to standard, and may include a dimensional check. The second is a functional test to ensure that the product performs to specification. Where line assembly is being used, the final inspection can be incorporated with the assembly operations. This is an advantage as it reduces the number of finished products waiting for test. In a batch assembly shop, where inspection is not in step with production, the storage of un-tested products that have left the assembly bench is often a most difficult problem.

GAUGE INSPECTION

If parts are to be made to a required standard of accuracy the means of checking these parts must themselves be maintained to a high standard. Generally, the tolerance on the accuracy of gauges is about 10 per cent of the component tolerance. In normal shop use gauges may wear until they are outside the allowed limits; for this reason a periodic examination of gauges is necessary. New gauges must also be examined to ensure they have been accurately made. This work is usually done in a standards room where conditions of temperature are closely controlled at 68°F (20°C) to eliminate expansion errors.

TOOL INSPECTION

The purpose of tool inspection is not so much to check the accuracy of tools against their drawings as to ensure that they are safe, functionally sound and will produce a component within the specified tolerance. A frequently-used method of checking consists of an inspection of sample components made from the tools. This applies particularly to press work where the assessment of bending and drawing tools is frequently made by trying them out. In addition, the safety officer may have to check that the tools are safe or adequately guarded.

INSPECTING FOR AUTOMATIC ASSEMBLY

With the increased pace of mechanization in component production, it is logical that there should be a trend toward automatic assembly as well. So far, most efforts in this direction appear to have been in the light engineering industries where quantities have justified the high cost of automatic assembly plant. Unfortunately a higher standard of component quality and uniformity is necessary if the automatic plant is to function without jamming. Consider the effect of automatically driving grub-screws into terminals on a five-terminal base. If the screws are 99 per cent good there is a risk of a jam on every twentieth assembly, which is unacceptably high. There are means whereby most faults may be overcome. The cost of total inspection would more than outweigh any gain made by automatic assembly, neither is total inspection a certain way of removing faulty parts. Automatic inspection may be possible, but many efforts to inspect small components automatically have proved costly and unreliable. However, modifications to design frequently overcome difficulties of automatic assembly. These modifications may involve a tightening-up of limits or a complete alteration of form. Where hopper-fed components are used it may be necessary to consider the position of the centre of gravity so that the components feed to the assembly point the same way up. It has been suggested that screw-driver slots with their inevitable percentage of burrs, missed or misaligned slots may give way to recessed heads or convex forms which allow the use of drivers which are less sensitive to slight imperfections and variations. It may also be necessary to increase the lead-in to tapped holes and to provide fool-proofing devices to prevent damage if any component is fed out of position to the assembly fixture.

It is certain that inspection problems will be greater where automatic assembly is used, and concessions are likely to be far more difficult to obtain since quite small variations in form may prevent the proper functioning of the assembly machine.

INSPECTION OBJECTIVES

It is extremely difficult to specify a system of inspection objectives that provides realistic targets in the production shops, but such a system is very desirable if the requisite efficiency of the production process is to be achieved and maintained. To a certain extent the cost of the scrap bill and the cost of rectification in terms of the total output may provide useful information, but other factors such as the return of unsatisfactory equipment from customers should also be considered.

Inevitably there will always be a certain percentage of work of an unacceptable standard, and when setting targets it is necessary to assess the minimum amount of sub-standard work that can be reasonably expected from the process. When first setting objectives, the original targets must be arbitrarily fixed from past experience, but subsequent targets should be based on achievement against the previous targets. The intention is to set targets which are high so that the objective is just capable of achievement. If the targets are consistently attained then they can be raised so that there is always something for which to strive.

A practical way of expressing achievement against these objectives is by means of a quality index, which is the arithmetic average of the indices for scrap, rectification and customer returns. These indices are calculated at convenient intervals, for instance, each month, and progress toward the target figure of 100 can be recorded on a graph. A typical quality index calculation is as follows:

SCRAP INDEX

If the target for scrap is £1 for every £100 of output, then 1 per cent scrap will represent a scrap index of 100; and 2 per cent scrap will represent a scrap index of 50.

Suppose that the cost of work scrapped in a given period is £852 when the total output is £50,000, then the scrap percentage is $\frac{852}{50,000} \times 100 = 1\cdot704$ per cent and the scrap index is $\frac{1 \times 100}{1\cdot704} = 59$.

RECTIFICATION INDEX

If the target for rectification is $\frac{1}{2}$ hour spent on rectification for every 100 hours productively employed, then 0·5 per cent of time spent on rectification represents a rectification index of 100.

Suppose the number of hours spent on rectification is 620 out of 30,000 productive hours, then the percentage of time spent on rectification is $\frac{620}{30,000} \times 100 = 2\cdot067$ per cent and the rectification index is

$$\frac{0\cdot5}{2\cdot067} \times 100 = 24.$$

CUSTOMER RETURNS INDEX

If a reasonable number of returns from customers is 1 in 700 units sold, 0·143 per cent returned represents a 100 index.

Suppose that 172 are returned out of 80,000 units sold, the percentage returned will be $\frac{172}{80,000} \times 100 = 0.215$ per cent. The customer return index will then be $\frac{0.143 \times 100}{0.215} = 66$.

OVERALL INDEX

This is the arithmetic average of the above, i.e. overall index

$$= \frac{59+24+66}{3} = 49.7.$$

A typical Quality Index Chart for a product is shown in fig. 10.1. Similar charts can be compiled for departmental quality targets.

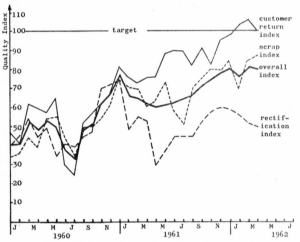

FIG. 10.1 *Quality Index Chart for a Product.*

STATISTICAL QUALITY CONTROL

Apart from being costly, experience has shown that total inspection often allows a high percentage of rejects to be passed, due to boredom and fatigue. In recent years many attempts have been made to control quality at the manufacturing process, to reduce inspection costs and to provide the high standards of interchangeability required by large-scale production. These requirements have led to the development of methods of statistical quality control (S.Q.C.), samples of the work being inspected to obtain, within known limits of error, a picture of the quality of the entire batch. Some of the problems besetting the engineer applying S.Q.C. are to find out what percentage of the output must be inspected, how samples are to be taken and what variations of sample quality may be accepted. The mathematical theory of S.Q.C. is complicated but a fundamental knowledge is unnecessary for control to be applied. Provided a few simple steps are followed and a set of the appropriate statistical tables are available, the limits necessary to exercise control may be easily determined.

Before discussing how S.Q.C. may be applied the advantages which may be derived from this system of inspection will be considered.

1. As sampling is performed at regular intervals while the operation is proceeding, immediate action can be taken to minimize the production of reject work. This results both in decreased scrap and in less time being spent on rectification of faulty parts.

2. Quality standards may be improved without increasing inspection costs or, alternatively, existing standards may be maintained at a lower cost.

3. Due to the higher standard of uniformity achievable in component quality the performance of assembly operators may be improved.

4. Where testing has to be of a destructive nature the adoption of a statistical sampling technique is the only reasonable guarantee of quality.

5. Results obtained from sample checks show if the process can be expected to produce consistently components of the required quality standard. These results also indicate when process accuracy is being affected by deterioration of the machine or tooling.

The rest of the chapter describes how S.Q.C. charts are applied where either:

(*a*) Samples of components are individually measured. Here sample means and ranges are calculated and recorded. to indicate if the process is working satisfactorily, i.e. in control.

(*b*) Components from samples are simply accepted or rejected as with a go or no go gauge. Results can be recorded on fraction defective charts to show if the process is in control. Fraction defective sampling can also be used to check the quality of incoming goods.

MEAN AND RANGE CHARTS

These charts are used when the parts sampled are individually measured. They are usually applied to running jobs where samples can be taken at regular intervals, the samples being of four or five components.

If many components from a batch are measured and the frequency with which each dimension occurs is plotted to form a frequency distribution, it will be found that the frequencies group themselves round a central value in a reasonably symmetrical curve approximating to the "Normal" distribution shown in fig. 10.2. This fact is

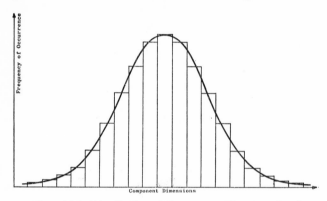

FIG. 10.2 *Distribution of Component Sizes in a Batch.*

used when compiling control charts, the limits on the chart being determined by the variation from the central value. The central value is known as the mean or grand sample average, and the spread of the distribution is known as the dispersion The most convenient measure of dispersion for a normal distribution is the standard deviation. This is found from the formula:

$$\sigma = \sqrt{\left\{ \frac{\Sigma (x - \bar{X})^2}{N} \right\}}$$

Where σ is the standard deviation of the individual components,
  $\bar{X}$ is the grand sample average,
  x is the size of an individual component,
  N is the total number of components in the distribution.

Figure 10.3 shows the percentage of the total population contained within one, two and three standard deviations on either side of the mean value. It can be seen that 95·5 per cent of the components lie within $\pm 2\sigma$ and 99·7 per cent lie within $\pm 3\sigma$. If the value of the standard deviation is found for any distribution of this sort, it is possible to specify limits in terms of standard deviations outside which only a small known percentage of parts will fall, provided the process is in control. For example, if limits are set at $\pm3\sigma$ from $\bar{x}$ on average only 3 components in 1,000 will fall outside them.

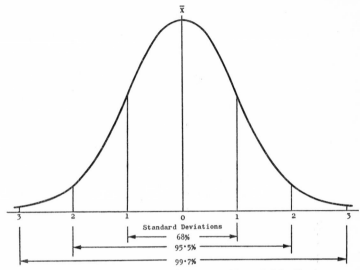

FIG. 10.3 *Dispersion of Population in a Normal Distribution.*

In practice the dimensions of individual components are not recorded on a control chart, but the average size of the sample. Hence, taking a sample of 4 components add their dimensions and divide by 4. The effect of this is to make the distribution of mean sample sizes round the grand sample average more compact; that is, the dispersion and the sample standard deviation decreases as the sample size increases. Actually, $\sigma_n = \dfrac{\sigma}{\sqrt{n}}$ where σ_n is the standard deviation of the sample averages of n components. This is shown in fig. 10.4. It follows, then, that the larger the size of the samples the closer to the mean will be the control limits on the mean chart, an example of which is shown in fig. 10.5.

To exercise complete control over a process a range chart must also be used. This records the maximum difference between the largest and smallest components in a sample and is plotted on a chart showing action and warning limits for sample range size. As the sample size increases, the average range also increases, so the limits on the range chart when taking large samples will embrace a larger variation of size than when taking small samples.

Control limits may be set to contain any required percentage of

L

the population, but it is usual for the action limits on the mean chart to contain 99·8 per cent of the samples (3·09 standard deviations) and for the warning limits, when used, to contain 95 per cent (1·96 standard deviations) of the samples. In other words, 1 sample in every 1,000 can be expected to fall outside the top action limit and

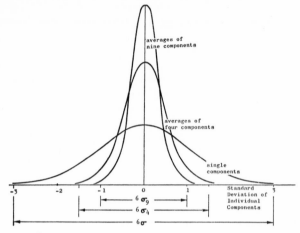

FIG. 10.4 *Effect on Standard Deviation of Increasing Sample Size.*

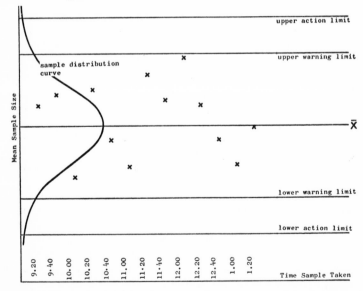

FIG. 10.5 *Typical Mean Chart Showing Action and Warning Limits*

1 in 1,000 outside the bottom action limit. They are therefore called the 1 in 1,000 control limits, while by similar reasoning the warning limits are called the 1 in 40 control limits. The action and warning limits on the range chart contain 99·9 and 97·5 per cent respectively and are known as the 1 in 1,000 and the 1 in 40 limits. Although these limits are worked out from a knowledge of the standard deviation, constants have been evaluated for different sample sizes which enable the limits to be calculated directly from the grand sample average and the sample range without finding the standard deviation.

When finding the limits for a control chart, a number of samples is checked at regular intervals and the sample average $\bar{x}$ and the sample range w are tabulated. After taking about ten samples the grand sample average $\bar{X}$ and the average range $\bar{w}$ are found by adding the values of $\bar{x}$ and of w and dividing by the number of samples taken. Then for the mean chart, using the tables in fig. 10.6:

Sample size	MEAN CHART warning limits	action limits	RANGE CHART warning limits	action limits	Modified limits warning limits	action limits	Critical examination of range chart
n	$A'_{0.025}$	$A'_{0.001}$	$D'_{0.975}$	$D'_{0.999}$	$A''_{0.025}$	$A''_{0.001}$	L
2	1·23	1·94	2·81	4·12	1·51	0·80	0·18
3	0·67	1·05	2·17	2·98	1·16	0·77	0·27
4	0·48	0·75	1·93	2·57	1·02	0·75	0·33
5	0·38	0·59	1·81	2·34	0·95	0·73	0·37
6	0·32	0·50	1·72	2·21	0·90	0·71	0·41

FIG. 10.6 *Constants for Use when Calculating or Critically Examining Limits on Mean or Range Charts.*

Warning limits $= \bar{X} \pm A'_{0.025} \times \bar{w}$

Action limits $\ = \bar{X} \pm A'_{0.001} \times \bar{w}$

and for the range chart:

Warning limit $\ = D'_{0.975} \times \bar{w}$

Action limit $\ \ = D'_{0.999} \times \bar{w}$

Additionally, there are lower action and warning limits for the range chart, but these are of little use in practice, and are seldom plotted.

The limits are now drawn in on the charts and sample averages and ranges plotted at regular intervals. From the pattern formed by these points, it is possible to see whether the process is stable; that is whether it continues with the original degree of accuracy and uniformity. The distribution of points on the mean chart will indicate the amount of tool wear, the ability of the setter to set near the mid-

tolerance, and the ability of the machine to produce at a given size without drifting toward either limit. Points on the range chart will show the ability of the machine or the operator to repeat consistently. Signs of instability are when a point occurs near the action limit or when two or more points in rapid succession appear near the warning limit.

It will be seen that the statistical limits bear no relation whatever to the design limits, and although the charts described may show the process to be stable, stability is of no use if the components are being produced outside the limits. In order that there shall be no appreciable production of defectives it is necessary that the whole distribution should fall within the design limits. As 99·7 per cent of the components fall within 3 standard deviations on either side of the mean, allowing the possibility of 0·3 per cent defectives being passed, the production is satisfactory provided the tolerance between top and bottom design limits exceeds 6σ (or 6·18σ if the statistical limits are set to enclose 99·8 per cent of the distribution). Now, since samples are taken of n components, the action limits on the mean chart will be $6·18 \dfrac{\sigma}{\sqrt{n}}$ apart, and the design tolerance must then equal or exceed $\sqrt{n}$ times the difference between the top and bottom control limits. Constants have been calculated to allow critical examination of control charts without first finding the standard deviation. The fundamental requirements are:

1. The average sample range must not exceed $L \times$ design tolerance. (L is a constant given in fig. 10.6.)

2. Mean chart control limits must lie between values of $A''_{0.001} \times \bar{w}$ above the bottom design and below the upper design limit.

Sometimes the process is controlled well within the limits allowed by the design tolerance, and if the statistical limits were worked to the components would be made to an unnecessarily high standard of perfection. To make these limits more realistic a drift is allowed on the mean value so that the tails of the distributions centred round the displaced means fall within the design limits by an amount equal to $\bar{w} \times A''_{0.001}$ (fig. 10.7).

The modified limits will then be as follows:

$$
\begin{aligned}
\text{Upper action limit} &= \text{upper design limit} - \bar{w} \times A''_{0.001} \\
\text{Upper warning limit} &= \text{upper design limit} - \bar{w} \times A''_{0.025} \\
\text{Lower warning limit} &= \text{lower design limit} + \bar{w} \times A''_{0.025} \\
\text{Lower action limit} &= \text{lower design limit} + \bar{w} \times A''_{0.001}
\end{aligned}
$$

The constants in fig. 10.6 give the limits most commonly used and

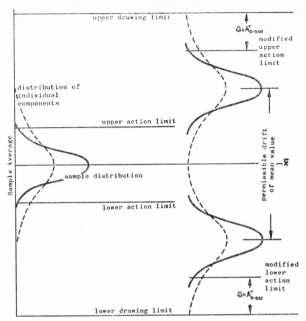

FIG. 10.7 *Modified Control Limits.*

recommended in British Standards B.S.600R "Quality Control Charts" and B.S. 2564 "Control Chart Technique when Manufacturing to a Specification". Frequently, control charts are used without warning limits and sometimes the range chart has been found unnecessary, but until they have been proved unnecessary in practice it is advisable to adopt the full charting technique.

FRACTION DEFECTIVE CONTROL CHARTS

Fraction defective charts are generally a poor substitute for range and mean charts but they are applicable in many cases where the decision to accept or reject does not depend on a dimensional measurement or where a simple go/no-go gauge is used. They have found considerable use where parts are purchased from sub-contractors or outside suppliers, or where testing is necessarily of a destructive nature. Due to their simplicity they are now frequently used in factories instead of the charts already described.

If a large batch of components contains p per cent within the specified limits, and q per cent outside the limits, then the probability that one component selected at random is a good one will be p, and the probability of its being a defective will be q, where $p+q=1$.

Selecting two at random, the probability of two good ones will be p^2 and of two defectives will be q^2. The probability of the first one being good and the second defective will be pq and the probability of the first being defective and the second good will be qp. Hence we can summarize the various probabilities as follows:

	Probability
2 good	p^2
1 good, 1 defective	$2pq$
2 defectives	q^2

By a similar process of reasoning it can be shown that if three components are selected at random the probabilities are as follows:

	Probability
3 good	p^3
2 good, 1 defective	$3p^2q$
1 good, 2 defectives	$3pq^2$
3 defectives	q^3

Anyone acquainted with the expansion of binomial expressions will quickly see that the probabilities may be found from the expansion of $(p+q)^n$, where n is the number of components in the sample. Thus:

$$\text{probability of no defectives} = p^n$$
$$\text{probability of one defective} = np^{n-1}q$$
$$\text{probability of two defectives} = \frac{n(n-1)}{1\times 2}p^{n-2}q^2$$
$$\text{probability of three defectives} = \frac{n(n-1)(n-2)}{1\times 2\times 3}p^{n-3}q^3 \text{ etc.}$$

Let us now consider a simple numerical example using this distribution, where the batch is 90 per cent good and samples of four components are being measured.

Then $p = 0.9$ $q = 0.1$ $n = 4$
$(p+q)^n = (0.9+0.1)^4$

$$= 0.9^4 + (4\times 0.9^3 \times 0.1) + \left(\frac{4\times 3}{1\times 2}\times 0.9^2 \times 0.1^2\right) +$$

$$\left(\frac{4\times 3\times 2}{1\times 2\times 3}\times 0.9 \times 0.1^3\right) + 0.1^4$$

$$= 0.6561 + 0.2916 + 0.0486 + 0.0036 + 0.0001.$$

Figure 10.8 shows this information plotted in the form of a frequency distribution. The other distribution shown dotted illustrates the effect

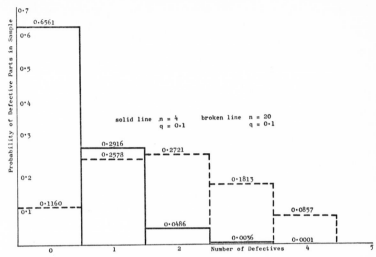

FIG. 10.8 *Effect on Distribution Curve of Increasing the Sample Size.*

of increasing the size of the sample to twenty, the greatest probability now being that there will be two defectives.

From these distributions the probability of *at least* a certain number of defectives being present in a given sample can be found. In the above example it can be said that:

Probability of at least one defective = $1 - 0.6561 = 0.3439$

Probability of at least two defectives = $0.3439 - 0.2916 = 0.0523$

Probability of at least three defectives = $0.0523 - 0.0486 = 0.0037$

Probability of four defectives = $0.0037 - 0.0036 = 0.0001$

This means that when sampling from a batch in which 10 per cent of the parts are defective, there is an expectation of 2 or more defectives per sample about once in every 20 samples. Similarly 3 or more defectives per sample occur only 3 or 4 times in each 1,000 samples taken, so the presence of 3 defectives in any sample show that the percentage defective probably exceeds 10 per cent. In practice such small samples are unreliable when dealing with a batch of relatively good components, and larger samples, particularly from batches in which the defective percentage is low, involve complicated arithmetic to calculate the limits, using the binomial distribution. For this reason it is more convenient to use the Poisson distribution, when the number of defectives is less than 10 per cent, as would normally be the case. The probabilities of defective parts occurring in samples of a given size taken from a batch having a known percentage of defectives, according to the Poisson distribution, are expressed by the terms of the expansion $e^{-m} \times e^{m}$ where m is the expected number of rejects in a sample and e equals 2·718.

$$e^{-m} \times e^{m} = e^{-m}\left(1+m+\frac{m^2}{\underline{|2}}+\frac{m^3}{\underline{|3}}+\frac{m^4}{\underline{|4}}+ \ldots\right)$$

where $\underline{|n} = n \times (n-1)(n-2) \times \ldots 2 \times 1$.

If we consider a batch which is 90 per cent good and the sample size is 20,

$$m = nq = 20 \times 0·1 = 2.$$
$$e^{-m} \times e^{m} = 0·1353\,(1+2+2+1·333+0·667+ \ldots)$$
$$= 0·1353+0·2706+0·2706+0·1803+0·0902+ \ldots$$

The following table shows the comparison of the probabilities obtained from both the Poisson and binomial distributions.

	Poisson	Binomial
Probability of no defectives	0·1353	0·1160
Probability of one defective	0·2706	0·2578
Probability of two defectives	0·2706	0·2721
Probability of three defectives	0·1803	0·1813
Probability of four defectives	0·0902	0·0857

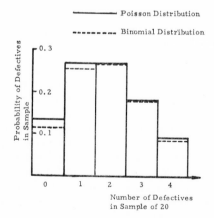

FIG. 10.9 *Comparison of Poisson and Binomial Distributions for a Sample Size of Twenty from a Batch which is 90 per cent Good.*

Both distributions are plotted in fig. 10.9 and it can be seen that, provided the sample size is large enough and that q is relatively small, the Poisson distribution may be taken as a good approximation of the binomial distribution. As q becomes smaller the approximation becomes closer. For various expectations of rejects the probability of the number of defectives in a sample exceeding a certain number has been calculated and tables have been published giving the maximum number of defectives which a sample may reasonably be expected to contain without causing concern.

The table of limit values in fig. 10.10 are calculated on the basis that the stated quantities of defectives will be equalled or exceeded with a frequency of less than one sample in 10 or one sample in 200 if the batch is of the quality expected.

	limits				limits	
m	1 in 10	1 in 200		m	1 in 10	1 in 200
0·1	1	2		2·0	5	7
0·2	2	3		2·5	6	8
0·3	2	3		3·0	7	9
0·4	2	4		4·0	8	11
0·5	2	4		5·0	9	13
0·6	3	4		6·0	10	14
0·7	3	5		7·0	11	16
0·8	3	5		8·0	13	17
0·9	3	5		9·0	14	19
1·0	3	5		10·0	15	20
1·5	4	6				

FIG. 10.10 *Limiting Values for the Number of Defectives in Samples which will be Equalled or Exceeded with a Frequency not Exceeding One Sample in Ten and One Sample in 200.*

Let us examine a case where a batch of work is considered acceptable if no more than 2 per cent of the components are outside the prescribed limits. Samples of 150 components are to be inspected. Then the average number of defectives m expected in a sample n equals nq or 3. Looking at fig. 10.10, where $m = 3$ the warning limit in a sample of 150 is 7 and the action limit is 9. This means that if the batch is of the required quality no more than one sample in 10 should contain 7 or more rejects. A typical fraction defective chart based on these values is shown in fig. 10.11. The last two points, both being round the warning limit, indicate that the process may be getting out of control, and action should be taken to prevent further deterioration.

The standard deviation of a Poisson distribution is equal to the square root of the mean of the number of defectives. In order to construct the control limits for a component being machined the

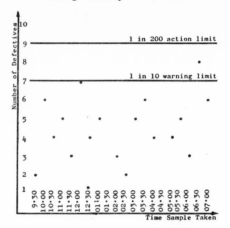

FIG. 10.11 *Typical Quantity Defective Chart Showing Action and Warning Limits.*

average number of defectives per sample over about 50 samples can be found and by taking the square root of this figure multiplied by 1·96 and by 3·09 and adding the results to the mean value gives us our 1 in 40 and 1 in 1,000 control limits. These limits will show whether the process is in control.

Each application of these charts requires its own special treatment but when sampling from a running job it is usual to examine between 5 and 10 per cent of the total output, the sample size being selected to give an expectation of 1 to 4 defectives per sample. This usually results in samples of between 20 and 50 components being used, but for a batch with a very low defective percentage the sample size may be considerably larger. Small samples always tend to indicate that the quality of the batch is higher than it in fact is.

In the consideration of fraction defective charts so far it has been assumed that a certain percentage of defectives is acceptable, but when it is desirable to avoid any defectives being passed a compressed limit chart is used. When using compressed limit charts, the gauges are specially set 0·2 times the design tolerance inside the design limits. This has the result of rejecting parts which are just inside the design tolerance, so that the expectation of defectives is raised without increasing the sample size. Charts of this type enable a smaller part of the total batch, usually not more than 2 per cent, to be inspected where the batch has only a small percentage of defectives; it also enables the fraction defective principle to be applied where it is desirable that no defective parts shall be passed. Constants to be used with compressed limit charts are contained in B.S.2564 "Control Chart Technique when Manufacturing to a Specification".

When sampling from batches of parts bought from outside suppliers it is desirable that the acceptance or rejection formula is previously agreed with the supplier. One of the best-known systems is that advocated by Dodge and Romig whereby a second sample is checked if the percentage defective in the first sample exceeds the acceptance limit but is less than the rejection limit. If the total number of defectives in the first and second samples do not exceed the rejection limit then the batch is accepted, but if they do exceed the rejection limit then the entire batch is rejected.

This section on statistical quality control is not intended to be an exhaustive treatment, but is simply to provide the student with an appreciation of the principles involved. There is a large number of excellent publications on the practice of the subject, some of which are mentioned in the bibliography. However, it will be found that symbols contained in British Standards are frequently not used, and the recommended control limits are by no means universally applied.

11

Measurement of Industrial Performance

COST CONTROL

If the financial position of a company is to be maintained, means must be provided to analyse production costs at regular intervals so that control can be exercised in the following ways:

1. Comparison of costs of products and spare parts with their selling prices, to show the measure of profitability.
2. Measurement of progress towards financial objectives.
3. Incorporation of flexibility in the expenditure budgets, so that variations in sales from the budgeted quantities may be compensated by adjustment to the various financial budgets.
4. Apportionment of overhead expenditure to products as accurately as possible.
5. Noting of variations from the accepted methods of production which may involve excess costs.
6. Use of the most efficient production process having regard to quantities required.

Different industries require a varying amount of emphasis on each control, and as a consequence a number of differing systems of cost accounting and budgetary control are found in practice. Generally, the choice of system is determined by the size of the company, the type of production and the relative ease with which the system can be applied to give the desired results.

In jobbing production, where the size of the undertaking is often small and the variety great, the most important requirement is to determine the product or job cost for purposes of pricing so that the products can be sold at a profit. If work is performed against a quoted contract price, this information is still desirable so that errors of quotation are not perpetuated. Process industries, where a single product or a very limited range of products is made by passing work through a pre-determined series of processes, need a close check on material utilization; therefore an important factor in process costing is the determination of wastage. Mass production factories, where a small range of products is made, are particularly sensitive to changes in cost due to variations in the volume of production and lend themselves to standard costing systems. Such systems are also generally the best means of cost control in batch production industries, but the expense and complications involved have deterred many managements from installing standard costing in this type of factory.

STANDARD COSTS

Standard Costs are estimated costs per unit of output for labour, materials and overheads, based on a prediction of material prices, labour rates and overhead expenses for a given future period. Breaking down product costs into their various contributory factors enables performance in all areas of activity to be compared with standard values. Variations from predicted performance can then be accurately determined and action taken to prevent their recurrence or to allow for them if they cannot be prevented. This is a case where control is exercised by exception, as only the variations from standard need be studied so that appropriate action can be taken.

A typical cost data sheet for a component is shown in fig. 11.1, and a standard cost sheet for a finished model compiled from cost data

| COMPONENT COST DATA SHEET | | | Part no. 265842 | | | | | |
| | | | Description bearing bolt | | | | | |

material specification	cost code	qty. required	std. price/lb	std. material cost				
$\frac{7}{8}$ " dia. 0·4% carbon bright drawn steel	427	1·231b	11·3d	13·90d				

Standard cost of direct labour and overhead

op. no.	description	dept. code	labour grade	std. time (min)	std. labour rate (pence)	std. labour cost (pence)	std. over-head rate (%)	std. over-head cost (pence)	cum. labour cost (pence)
1	capstan	61	M3	8·3	92·2	12·75	220	28·05	12·75
2	capstan	61	M3	3·4	92·2	5·22	220	11·48	17·97
3	mill	52	F3	1·2	49·6	0·99	250	2·47	18·96
4	drill	51	F3	1·5	49·6	1·24	270	3·35	20·20
5	grind	66	M4	2·4	96·3	3·85	240	9·24	24·05
6	bench	74	M3	3·6	92·2	5·53	180	9·95	29·58
7	etc								
8	etc								
9									
10									
						29·58		64·54	

STANDARD COST SUMMARY

material	13·90
labour	29·58
overhead	64·54
total cost	108·02

FIG. 11.1 *Component Cost Data Sheet.*

(a)

| STANDARD PRODUCT COST - LABOUR | | Product | 128 control board |

part no.	no. off	departmental cost per unit (pence)									total cost per unit
		auto 62	capstan 61	short order 39	milling 52	drilling 51	bench 74	grinding 66	metal finish 54	assy. 13	
265264	2	–	14 ·28	–	2 ·42	–	3 ·42	–	–	–	20·12
265384	1	3·31	10 ·28	15 ·16	–	–	3 ·68	–	–	–	32 ·43
265396	3	–	–	16 ·41	2 ·40	–	10 ·41	–	–	–	29 ·22
265842	1	–	17 ·97	–	0 ·99	1 ·24	5 ·53	3 ·85	–	–	29 ·58
etc assembling									548·22		548 ·22
total deptmtl. std. cost/unit		3·31	42 ·53	31 ·57	5 ·81	1 ·24	23 ·04	3 ·85	–	548·22	659·57

(a)

(b)

| STANDARD PRODUCT COST - MATERIAL | | Product | 128 control board |

part no.	no. off	material cost per unit (pence)							total cost per unit
		mild steel 425	bright drawn steel 427	alloy steel 478	non-ferrous bar 462	iron castings 487	aluminium castings 468	forgings 456	
265264	2					246 ·22			246 ·22
265384	1						148 ·70		148 ·70
265396	3	46 ·23							46 ·23
265842	1		13 ·90						13 ·90
total material cost/ unit		46 ·23	13 ·90			246· 22	148· 70		455 ·05

(b)

(c)

| STANDARD and CURRENT PRODUCT COST | | | | Product | 128 control board |

	standard cost				current cost			material cost			
dept.	labour		overhead		factor	labour	o'head	code	std.		current	
	s	d	rate	s d	lab. o'head	s d	s d		s	d	s d
13 assemble	45	8·22	220	100 5·08				425 mild steel	3	10·25	
39 s'order	2	7·57	230	6 2·61				427 b.d. steel	1	1·90	
51 drilling		1·24	270	5·35				456 forgings			
52 milling		5·81	250	1 2·52				462 non-f. bar			
61 capstan	3	6·53	220	7 9·57				468 alum.cstg.	12	4·70	
62 autos		3·31	600	1 7·86				478 alloy st.			
66 grinding		3·85	240	9·30				487 iron cstg.	20	6·22	
74 bench	1	11·04	180	3 5·44				etc			
total	54	11·57		121 10·73					37	11·05	

TOTAL COST	standard £ s d	current £ s d
labour ·	2 14 11·57	
material	1 17 11·05	
overhead	6 1 10·73	
TOTAL	10 14 9·35	

(c)

FIG. 11.2 *Product Standard Cost Cards.*

sheets for the components used on the model is shown in fig. 11.2. From component cost data sheets together with wages bookings and scrap records it is possible to calculate the following information:

1. Standard cost of work done in each department during the reference period.

2. Scrap and rectification cost attributable to each department.

3. Standard cost of direct materials, from which the material usage variances may be computed.

4. Cost of components, as a means of price fixing for spare parts or as a cost comparison when obtaining sub-contract quotations.

5. Basic data from which to calculate standard model costs as shown in fig. 11.2.

From fig. 11.2 it is possible to calculate a factory labour load for a given sales programme by converting the standard labour costs in each department to complete the programme in terms of hours. This load will indicate how much labour of each grade is required, but will not show the particular type of machine needed to accommodate such a work load. If a statement of plant load was required it would be necessary to code all plant according to type, and record the standard labour costs according to the plant code and not according to department.

The value of work-in-progress in the factory may be obtained, at any time throughout the year, from a knowledge of its value at the last stock-taking and the movement into and out of the factory since that date.

The period for which standard costs are to be valid varies considerably, although from an accounting point of view a year is often an obvious choice since business plans are usually for a year or for multiples of one year. Shorter periods than a year involve heavy clerical costs, and changing standards will make it increasingly difficult to follow the progress of long-term plans. Longer periods will demand higher degrees of flexibility to enable adjustments to be made for current conditions.

When calculating standard prices for materials, the values of stocks already purchased and of purchases already contracted should be taken into account as well as the forecast price level in the standard costing period. Standard direct labour costs can only be calculated from a knowledge of the standard time and wage rate for each operation. Knowing this, and also knowing the average operator performance expected for each labour grade during the cost period, it is possible to evaluate the direct labour standard cost per component for each operation. The calculation of the standard overhead recovery rate for each department depends firstly on the apportionment to departments of the general overhead expense. This is added to the budgeted expense for the department, and the resultant figure divided by the budgeted production gives the standard overhead recovery rate. It will be realized that the initial assessment of the value of overheads can be arrived at only as a result of a budget based on the planned output. The unit of production used will depend on the industry, some using the unit of output, e.g. the pound weight, others, including most engineering companies, using the standard machine hour, the standard direct labour hour, or the standard direct labour cost.

The use of standard costs has led to a change of emphasis in the rôle of cost accounting from one of historical analysis, the ascertainment of product costs after they have been incurred, to one of forward planning and the provision of a regular service of cost information to management. This enables a close control to be exercised to ensure that performance corresponds to the planned budget.

Many excellent books have been written by accountants on standard costing, some of which are recommended to the student requiring detailed information on the subject. The foregoing paragraphs have been written to give some idea of the general principles involved so that when reading the following pages it will be easier to appreciate the type of basic data from which the control information may be calculated.

MANAGEMENT ACCOUNTING

Management accounting is the presentation to all levels of management of figures which will assist them to perform their jobs efficiently. These figures may be in any units, not necessarily related to money, which have a significance to the manager or supervisor receiving them. Although management accounting is not necessarily geared to a system of standard costs, it will be realized that standard costing procedures lend themselves readily to the collection and analysis of data necessary for management accounting purposes.

The development of management accounting would have no doubt occurred at an earlier date if managements had realized what services could be offered by cost accountants, but the additional cost of such services and the reorganization of data collection and distribution needed, encouraged the continuation of old and tried systems. Also, the failure to introduce a standard terminology for management accounting led to confusion not only of managers, but of cost accountants themselves. This was due mainly to the uncoordinated individual efforts which were taking place simultaneously along parallel paths in several countries. Another delaying factor was the totally different type of control information required by different industries.

Although most manufacturing businesses have, in the past endeavoured to produce and work to a plan covering all financial expenditure, the growing competition for markets since World War II has more than ever demanded that production should be planned to give the optimum return on material, manpower and equipment. Competition has necessitated a much closer control of expenditure, so that, when working to the close cost margins required, products may be sold at prices which are competitive but which ensure a reasonable return on investment. Inevitably, as tariff barriers fall, this competition will grow, and the accurate preparation of budgets will become of still greater importance.

BUDGETARY CONTROL

The basic principles of standard costing, namely the comparison of actual performance and predicted performance, with suggestions for corrective action where necessary, apply also to budgetary control. Budgetary control applies these principles to the business as a whole, or to departments within the business, whereas standard costing applies them to individual products and to production processes.

If budgetary control is to be successful it is necessary that the budgets are planned in an atmosphere of co-operation, so that the initial financial requirements of departments for the period in question shall be compiled by the departmental managers concerned, and the development of the final draft budgets shall be agreed with them before being submitted to top management. This ensures that managers are made aware of their financial responsibilities and that they are not in a position to claim at a later date that their departmental budget is unworkable or unrealistic.

It is necessary to know how far ahead a business can be planned. Generally, long-term and short-term budgets should be prepared, long-term budgets covering periods varying from 2 to 10 years, and short-term budgets covering periods up to one year. The long-term budgets are based largely on conjecture and are subject to considerable modification. They are none-the-less necessary, as many of the decisions affecting the ultimate success of a company, such as embarking on a new line of products, require this sort of forward planning. Short-term budgets, generally covering a period of one year, are the tools by which day-to-day control is exercised. Periodic progress reports are circulated showing the achievement against the plan so that action may be taken to see that expenditure is controlled

M

and income is maintained. The main budgets which are required are listed below:

1. Sales budget.
2. Production budget.
3. General expense budget.
4. Capital expenditure budget.
5. Working capital budget.
6. Cash budget.

In their final form these budgets will enable next year's profit-and-loss account and balance sheet to be estimated.

SALES BUDGET

This is the budget to which all others must be geared. The estimated sales volume must be a realistic assessment of what can be sold. Quantities sold will generally be affected by selling price, so it will be necessary to estimate sales over a range of prices. By this means it should be possible to determine an optimum price which would give the maximum profit. Figure 11.3 shows how, for an article having an elastic demand, the volume of sales is affected by price. Figure 11.4

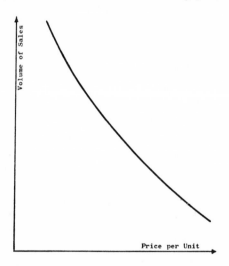

FIG. 11.3 *Effect on Sales Volume of Price for an Article having an Elastic Demand.*

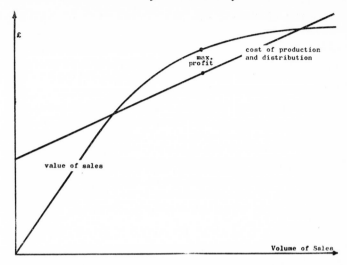

FIG. 11.4 *Effect of Sales Volume on Profit Margin.*

shows how the total value of sales for such an article increases as the volume of sales increases. From this graph a point of maximum profit, where sales value exceeds costs by a maximum amount, may be found. It is not suggested that the maximum profit alone is the only factor determining price, but it certainly limits the permissible range of prices. Maximum profit does not necessarily imply the maximum return on existing capital, since the sales volume at which this occurs may involve considerable additional investment in fixed assets. Also the question of market standing must be considered. If the company is to increase its share of a given market it may be expedient to produce in larger quantities and accept a smaller margin of profit, particularly if this is likely to lead to better production techniques at a later date.

The anticipated sales may not be the potential of the market; production may be limited by machine capacity, availability of capital, materials, or labour, or by a number of other factors. These sales estimates, then, serve the dual purpose of providing the cash value of sales for the budget and sales quotas for agents and salesmen.

PRODUCTION BUDGET

The production budget is usually the responsibility of the production manager with the assistance of his departmental heads. Its purpose is to find the cost of producing the estimated volume of saleable product. This quantity may be affected by inventory considerations. For instance, if the volume of sales is increasing, the budgeted value of warehouse stocks at the end of the period will also have increased to allow the requisite buffer stocks to be maintained.

A production plan is calculated in terms of the number of units to be produced in each period; the standard period may be of any duration but a month is a useful time to select. Estimates are made of requirements of labour, plant, floor-space and materials necessary to meet the plan. If standard costs are used these estimates can be more easily found and converted to money values, but failing this, estimates must be made by other means.

The production budget may be compiled on a departmental basis, in which case it can be used to measure periodically the effectiveness of departments, or it may be compiled under cost headings, e.g. direct material cost, direct labour cost and factory overheads.

GENERAL EXPENSE BUDGETS

These budgets cover all aspects of general expenditure such as selling and distribution, development and research, and administration. They are prepared initially by the managers responsible and integrated with the overall plan with the assistance of the accountant.

CAPITAL EXPENDITURE BUDGET

The justification for the purchase of individual items of capital equipment will be as stated in Chapter 4. Usually there is insufficient money available to indulge in all the capital expenditure which appears justified. Capital expenditure will therefore have to be related to the cash position of the business and pruned accordingly.

Departmental expense budgets will include small unspecified items, but all equipment subject to annual depreciation must be included in the capital budget.

WORKING CAPITAL BUDGET

The successful functioning of a business depends largely on the correct allocation of working capital, which is the difference between current assets and current liabilities. Current assets are mainly composed of stock, work-in-progress and debtors, while current liabilities consist mainly of creditors. Stock and work-in-progress levels will be dictated by company stock policy, which will be influenced by the time required to obtain material while money payable and receivable by the company will be largely determined by purchasing and selling policy.

CASH BUDGET

It is necessary that sufficient cash is available at all times to ensure the day-to-day operation of the business. Account must be taken of the varying rates at which cash will be received and paid out during the business cycle. The other budgets are integrated in the cash budget to provide the overall financial plan for the period under consideration. This budget will indicate whether additional funds will be necessary or, alternatively, will show if excessive cash is likely to be accumulated.

Sometimes labour costs and purchases are extracted from the production and general expense budgets and expressed as separate budgets so that a more direct control can be exerted on the ratio of direct to indirect labour or on the execution of the purchasing policy.

Budgets are estimates intended to provide a reasonable profit at a given sales volume, and every effort must be made to achieve the budgeted level of activity. However, it is necessary to allow some elasticity provided this does not jeopardize the overall operation of the plan. For this reason a knowledge of the effects of flexibility in budgeting is desirable.

FLEXIBLE BUDGETS

The components of cost do not, unfortunately, bear any direct relationship to the volume of output in most cases. Certain expenses such as direct materials and direct labour may be assumed to be directly proportional, while the overhead expenses are fixed, directly variable and semi-variable in character. Usually the semi-variable expenses are resolved into fixed and directly variable components. In practice most expenses, irrespective of their variability, follow a reasonably linear law. Figure 11.5 shows how these expenses may be compounded to show the cost of producing over a large range of sales volume. Bearing in mind that the budgets are calculated for a specified sales price, the value of sales can be shown by a straight line passing through the origin. From this simple graphical representation, it is possible to find the estimated profit at the budgeted volume of sales and the effect on profit of exceeding or falling short of this figure.

In practice the cost will not usually increase exactly in this uniform manner with increased volume of sales, nor will it decrease as smoothly. Typical reasons for this are the tendency to retain a higher labour force than is necessary during slack periods and the need for increased supervision expenditure if production is to be raised beyond certain levels which represent the maximum capacity of existing plant and buildings. However, allowing for these retentions, the general trend will approximate fairly closely to the graph.

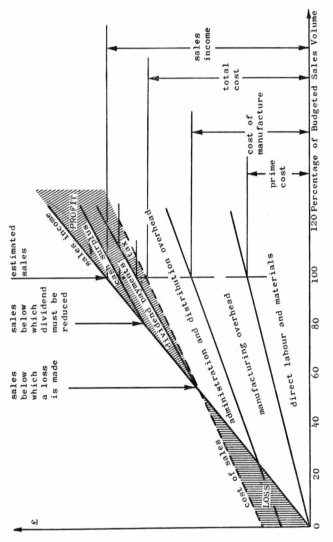

FIG. 11.5 *Effect of Sales on Estimated Profit.*

Divergence between predicted results and actual results will be due to two factors, one called revisions variance and the other controllable variance. Revisions variance is caused by cost variations beyond the control of the departments concerned, such as price changes or increased wages resulting from national awards. In the event of excessive variances occurring to make the budget unworkable a revised budget based on the new costs is created, which is then used in parallel with the original budget. Controllable variance is due to departmental performance differing from the budgeted performance as a result of factors over which the departmental manager may be expected to have some measure of control. These factors will include labour utilization, material utilization, quality, indirect labour costs, indirect materials, or non-standard processes. Since departmental managers have no control over the revisions variance it is advisable that departmental operating sheets supplied to them should contain only controllable variances analysed so that appropriate action may be taken. A typical departmental operating sheet suitable for issue to the foreman of a works department where a bonus scheme is in operation is shown in fig. 11.6. In process industries direct material variances would probably also appear on the

Foreman Mr W.Jones Period W/E 21/10/61	Department 13 Assembly Shop				DEPARTMENTAL OPERATING SHEET				
	planned budget	actual result	adjusted budget for output	diff + or −	analysis of labour losses	direct responsibility hours £		indirect responsibility hours £	
Output labour hours	6548	6361	97% ACHIEVED		daywork training excess costs			18	2½
Direct Operators no. of directs total clock hours total wages (£) piecework perf. (%) % directs under 175% hours lost cost of labour losses (£)	65½ 2816 786 250 − 197 131	60 2714 747 250 13.7% 171 104	63½ 2729 762 − − 191 127	−3½ −15 −15 − − −20 −23	rectification waiting make-up awards overtime over-rated labour	138 45 15 3½		1½ 1½ 34	
Indirect Operators no. of indirects indirect hours indirect wages (£)	3 186 58½	3 287 76	3 186 58½	− 101 17½	indirect labour supervision setters from directs	budget no. hours £ 1 48 17½ 2 92 26¾ 46 14¾		actual no. hours £ 1 48 16 2 107 31 130 29¼	
Indirect Materials consumable tools (£) consumable materials (£)	11½ 8	5¾ ½	11 7½	−5¼ −7					
Tool Maintenance materials (£) labour (£)	9 13	− 19½	8½ 12½	−8½ 7					
Quality scrap (£) scrap as % output cost of rectif. as % output at std.cost	72	95½	70	25½	notes				
Rating	output 97	labour use 93·7	quality 95	rating 95·2					

FIG. 11.6 *Departmental Operating Sheet.*

sheet, but in a batch production factory where much of the work is performed in different departments the material variances could not be attributed to any single department. The value of scrap provides a more suitable measure in such cases.

MACHINE AND LABOUR UTILIZATION

MACHINE UTILIZATION

This is defined as the ratio of the number of hours a machine is productively employed on standard operations to the total number of working hours in the period under consideration. Information on machine utilization should be analysed so that the utilization of specific machine groups is shown. A single figure for the utilization of all the plant in a department containing a number of different machine types gives no indication of where losses of productive capacity have occurred. Machine utilization is affected by:

1. Work load available relative to the number of machines in the section.

2. Direct labour available.

3. Availability of setters, i.e. setter/operator ratio.

4. Efficiency of setters and operators. Good setters and poor operators may create the impression of high utilization.

5. Recording of working hours. If, as a consequence of running a skeleton night-shift, all machine utilizations are recorded on a double-shift basis, the percentages will be low.

6. Size of batches. This affects the percentage of time the machine is being set.

7. Flow of work from previous operations, or of material from stores.

8. Amount of work requiring rectification.

9. Machine or tool breakdown.

10. Flexibility of production equipment.

Sometimes the time spent by direct operators on rectification work may be included in the utilization percentage, on the basis that this work would need to be performed on a machine anyway, and the available capacity must allow for the time spent on rectification.

LABOUR UTILIZATION

This is the ratio of direct labour hours booked on standard operations to total clock hours. It is affected by the following considerations:

1. Work load relative to the number of direct operators.
2. Setter/operator ratio.
3. Lateness or absenteeism of setters or, sometimes, of other operators engaged on previous operations.
4. Machine or tool breakdown.
5. Size of work batches. This will affect the setter/operator ratio necessary to maintain the labour utilization percentage.
6. Flow of work from previous operations.
7. Flexibility of labour.
8. Percentage of work requiring rectification.
9. Operations performed as excesses due to non-standard methods being employed.
10. Daywork due to operation not having been timed, or the time not having been accepted.
11. Trainee labour not employed on the bonus scheme.

Time lost due to the above factors can be analysed and the responsibility pinpointed. Foremen or departmental managers can then be required to explain the reasons, so that corrective action can be taken or negligence censured. Labour utilization is controllable by the foreman to a greater degree than machine utilization as he can vary the labour force to meet changing circumstances; he is not normally able to alter the number of machines in his department.

Machine and labour utilizations can be calculated by inserting the machine number on the operator's work ticket, which provides the necessary information for calculating operator performance, hence his wages. A typical work ticket is shown in fig. 11.7. The analysis number indicates the type of operation, for example, time piecework, daywork, rectification, or additional operation due to faulty material.

If any benefit is to be derived from these figures it is important that the reasons for low utilization are established as they frequently show a shortcoming in the system, and idle plant produces no return on invested capital. For example, foremen paid a bonus which depends in part on the labour utilization obtained have been known deliberately to limit their labour force so that the labour employed showed a higher utilization, the excess work then having to be sub-contracted. This would, of course, be shown up by the low machine utilization achieved.

WORK TICKET		
date	name	works no.
part no. and operation		piecework time
time on	time off	hours
qty. produced		p/w performance
m/c no.		analysis no.
bonus clerk's initials		

FIG. 11.7 *Operator's Work Ticket or Time Card.*

ESTIMATING

Some form of estimating is necessary in any type of manufacturing industry, although estimates may be used for different purposes under different conditions of production. In a jobbing company, where products are made in small quantities, accurate estimates are of great importance as a basis for delivery promises, pricing and tooling requirements. The degree of accuracy obtained by estimating depends on the detail with which the job is analysed. Sometimes, as in engineering products, the individual components are costed on an operation basis, and an estimate is made of the assembly cost. This highly detailed analysis is expensive and takes a considerable time; some industries do not lend themselves to such a detailed approach. Typical of these is the building industry, where costs may sometimes be determined from a calculation based on the cubic capacity of the building. Different cost factors would obviously have to be used for different conditions of construction, i.e. ground floor, first floor, or second floor, but for a particular sort of structure the use of factors based on cost per cubic foot will often give a quick and reasonably accurate figure. Other industries find that cost is nearly directly proportional to the weight or to the surface area of the product. Factors based on these characteristics are sometimes used in foundries and sheet-metal factories. In engineering factories, estimates are sometimes made from comparison with existing products, where a marked similarity exists.

In batch or mass production industries estimating is largely used to find whether a product can be sold at a given price and yield a reasonable profit. The price is determined by a knowledge of the market and of competitors' products. If the estimates indicate that the price is uneconomic it will probably be necessary to modify the design. Frequently, savings of considerable magnitude can be effected by examination of the materials used, since material costs often represent about half the total cost of a product. Estimates must possess a high degree of accuracy if heavy losses are to be avoided on "big-selling" products through under-estimating. Over-estimates may also lead to unnecessarily low sales due to high prices and possibly uneconomic manufacture, since there is a tendency to treat the estimated cost as an objective.

Estimates will be affected considerably by the volume of sales predicted. A forecast of large sales may result in an expensive tooling programme, which will not be recovered if sales fail to reach expectations. This often leads to a reluctance to change design until the tool cost has been recovered. Under-tooling, however, is probably a greater and more frequent error brought about by a low initial sales forecast, followed by a steadily increasing demand, which can eventually be satisfied only by improved production methods.

Overheads must be included in all estimates. Depending on the

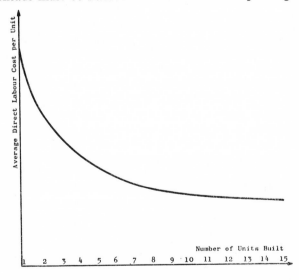

FIG. 11.8 *Decrease in Direct Labour Cost with Increase in Manual Dexterity.*

type of factory the overhead may either be calculated as a fixed percentage of total direct labour costs, or may be worked out in greater detail as a percentage of direct labour costs incurred in each department. The second method is more accurate, particularly where different departments carry a widely varying factory overhead.

Apart from the improved performance obtained by expensive tooling, manual dexterity plays an important part in costs. The effect of this is particularly noticeable during the early stages of production, when operators are acquiring skill. Where production is on a large scale the initially low output is soon overcome and cost savings due to increase in operator skill will then cease. However, if only a strictly limited number of a certain design is to be built, as is often the case in the aircraft industry, the estimate must take account of the fact that the average direct labour cost will be affected markedly by the quantity ordered, as shown in fig. 11.8. This effect is particularly noticeable where total quantities are small, total cost is high, and assembly operations represent a major part of the total cost.

As an approximation when assembling small batches it is possible to express the direct labour cost l for the Nth assembly by the following equation,

$$l = C.N^{-b}$$

where C = labour cost for the first assembly,
          b = a parameter $(0 < b < 1)$.

Research in a number of labour intensive assembly industries suggests that b takes a value of about $\frac{1}{3}$ irrespective of the type of assembly. This equation implies that labour cost approaches zero for very large numbers of assemblies and hence it is likely to be a poor approximation for batches in excess of one hundred.

12

The Production Control Department

THE control of quality and cost have been discussed in earlier chapters, the planning and control of production has yet to be dealt with. The department chiefly concerned with these functions is known as the Production Control Department (P.C.D.). It plans the assembly of finished products to meet sales requirements, it also plans the manufacture of parts required for assembly and does much to help ensure that the plan is fulfilled by the departments concerned. Production planning and control is not difficult if products contain only a few parts or if flow production layouts are used. It does, however, become very complex when products contain a large number of components and sub-assemblies, or a wide variety of products is being manufactured. These complex conditions are often found in engineering companies where it is not unusual for more than 10,000 different components and sub-assemblies to be required to meet current sales demand.

FUNCTIONS OF PRODUCTION CONTROL DEPARTMENT

The following list of duties is a comprehensive one and, quite often, some of the tasks are undertaken, wholly or partly, by other departments.

1. Estimate future factory load.
2. Issue information on equipment and labour requirements to meet the production plan.
3. Convert sales requirements into a factory assembly plan.
4. Determine component and material requirements either by analysis of the assembly plan and addition of spares requirements, or by other means.
5. Maintain raw material, component and finished product stores.
6 Unpack and check the quantity of goods received.
7. Despatch finished products and spares.
8. Maintain stock records.

9. Provide a timetable to guide the factory in the assembly and manufacture of parts.

10. Authorize the manufacture of parts and the issue of material by means of orders and material requisitions.

11. Assist supervision with the loading of their sections, so that work is processed to comply with the manufacturing timetable.

12. Control works order documents in the factory, count and record the quantity of finished work.

13. Control internal transport.

14. Maintain a record of outstanding orders.

15. Expedite late work.

16. Re-plan programme arrears.

17. Inform sales department of the performance of the factory against the assembly programme.

18. Implement design changes.

Most of these functions are self-explanatory, they will almost all be described in detail in the ensuing chapters.

RELATIONSHIP WITH OTHER DEPARTMENTS

Production control is expected to satisfy a number of requirements, some of which conflict. Let us examine what is required of the P.C.D. by other departments.

1. The sales department will be concerned that the customers are satisfied, often to the extent of trying to insert last-minute customer additions and cancellations in the production plan. They will also be anxious that satisfactory delivery promises are made to the customers and that these promises are kept.

2. Factory management and supervision will require a steady work load and plenty of prior notice of changes. They will also want long production runs with all parts and materials available when required.

3. The production engineering department will be keen to see that the equipment which they have specified has a high utilization and will generally demand long production runs. They will also ask for prior notice of changes in production requirements so that arrangements can be made to increase manufacturing capacity.

4. The purchasing department will require adequate notice of requirements of bought-out parts and materials. This will enable them to buy in the best markets and to maintain the continuity of

supplies. If long-term contracts are to be placed with suppliers estimates of requirements for periods from six to twelve months ahead will be required.

5. The accountant will attempt to ensure that stocks and work-in-progress do not exceed their budgeted values. He will also require that stock records are correctly maintained and that adequate control is kept of work-in-progress.

6. The department responsible for design and development will want new products and design modifications incorporated with little regard for disruption of output or the balancing of stock to avoid component redundancies.

The P.C.D. will have an impossible task if it tries to please all the departments with which it works. For instance, long runs and low stocks oppose each other, except in flow production. It will frequently be impossible to make last-minute changes to the assembly plan to suit the sales department without upsetting factory management.

PRODUCTION CONTROL SYSTEMS

Production control systems are best if they are designed for the requirements of the particular factory, and disaster often awaits the person who tries to lift the production control system out of one company and rigidly apply it elsewhere. There is, however, a number of principles of good production control which are universally applicable and these must be woven into a system which successfully meets local requirements. Management consultants have had much experience in this field and there is a considerable demand for their services.

In the past, and in some instances even at the present time, the importance of good production control to the general efficiency of a company goes unrecognized by management. Consequently the staff appointed to senior production control positions are often inadequate; loyal and thrustful progress chasers frequently make unsuccessful production controllers. These people devote their considerable energy to clearing today's shortages without giving much objective thought to the system which created the shortages. Their do-or-die attitude is evidenced by the brave mottoes sometimes seen hanging in their offices, such as "The difficult we do now, the impossible takes a little longer".

Often the circumstances under which P.C.D.s have to operate are little short of impossible; last-minute changes to assembly programme have to be accepted, short runs are forbidden and stocks are expected to be held at an unreasonably low level. In addition, the direct labour force is often insufficient to cope with the factory load. Under these circumstances it is not surprising that the P.C.D. proceeds from one crisis to the next, the production controller accepting them as inevitable and being left in a position to receive management censure for failing to achieve targets which are impossible of simultaneous achievement. Do not think that all companies operate under these conditions, but many do, and in these fundamental thinking is necessary to plan a new framework for production control. Agreement will have to be reached on the compromise to be struck between the conflicting requirements of other departments, sensible targets will have to be set, and a sound system of planning and control installed.

If close control is required the system will be expensive to operate but there will be fewer mistakes and less interruption of production. Simpler arrangements will leave more to chance but will be cheaper to operate. In designing a system of production control a satisfactory balance between cost and control will have to be struck. Most companies appear to suffer from lack of control rather than too much of it.

Although a production-control policy is bound to contain a series of compromises there should be no vacillation in the application of the policy once it has been decided upon. If there is weakness here the department will lose the respect and authority necessary to carry out its functions.

ORGANIZATION OF PRODUCTION CONTROL DEPARTMENT

Production control is usually considered the responsibility of factory management, although it is occasionally under the charge of the accountant or the company secretary. In small firms employing less than 100 people production control does not usually exist as a separate function, the necessary work often being done jointly by factory management and the sales department. A satisfactory arrangement in larger companies, which enables a reasonably independent policy to be followed, is to make the P.C.D. the responsibility of the general manager or the general factory manager.

The functions of the department have already been listed. It will be found that there is a considerable variation from one company to another in the duties of the P.C.D. The planning of production and the progressing of late work are almost invariably included, but stores, stock records and internal transport are often omitted. If the P.C.D. has only a narrow range of responsibilities it may have to depend on the accountant for stock balances, the chief storekeeper for assembly set shortages, and on a third department for moving work within the factory, not a very satisfactory state of affairs. The narrower responsibility will also reduce the status of the department and make the job of production controller a less attractive one. Apart from size of company and span of responsibility, a third factor affecting the size of the P.C.D. is the type of work being processed in the factory. Simple products made in large quantities on flow production layouts usually require a smaller P.C.D. than a similar size batch-production factory manufacturing a wide range of products. A typical production control organization for a medium-sized company is shown in fig. 12.1.

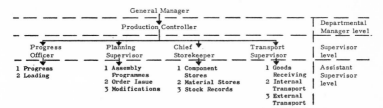

FIG. 12.1 *Organization Chart for Production Control Department.*

N

Planning for Component Manufacture

FORECASTING

A company will undertake several types of forecasting. Production control will not be greatly concerned with forecasts of the level of economic or industrial activity several years ahead. This information will be required by the Board of Directors to plan its general business policy and to decide whether or not to manufacture new products or build new factories.

Shorter term forecasts running up to a year ahead and broken down into detailed requirements are, however, of interest to the P.C.D. This type of forecast is usually made by the sales department but occasionally it is the responsibility of the P.C.D. itself. Salesmen frequently alternate between over-optimism and over-pessimism and care must be taken that these extremes are not reflected in the final sales forecast. Short-term forecasts are often divided into two parts, tentative and firm. The tentative forecast is used to check manufacturing capacity, and the firm forecast, covering only a few months ahead, is used as the basis of the manufacturing programme. In companies which are not manufacturing for stock, such as those engaged on jobbing production, there is no need to use forecasts as a basis of the manufacturing programme, as this will be composed of firm orders. When a company is acting as a sub-contractor it usually relies on firm orders, although in some instances it may have to compile its manufacturing programme from customers' tentative requirements.

THE ASSEMBLY PROGRAMME

Assembly programmes are issued by the P.C.D. and prepared by them in co-operation with the sales department and factory management. They show details of finished product output required from the factory during a given period. The period covered by the programme will vary, but one month is frequently used. In addition to the firm factory programme a tentative one, covering say an additional two months, is sometimes also prepared.

A factory usually operates most efficiently near to its maximum capacity, as it cannot rapidly increase its output nor can it economically lower it. Sales demand may, however, be at a different level from factory capacity, and subject to violent fluctuation. How then are the sales and factory requirements to be reconciled? Some warning of changes in the volume of sales should have been given by sales forecasts, thus enabling capacity to be increased or decreased accordingly. Often there is no such warning and a change in the policy of an overseas government can create or destroy an export market overnight. Although output can be reduced at comparatively short notice, a longer period is needed to obtain increased production, particularly when the factory is already operating near to its maximum capacity. Most companies do not know their maximum capacity and many issue assembly programmes slightly in excess of "maximum" capacity to try to squeeze a little more output from the factory. It is, however, bad practice to issue assembly programmes knowing that they will seriously overload production facilities. When preparing assembly programmes, any arrears outstanding from previous programmes must be taken into account and new programmes reduced accordingly, thus enabling the arrears to be cleared.

In factories which have a regular pattern of varying demand, such as the toy trade, the assembly plan can be arranged to keep the factory running at a fixed output, the stocks built up during the period of slack demand being cleared when sales demand increases. In other industries it is most unwise to build up large stocks of finished products in the hope of trade improving. Most companies impose a strict financial limit to the amount of finished product stock which can be held. It may, however, be expedient to raise temporarily the maximum limit of finished product stock, provided there are good reasons to believe, not hope, that demand will improve. Many assembly programmes aim at keeping a buffer of finished stock between factory and customer provided there is a likelihood of a continued demand. This buffer stock enables sudden changes in demand to be accommodated, as well as providing a short breathing space for the factory to increase capacity if needed. Stock may also be required to allow the factory to produce the customer requirements in one batch, say at the end of a monthly programme, yet to supply the customer with finished products each week of the month. This stock is often referred to as planning stock. When the demand for a particular model is low, small assembly batches can be avoided by making several months' requirements in one build and supplying the customer from stock. Although the holding of finished product stock tends to isolate the activity of the factory from customer demand, difficulties are likely to arise if production and sales remain out of step for very long.

When compiling assembly programmes it is necessary to know the current maximum capacity of the factory. Usually this is based on past achievement, although sometimes it can be calculated from machine capacities or from standard times and operator performance. By sub-contracting or by increasing shift work much can often be done within a few months to increase output. Although the capacity of most factories is elastic, the rate at which output can be increased must be correctly estimated so that in times of rapidly increasing demand the assembly programme remains in step with factory capacity.

OPTIMUM STOCK HOLDING POLICY

In companies where the products manufactured are expensive and where orders are likely to be lost if immediate delivery cannot be guaranteed an optimum stock holding policy is particularly important. To achieve such a policy it is first necessary to know the probability of demand during the period of manufacture, and the penalty cost of unsatisfied demand. Generally, the penalty cost is the estimated loss of profit due to lost orders.

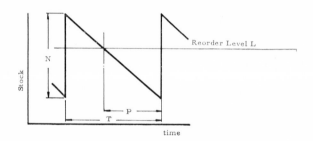

FIG. 13.1 *Idealized Stock-time Graph.*

Fig. 13.1 shows a typical stock-time graph based on average order levels, where N is the batch size of manufacture, L is the re-order level, P is the manufacturing time and T is the total cycle time between orders. Although the average rate of sales is R, the actual sales may show considerable variation during the cycle.

Assume the frequency distribution of sales during the manufacturing time P is as shown in fig. 13.2 where $P.R.$ is the expected sales,

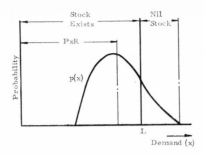

FIG. 13.2 *Probability Distribution for Demand during Procurement Time.*

and the probability of selling a quantity x is $p(x)$. Then the probable unsatisfied demand in any cycle =

$$\int_L^\infty (x - L).p(x)\mathrm{d}x.$$

The average penalty cost/re-ordering cycle

$$= K \int_L^\infty (x - L).p(x)\mathrm{d}x = A$$

where K = profit on one unit of output.

Average penalty cost of shortages per unit time

$$= \frac{A}{T} = \frac{A.R}{N}$$

From the geometry of fig. 13.1, the average carrying cost of stock unit time

$$= \left\{ \frac{N}{2} \cdot T + (L - R.P)T \right\} \frac{C}{T} = \left\{ \frac{N}{2} + (L - R.P) \right\} \cdot C$$

where C = carrying cost per unit of production during unit time.

Ordering and setting cost/unit time $= \dfrac{S}{T} = \dfrac{R.S}{N}$

where S = ordering and setting costs associated with one batch.

Total variable cost/unit time

$$= V = \frac{A.R}{N} + \left(\frac{N}{2} + L - R.P \right).C + \frac{S.R}{N}$$

$$\frac{\partial V}{\partial N} = \frac{-A.R}{N^2} + \frac{C}{2} - \frac{S.R}{N^2} = 0 \text{ for min cost/unit time.}$$

$N = \sqrt{\dfrac{2R(A + S)}{C}}$ if the optimum order quantity is calculated

to allow for penalty costs. However, A is a function of L, the re-order level, so N is also a function of L.

$$V = \frac{R(A + S)}{N} + \frac{N.C}{2} + L.C - R.P.C.,$$

but $R(A + S) = \dfrac{N^2C}{2}$

$$V = N.C + L.C - R.P.C.$$

The variables in this equation are N and L, so to minimise V, $N.C + L.C$ must be a minimum.

i.e. $N + L$ must be a minimum.

If the probability function has a mathematical definition the values of $L + N$ can be calculated, it is however, more likely that the

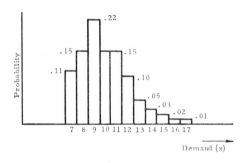

FIG. 13.3.

distribution will be discrete, as shown in fig. 13.3, and a numerical solution is necessary. When this is so the expected loss A becomes

$$K. \sum_{x = L + 1}^{\infty} (x - L).p(x).$$

Example.

The average annual sales (R) of a product are 100, carrying cost/unit/year is £200, ordering and manufacturing time $P = \frac{1}{10}$ year, profit per unit sold (K) = £400, S = £100. The probability of receiving orders during P is shown in fig. 13.3. Calculate the optimum re-order level and re-order quantity.

L		17	16	15	14	13	12	11
$A = K \sum\limits_{x=L+1}^{\infty} (x-L).p(x)$		0	4	12	28	56	104	192
$N = \sqrt{\dfrac{2R(A+S)}{C}}$		10	10·2	10·6	11·4	12·5	14·3	17·1
$N+L$		27	26·2	25·6	25·4	25·5	27·3	28·1

The minimum value of $N + L$ occurs when $L = 14$ and $N = 11·4$ and the optimum re-ordering system will be when the stock falls to 14 and the re-order quantity is 11.

In practice, the probability distribution as shown in fig. 13.1 is difficult to obtain, so a prudent inventory policy would allow for about 95 per cent certainty of meeting orders during P without carrying a re-order stock in excess of the maximum requirements.

ORDER QUANTITIES

There has probably been more consideration given to order quantities than to any other aspects of production planning. Let us consider some of the factors affecting order size.

1. PREPARATION COST

It may take from a few minutes to several days to set a machine to manufacture a part. These setting and other preparation costs, such as the cost of order issue, although lost in the general overhead charge, are significant and must be taken into account when considering order quantities. Although the setting cost for the batch is considered fixed the setting cost per part is inversely proportional to the batch size. Economic batch formulae normally assume that once a job is set it will run until completion, a dangerous premise in many factories, where the arrival of more urgent work often means that the part-completed batch is taken off the machine and reset later.

2. MACHINE UTILIZATION

The longer machines are kept running, the better the machine utilization and the higher the return on the capital investment. Large batches of work will increase machine utilization.

3. TYPE OF PRODUCTION EQUIPMENT

Once equipment has been purchased there is often considerable pressure to feed it with the sort of order quantity that suits its appetite. Much modern high production equipment has a hearty appetite which cannot be satisfied by small order quantities.

4. OPERATOR UTILIZATION

Operator utilization usually improves with the longer runs resulting from larger batch size. As a consequence of longer runs, operator earnings will probably be improved and waiting time reduced. These factors, which are often only marginally improved, influence operators and supervisors in favour of large batches. The influence on supervisors is particularly great if they are paid by a bonus scheme which penalizes them for waiting time and low operator performance.

5. INVENTORY CHARGES

These charges are made up of a number of items such as cost of storage and losses due to redundancy or deterioration. In addition, stock represents idle capital, and account should be taken of the fact that if capital was not frozen in stock it could be invested elsewhere and made to earn money. The value of inventory is increased by large batch quantities and the annual total cost of carrying engineering inventory is often in the range of 15 to 25 per cent of the average value of stock.

ECONOMIC BATCH FORMULAE

Much has been written on the size of economic batches, and scores of formulae, many of them highly unmanageable, have been evolved to calculate the best order quantity. A basic method of calculating economic batch quantity is shown below:

Total cost of each part produced, E can be expressed as

$$E = C + \frac{S}{N} + kN$$

where C = constant cost per part (material, direct labour and overheads),

S/N = preparation cost per part (S being the preparation cost of batch and N the batch size)

and kN = inventory carrying cost per part.

Differentiating the total cost relative to batch size

$$\frac{dE}{dN} = \frac{-S}{N^2} + k$$

Equating the differential to zero for minimum cost per piece

$$O = \frac{-S}{N^2} + k$$

and $N = \sqrt{\dfrac{S}{k}}$

The variation with batch size of the factors which make up total cost per part is shown in fig. 13.4. It will be seen from the graph that the total cost per piece does not increase greatly for small variations

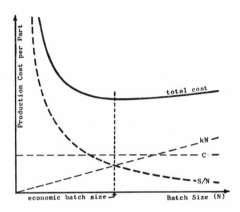

FIG. 13.4 *Production Cost per Batch with Different Batch Sizes.*

from the batch quantity giving minimum cost per piece; provided a batch size in this region is chosen the cost per piece will remain substantially constant. Very small batches should, however, be avoided, otherwise excessively high production costs per piece will be incurred and the production capacity of the factory reduced.

Economic batch formulae derived from the basic method shown above vary considerably in their complexity. The more complicated ones, some containing twenty or more terms, will not be considered as they are seldom used. Many of the items which could be included as part of preparation or inventory cost have little effect on batch size and can be neglected.

A simple formula frequently used is

$$N = \sqrt{\frac{2RS}{CI}}$$

where N = economic batch quantity,
  R = annual requirements,
  S = preparation cost,
  C = constant cost per part (material, direct labour and over-heads),

and I = inventory carrying charge rate per year (usually between 0·1 and 0·25)

The formula is derived by assuming a stock/time graph as shown in fig. 13.5.

Average inventory = $N/2$

Average value of inventory = $NC/2$

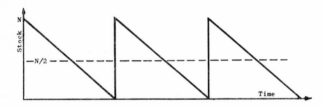

FIG. 13.5 *Stock/Time Graph.*

Total inventory carrying cost per year $= \dfrac{NC}{2} \times I$

Total inventory carrying cost per part $= \dfrac{NCI}{2R}$

but inventory carrying cost per piece $= kN$

$$\therefore kN = \frac{NCI}{2R}$$

and $k = \dfrac{CI}{2R}$

It has already been shown that

$$N = \sqrt{\frac{S}{k}}$$

$\therefore$ substituting for k

$$N = \sqrt{\frac{2RS}{CI}}$$

When considering minimum manufacturing cost per piece the term I will include an interest charge on the value of inventory. In practice, however, it is usual to increase the value of I to reflect the desired return from investment in inventory. As the required return on inventory investment is usually about three times the interest charge, the economic batch quantities normally calculated using the higher value of I are considerably less than those using the lower value.

Example. Calculate the economic batch quantity when estimated annual requirements are 10,000, setting cost is 50s., material, direct labour and overheads are 5d. and inventory carrying charge rate 0·2 (20 per cent).

$$N = \sqrt{\frac{2\,RS}{CI}} = \sqrt{\left(\frac{2 \times 10,000 \times 50 \times 12}{5 \times 0\cdot2}\right)}$$

= 3,460 or just over 4 months' supply.

It should be noted that economic batch formulae do not normally take into account the effect of batch size on the utilization of capital equipment. Small batch sizes reduce machine utilization due to the increased proportion of setting to running time. In batch production factories which use expensive plant that requires long setting times, batch sizes greater than those giving the minimum cost per piece provide a higher return on total capital employed.

In practice some of the factors listed below may affect policy on economic batch quantities:

1. Capital invested in manufacturing equipment.

2. Risk of stock becoming obsolescent.

3. Liability of stock to deteriorate in storage.

4. Availability of capital and its earning ability if used elsewhere.

5. Storage space available.

6. Availability of setters.

The great emphasis on the cost of carrying stock which often results in the indiscriminate holding down of inventory has, to some extent, put economic batch ordering out of favour. Economic batch formulae are, however, worth consideration as they do provide an analytical basis for judging batch sizes. The foreman who demurs at setting a job on an automatic lathe because it will run for less than one shift and is convinced that such a short run is uneconomic can have his opinion tested, provided there is someone who knows and can use an economic batch formula. The rigid application of economic batch quantities is, however, most unusual. Imagine the control problem of providing economic batch quantities at each operation for multi-operational parts. Between each process the batch would have to go to an inter-operation stores where it would have to be re-batched and then issued at the new economic batch quantity for the next operation.

CLASSIFICATION OF PARTS BY COST

Most engineering products are found to consist of a large number of relatively inexpensive parts, a small number of medium cost items, and an even smaller quantity of expensive parts. A typical distribution of the inventory value of the components of an engineering product is shown in fig. 13.6.

The control exercised over each category of part can be made to differ. As the expensive items have a disproportionately large effect on inventory they are processed in small batches, are scheduled to move quickly through the factory, and any buffer stock is kept to the absolute minimum. The cheap items can be ordered in "economic" quantities by simple re-ordering systems such as the stock-level method, described later in this chapter, records can be kept to a minimum, and the parts may be issued from stores without requisitions. It may be thought that the loose control used will cause

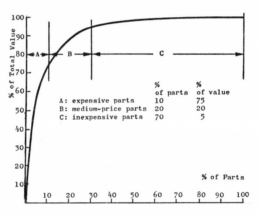

FIG. 13. 6 *Distribution of the Value of Parts in a Typical Engineering Product.*

wastage, but normally very little additional wastage results and this should be adequately compensated for by savings in control cost. The economies made in the control of inexpensive parts should also more than pay for the closer control which has to be exercised over the expensive items.

PLANNING COMPONENT MANUFACTURE

Components and sub-assemblies must be available to build finished products and satisfy spares requirements. In jobbing and flow production, component ordering is a comparatively simple matter. The parts for jobbing production are ordered in strict accordance with the assembly breakdown, and those manufactured by flow production are produced at the same rate as the product is assembled. It is batch production which provides the problems of component planning and most of the discussion in this chapter will be centred around providing parts for batch production.

The requirements of an ordering system are:

1. not to run out of stock,
2. to hold no surplus stock,
3. to avoid issuing orders for uneconomically large or small quantities of parts,
4. be simple to operate.

There are two basic methods by which components can be planned for batch production. The first assumes what has been used before will be needed again and maintains adequate stocks of each part to meet future requirements. This system is called stock-level ordering or maximum and minimum stock ordering. The second method orders only those parts actually required, making no provision for surplus stock and ignoring economic batch order quantities.

STOCK-LEVEL ORDERING

This system is the simplest method of ordering components and sub-assemblies; it however produces higher inventory than periodic re-ordering. The stock/time graph shown in fig. 13.7 can be used to

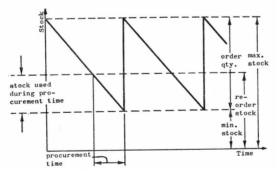

FIG. 13.7 *Stock/Time Graph assuming Constant Usage.*

demonstrate the operation of stock-level re-ordering. In drawing the graph it has been assumed that the order is delivered as a single lot and that the rate of usage is constant. The re-order point is chosen sufficiently above the minimum stock so that the re-ordered parts arrive in stores just as the stock has fallen to the prescribed minimum level. This arrival restores the stock to its maximum level. In practice, stock is not normally used at a constant rate or at the expected rate; orders may not be delivered in one batch or may take a longer or shorter time to obtain than estimated. A graph showing the typical movement of component stock is shown in fig. 13.8. Instead of

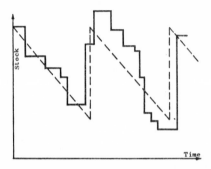

FIG. 13.8 *Actual Movement of Stock.*

expressing stock in numerical terms it can also be stated in terms of time, for instance if the stock of parts is 500 and the average usage is 100 per week this represents 5 weeks' stock. This method of talking about stock is most useful when discussing ordering systems. Let us now consider the various aspects of stock-level re-ordering in greater detail.

MINIMUM STOCK

This buffer stock provides a margin of safety when orders take longer to obtain than estimated or when usage is greater than expected. Very large and costly buffer stocks will be necessary if the very worst cases are to be guarded against. Buffer stocks should not therefore aim at complete protection against running out of stock. When deciding on the level of buffer stock to carry, help can be obtained from looking back over past records to find the occurrence of nil stocks and then setting the buffer stock level so that there is a low risk of nil stocks occurring in future. The likelihood of stock shortages will increase if the batches taken from stock for assembly are increased in size. For instance if the minimum stock is 4 weeks' usage then the chances of running out of stock will increase greatly if it is decided to withdraw parts from stores in 4-weekly instead of weekly batches. The nil stocks created by large stock withdrawals from stores will not, however, stop production until all of the parts available on the assembly lines have been used.

RE-ORDER POINT

The re-order point is equal to the minimum stock plus the expected usage of stock during the procurement period. The procurement period will usually be composed of two parts, the time for raising the necessary order and the actual processing time for the part. The order raising period is comparatively short, about a week, although in the case of bought-out items a longer period may be required. The processing time will vary with the part concerned. Allowance will have to be made in the processing time for work waiting between operations, and for inspection. Usually the processing time is much greater than the sum of the batch processing times for each operation. Generous process times can be allowed for less expensive parts as these have a much smaller influence on work-in-progress than the more expensive parts. The generous process allowances on cheaper parts should allow much tighter schedules to be maintained on expensive parts. The slack allowed in processing times should enable the batch quantities on most parts to be varied within reasonable limits without making it necessary to increase or decrease processing times. On bought-out items, such as raw material, where considerable fluctuations in procurement time occur, the purchasing department must keep P.C.D. informed of these changes.

Both stock and outstanding orders should be considered when deciding if a part is due to be re-ordered. If outstanding orders are not taken into account unnecessary orders may be issued and excessive stocks will result. A new order should be issued only when the sum of stock plus outstanding orders is less than the re-order point.

ORDER QUANTITY

This is usually a predetermined quantity which may represent a given number of weeks' usage, or may be calculated from economic batch formulae.

AVERAGE FINISHED PARTS STOCKS

When installing a re-ordering system some idea of the expected level of finished parts stocks and part-processed stocks will be required.

The average finished parts stock for each part ordered by a stock-level system can be found by adding the minimum stock to half the order quantity, see fig. 13.9. The total target value of finished parts stock can be found by summing the stock values for each part ordered.

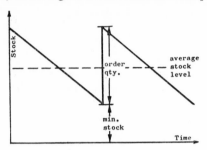

FIG. 13.9 *Finished Parts Stock.*

AVERAGE PART PROCESSED STOCKS
It is also possible to calculate the effect that each part has on the level of part-processed stocks. This is represented by the shaded area in fig. 13.10. If the process time is 3 weeks for a part re-ordered each 10 weeks its average contribution to the value of part-processed stocks

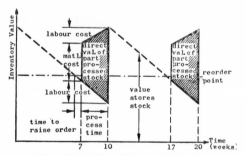

FIG. 13.10 *Part Processed Stock.*

can be assumed to be $3/10 \times$ order quantity $\times$ (material cost per part plus half of the direct labour cost, plus factory overhead). To establish the total value of work-in-progress the sum of the contributions made by each part will have to be found.

WHEN TO RE-ORDER
There are two main methods of knowing when a new order should be issued: one depends on a record of stock and outstanding orders and the other on sealed re-order quantities.

In the first method postings are made on the relevant stock record card for all orders issued and for all stores receipts and issues. When postings from stock are made the stock balance is added to the amount of any orders outstanding and compared with the re-order point. Sometimes the comparison is made by the clerk posting the record card, in other cases it may be possible for the posting machine itself to make this comparison, as described in Chapter 15.

The sealed-stock method depends on physical quantities, and stock records need not be used. When an order arrives in stores the re-order quantity is removed and put into a sealed container; this could be a sealed bin or a heat-sealed polythene bag. Before the parts are sealed a re-order chit is put with the parts. The storekeeper issues from the non-sealed stock but when no more parts are available he breaks into the sealed stock and issues from it. At the time the seal is broken on the sealed stock the re-order chit is removed and sent to the order issuing section of the P.C.D. who prepare a new order. This method of re-ordering is simplicity itself and is recommended for very cheap parts such as nuts, bolts and washers. Orders for these parts are usually large, but as the processing times are short the chance of there being a previous order outstanding is not high. Although this can be a simple and effective method of re-ordering it depends for its success on efficient storekeeping.

EFFECT OF COMPONENT ORDERS ON MATERIAL STOCKS

If material is ordered on a stock-level basis the material inventory will, to some extent, reflect the order quantities of the parts using the material. If a material is exclusively used for one part, then enough stock should be available to satisfy the order quantity issued for that part. If, for instance, the order quantity for the part is three months' usage then the minimum stock of the material should also be at least three months usage. When the material is used to manufacture several components then the minimum stock need not equal the combined size of the component orders as it is unlikely that material for all the parts will be required on the same day.

A similar position to that on material occurs on components used in sub-assemblies. If both components and sub-assemblies are ordered by the stock-level method the minimum component stock will have to reflect the sub-assembly order quantity.

CHANGES IN DEMAND

Although the stock-level method of ordering has flexibility the actual usage must, from time to time, be compared with the usage employed

o

for ordering purposes and the latter adjusted if necessary. Figure 13.11 shows what will happen when actual usage is (*a*) double and (*b*) half that used for ordering. It will be seen in fig. 13.11(*a*) that a higher than expected usage results in the more frequent issue of orders and reduced buffer stocks. In the example shown the buffer stock, in terms of usage, has been reduced to almost a quarter of that intended.

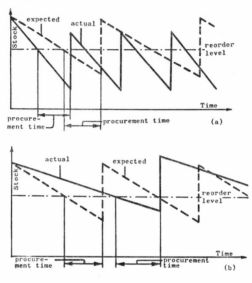

FIG. 13.11 *Effect on Stock of Variation in Rate of Usage.*

(a) *Actual Usage Double that Expected,*
(b) *Actual Usage Half that Expected.*

When the usage rate is less than that anticipated, unnecessarily large stocks of parts are carried. Figure 13.11(*b*) shows that the average stock level, in terms of usage, has been more than doubled.

ADVANTAGES AND DISADVANTAGES OF
STOCK-LEVEL ORDERING

Advantages:

1. Simplicity.
2. Flexibility.
3. Inexpensive to install and operate.

Disadvantages:

1. Produces a high inventory, particularly if used to order expensive parts.
2. Much clerical work is necessary to compare usage employed for ordering with actual usage and to adjust where necessary.
3. It does not provide an even factory load and makes the advance calculation of factory load difficult.

ORDERS BASED ON ANALYSIS OF ASSEMBLY PROGRAMME

This system, which is fundamentally different from stock-level re-ordering, orders parts from a breakdown of the assembly programme. It is, therefore, possible to order only just what is required to meet sales and service requirements and thus keep inventory at a very low figure indeed. There are many variations of this method of ordering; they all retain a breakdown of the assembly programme, but go part or all the way toward ordering parts in "economic batches". These variations, while meeting objections to small batch orders,

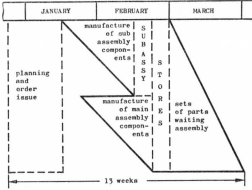

FIG. 13.12 *Monthly Planning (for March)*.

result in higher inventory charges. The general features of the system can be illustrated by the chart in fig. 13.12. This chart has been drawn assuming

(*a*) assembly programmes are issued each month,
(*b*) planning and order issue takes 3 weeks,
(*c*) the longest component manufacturing time is 4 weeks,
(*d*) sub-assembly takes 1 week,
(*e*) at least 1 week is required in stores, and
(*f*) the assembly operation itself takes only a few hours to complete.

If the parts were manufactured in weekly batches instead of monthly ones, less inventory would be required due to the smaller order quantities. Although inventory is reduced with shorter period planning, machines, other than those which are permanently set up, will have to be re-set more frequently due to the smaller batches. If the period covered by the assembly programmes is further shortened this type of planning ultimately reduces to feeding into the factory material for processing at the same rate as it is needed for the assembly programme. It is, in fact, flow production planning.

AMENDMENTS TO PROGRAMME

In the example illustrated in fig. 13.12 the assembly programme must be known 13 weeks before the completion of the assembly programme. In many companies it is difficult to be certain that the models being planned today will be what the customers will require two to three months hence. If the customer changes his mind and the buffer stock of finished models will not accommodate this change, then an amendment to the assembly and component manufacturing programme can be issued. A few amendments can be dealt with satisfactorily but a flood of amendments will produce chaos in the factory.

There are two factors which affect the time interval between planning and assembly; they are (*a*) the time required for the part with the longest process time to be ready for assembly and (*b*) the period covered by the assembly programme. In our example, if the planning time could be reduced by one week, the process time of the longest part by two weeks, and the time in stores prior to assembly by half a week, then customer requirements would not need to be known until $9\frac{1}{2}$ weeks instead of 13 weeks, before the completion of the assembly programme. If the period covered by the assembly programme was one week instead of one month, then another 3 weeks could be cut off the lead time, and it would now be $6\frac{1}{2}$ weeks instead of 13 weeks. This reduction can be seen by comparing figs. 13.12 and 13.13.

If only a few parts have long process times they can be dealt with as exceptions, thereby preventing them from extending the programme lead time. In our example of a March assembly programme, if there were a few parts which needed up to a 9-week processing time, then these would be planned and ordered a month ahead with the parts for February assembly. The quantities planned for these long process-time parts would be of course tentative ones as the firm requirements would not be available until a month later. Provided a small buffer

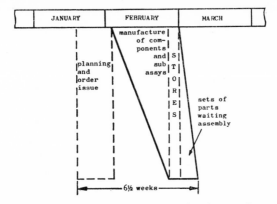

FIG. 13.13 *Weekly Planning (for first week in March).*

stock is held and the difference between tentative and firm requirements is adjusted on the next batch of orders this system should work satisfactorily. When it is necessary to keep the programme lead time short a similar system can be used to plan the production of all parts, although the additional clerical work involved is considerable.

COMPILING THE ASSEMBLY PROGRAMME

Sales requirements have to be converted into an assembly programme so that due allowance can be made for arrears, for the content of earlier assembly programmes still current, and for finished product stocks. This can be done on a planning sheet similar to that shown in fig. 13.14. Any adjustment to programme such as cancelled customer arrears can be made in line 7. Line 10 gives the minimum build necessary to satisfy the March sales requirements. After a quantity has been added to replenish the buffer stock, in this case kept at about 2 weeks' sales requirements, the tentative assembly build can be found for each model. An addition for planning stock may also be necessary if the customer is not prepared to accept delivery at any time during the month. If, for example, the customer stipulates delivery each week and the requirements cannot be assembled as weekly batches, or as a single batch at the beginning of each month, then additional buffer stock may have to be added to provide more elbow room for arranging the assembly builds. It will usually be possible by adjusting the stock build figures slightly, to bring the

1	Product No.	712/A	971/C	873/B
2	Sales Require-ments March	100	210	10
3	Stock at 1st January	52	81	30
4	Assy. Arrears at 1st January	nil	12	nil
5	Planned for Jan & Feb	190	400	60
6	Total Availability (3+4+5)	242	493	90
7	Jan/Feb Sales Requirements + Adjustments	205	420	70
8	Surplus or Shortage (6-7)	37	73	20
9	Current Sales Requirements (2)	100	210	10
10	Balance needed to meet Requirements (9-8) March	63	137	- 10
11	Quantity for Stock	50	100	nil
12	March Assembly Programme (10+11)	113	237	nil

FIG. 13.14 *Assembly Plan for March.*

planned build into line with factory capacity. Care must be taken when planning assembly programmes not to exceed the stock limits set by management policy.

ANALYSIS OF ASSEMBLY PROGRAMME INTO
COMPONENT REQUIREMENTS

There are two main methods of performing this operation: manually with a parts list, or mechanically using punched cards or a computor. The mechanized methods will be described in Chapter 17.

The manual method consists of going through the parts list for each model ordered and multiplying the number of each part used in the model by the quantity planned on the assembly programme. Part of this process is shown below:

Model 127/A (*113 planned for March*)

Description	Part No.	No. off	March requirements
Stator	127981	1	1×113
Lamination	821971	52	52×113
End Plate	891752	2	2×113
Shaft	179673	1	1×113
etc.	etc.	etc.	etc.

Model 971/C (24 planned for March)

Description	Part No.	No. off	March requirements
Stator	129871	1	1×24
Lamination	821971	44	44×24
End Plate	891752	2	2×24
Shaft	179675	1	1×24
etc.	etc.	etc.	etc.

It will be noticed from the partial analysis of the two models that they have the same laminations and end plates. When the total parts requirement has been found by summing the model requirements a single figure of common usage parts will be available.

DEDUCTION OF SURPLUS STOCKS

If only the exact quantity of parts to meet the assembly requirements were ordered there would be insufficient available due to scrap losses in manufacture. An addition is therefore made to the order quantity to cover normal scrap losses. Often the full scrap allowance is not required and parts become surplus to requirements. This surplus stock is then available to reduce future orders. So that the amount of surplus stock is known, a suitable stock record will have to be posted. The form of such a free stock record is described in Chapter 15.

ADDITIONS FOR SPARES REQUIREMENTS

In this type of planning spares requirements cannot be obtained from factory-held stock. Spares needs will have to be specifically ordered and the service department should present their requirements each time the programme is planned. In our example the spares requirements will be presented monthly and it will take just under two months before the parts are delivered. These deliveries will replenish spares stock which will probably be ordered on a stock-level basis.

ADDITION OF SCRAP ALLOWANCE TO ORDER QUANTITY

The last stage in determining how many parts to order is to add the scrap allowance. It is better slightly to over-estimate the probable scrap, and standard scrap allowances ascending in steps of 5 per cent are usually adequate. These allowances will not cover exceptional scrap; if this occurs a scrap replacement order will have to be issued.

The order quantity is now at last available, it having been obtained by:

(a) preparing assembly programme from sales requirements,
(b) breaking assembly programme down into component requirements
(c) adding spares requirements,
(d) deducting surplus stock, and
(e) adding scrap allowance

MATERIAL REQUIREMENTS

Material requirements can be obtained from the component order quantities. With a knowledge of the material specified for each part and of the standard material usage (the amount of material for a given number of parts) it is possible to calculate the amount and type of material required to manufacture the assembly programme. Reverting to our example, it will be seen that the material requirements schedule will be available only a week or so before the first components are due to be manufactured. Material schedules will therefore have to contain a forecast material requirement if they are to provide sufficient time for the buyer to procure material.

SYSTEMS ORDERING MORE THAN MINIMUM QUANTITIES

The system of planning described will order only sufficient parts to satisfy each assembly programme. These quantities may be thought to be below those which provide reasonable machine utilization, particularly for high-production machine tools such as automatic lathes and presses. Once the minimum order quantities have been determined as described they may be increased to any desired amount. In fact economic batch quantities could be calculated for each part in use. Larger order quantities should, however, be staggered over a number of programmes, otherwise the factory load would be seriously out of balance. The system will be self-regulating so far as order quantities are concerned; when larger batches have been ordered the surplus will appear as a free stock, enabling future orders to be cancelled.

ADVANTAGES AND DISADVANTAGES OF ANALYSIS OF ASSEMBLY PROGRAMME

In compiling this list of advantages and disadvantages the system which provides minimum and not "economic" order quantities has been considered.

Advantages:

1. Produces the minimum possible inventory.
2. Production is kept in balance with sales requirements.
3. Write-off of stock due to redundancy or deterioration almost eliminated.
4. Modifications and new products can be introduced quickly without waiting for old stocks to be used up.

Disadvantages:

1. Often produces low machine utilization as order quantities are unsuitable for the production equipment.
2. More setters required due to short runs.
3. Considerable work involved in calculating order requirements.
4. Cannot deal with a demand which is unknown or which is subject to frequent amendment after planning has started.
5. Free stock records are necessary for each component; these are more difficult to keep accurate than simpler forms of stock record.

MODIFICATION TO DESIGNS

Much of the work concerned with the introduction of design modifications falls on the planning section of P.C.D. Design modifications usually result in losses of production and sometimes the replaced parts and their tooling have to be written off.

One method of introducing modifications is by a co-ordinating committee consisting of members of the design staff, research department, production engineering department and P.C.D. This committee decides on the action to be taken in each case. It determines the introduction date of the new design taking into account:

(*a*) urgency of the modification,

(*b*) whether new tooling will be needed or the old tooling adapted,

(*c*) availability of new parts and materials,

(*d*) the need to test samples of the modified product, and

(*e*) whether existing stocks of old parts and materials are to be exhausted, scrapped or used for spares.

Alternatively, the co-ordination can be performed by a member of the P.C.D. who supplies the design staff with information which enables them to fix an introduction date.

When the modification is suitable for release the drawing office sends details to the production shops; this can be done by a Drawing Alteration Note, similar to that shown in fig. 13.15. Simultaneously

DRAWING ALTERATION NOTE		No. D.A.2456 Sheet 1 of 3
109/22 control board	Disposal of Stock	

	warehouse	assembly	comp. stores	work in prog.	spares and service store
use					x
use for spares			x		
withdraw and rectify	x	x			
modify to new issue				x	
scrap					

2468706 ass. base drawing issue raised to 3
2468707 base drawing issue raised to 2
2468902 terminal replaces 2468708 5 off
2468903 connector replaces 2468709 3 off
2468710 connector 2 off deleted

Note
when old parts are used up
supply new sub-assembly as spare

Origin of Alteration
customer request

date 16/3/62

form 638

FIG. 13.15 *Typical Drawing Alteration Note.*

the modified drawing cross-referenced to the Drawing Alteration Note is released to the factory. Some of the most important information in the Drawing Alteration Note is that concerning the disposal of unmodified stock. When a modification is not urgent, balancing orders are often issued so that all the unmodified parts are completely used.

By adhering to a sound system of introducing modifications it is possible to ensure that changes are introduced economically and with the appropriate priority.

Works Order Documents
and their Use

In the previous chapter we have seen how order quantities are determined. These order quantities must now be transmitted with other manufacturing information to the factory. The works order authorizes production, provides manufacturing instructions and enables output to be recorded at each stage of manufacture. As the works order indicates where the batch of work is to be processed it is sometimes referred to as a route card. Additionally, a material requisition must be provided to enable the correct type and amount of material to be withdrawn from stores. Other documents, such as machine loading cards, may also be issued if required. The works order and the material requisition are, however, essential if control is to be exercised over work-in-progress and the issue of materials.

WORKS ORDER

The following list indicates typical information supplied on works orders. Details such as part number, quantity and operation sequence are essential, other information can be included depending on the requirements of the system.

1. Part number and description of part to be manufactured; sometimes the description is omitted, although this is undesirable.

2. Quantity to be manufactured; often two quantities are shown, the first being order quantity allowing for scrap, the second being the minimum quantity below which insufficient parts would be produced to satisfy the current assembly programme. If the quantity being processed falls below the minimum requirement a supplementary order must be issued.

3. Sequence of operations necessary to manufacture the batch. The amount of detail provided here varies considerably from a full description of the operations, as shown on the manufacturing layout, to the briefest indication of the process and the department in which it is performed. With the briefer operation description, it is necessary

to refer to a copy of the manufacturing layout at each stage of manufacture for details of process and tooling.

4. Order completion date. This date is essential if orders are to be processed in the correct priority to ensure that parts are available in stores when planned.

5. Manufacturing time-table. Although not shown on all orders it is very desirable that a time-table should be provided. To avoid putting actual dates alongside each operation every time an order is issued, the time-table is often indicated by week numbers alongside the operation description. The numbers are frequently referred to as "minus weeks" and show the number of weeks before order completion date by which each operation should be finished. So that specific weeks can be conveniently referred to many companies issue works calendars dividing the year into numbered weeks.

6. Material specification and standard weight. While this information is not essential on works orders, it may be useful to check that the correct type and weight of material has been issued. These details are, of course, included on the material requisition, but once the requisition has been presented this information may not readily be available from other sources.

7. Labour grade and standard time. This information is useful for machine loading if a separate system of machine loading is not in operation.

THE WORKS ORDER AS A PRODUCTION RECORD

The works order is not only an authority to manufacture but it also acts as a record of what has happened to the batch as it passes through the factory. In some cases the order remains physically with the parts and identifies them in the shop, finally going with them into stores. The quantity received into stores is entered on the order and the stock record card is posted from the works order information.

In addition to the quantity entering stores, the number of good parts produced at each stage of manufacture is entered on the works order. Any scrap or other losses in production should also be entered, so that a balance between the parts arriving on the section and those leaving it can be obtained.

COUNTING OF WORK

Responsibility for counting parts varies from one company to another. Often the inspection department deal with quantity as well as quality; sometimes counting is done by the bonus clerks responsible for wages booking, or it may be done by a separate section of the

P.C.D. Entries on the orders should be made in ink. To enable errors to be traced back to the person making them, all entries should be identifiable; one way of ensuring this is to issue individual rubber stamps for use alongside each order entry.

The method of counting work will vary with the type of part. Expensive or fragile parts may be arranged in special trays carrying a fixed number of parts, when, after checking that the trays are full, it is a simple matter to calculate the number of parts processed. Small quantities or bulky parts are often individually counted; this, however, is a time-consuming task, and larger quantities are usually counted by weighing. Counting scales are available with 9-to-1 and 99-to-1 ratio pans which enable several thousand parts to be counted in a few minutes. The quantity to be counted is placed in the large scale pan, parts are taken from this pan and placed in the two smaller ratio pans until a balance is obtained. The total number of parts is equal to the number of parts in the 99-to-1 pan × 100 plus those in the 9-to-1 pan × 10. Although the weighing method is not so accurate as good individual counting, it is quite accurate enough for most purposes; with suitable scales the limit of error is about ±2 per cent. Where standard work containers are in use and platform counting scales are available, work can be counted without taking it from its container. A tare weight is used to compensate for the weight of the work tin or pallet.

If work is moved by conveyor it may be possible to count it by arranging that the work breaks a beam of light directed on to a photoelectric cell. Counters operated by the cell can be wired to a central point at a convenient position in the factory.

Presses and some other high-production equipment have counters which are operated by each stroke of the machine. These counters are often used to determine the quantity of parts produced. Unscrupulous operators can, however, increase their earnings by running the machines without material or, on certain designs of counter, the readings can be increased by rotating the figures with a scriber.

CARE OF WORKS ORDERS

The proper care of works order documents is important if they are to control work-in-progress efficiently. If works orders physically accompany the work between operations, a rather dangerous procedure as they may be lost, they should be protected by polythene envelopes. Although, from time to time, works orders will be mislaid they must be hunted down immediately; duplicate documents should be issued only after an exhaustive search has failed. A better method, which ensures safe custody of orders, is to set up a control point in each section of the factory where a member of the P.C.D. has adequate facilities for checking and recording orders. When work is moved from one section to another the order also should be promptly handed over to the next control point.

Once work has been counted it should be cleared from the section, or placed so that it is out of the way of operators. If this is not done and a piecework system is in operation, there will be a strong temptation to "borrow" some counted work from a previous shift if the job is still running on a later shift.

TYPES OF WORKS ORDER

There are two main types of works order: one for work intended to move as a complete batch through all its operations, and the other for work which progresses from one operation to the next without waiting for completion of the whole batch.

The first type, sometimes called a route card, is illustrated in fig. 14.1; it consists of a card showing all operations in their standard

WORKS ORDER								
part no. 78172B	description Bracket				quantity 10,500			
to finish by 30/12/61 (2)	order no. 67802				min. qty. 10,000			
material specification CR EN 2B 0·109" x 1·5" Coil					wt/ 1000		31·81b	
minus week	op. no.	operation	m/c group	labour grade	std. min/	qty. good	qty. reject	date stamp	insp. stamp
2	10	Blank & pierce	PD2	M4	0·82	10,800	nil	19DEC	(12)
1	20	Form	P4	F	22·5	10,300	500	21DEC	(12)
1	30	Tumble	B1	M4	–	10,300	nil	29DEC	(7)
		Parts store				10,100	–	29DEC	[3]

FIG. 14.1 *Works Order for Parts Moved as a Complete Batch.*

sequence on the same document. Occasions will arise when it is impossible to process all the parts together as a single batch; for instance, if an order is running behind schedule some of the parts may be urgently needed to clear an assembly shortage. In these circumstances it will be necessary to sub-divide or split the batch, the split quantity being pushed rapidly ahead and the rest of the batch left to proceed at normal speed. When a batch is split a duplicate works order must be issued to accompany the split quantity. A panel should be provided on the works order to show what splits have been made from it. Although the route-card type works order will cope satisfactorily with the occasional split batch, where splitting is frequent, as is usual in some factories, it will prove a most unsatisfactory document.

The other type of order, which is usually referred to as a batch book, consists of a separate order card for each operation; the order cards are stapled together and issued in the form of a book to the first operation. A single page of a typical batch book is shown in fig. 14.2. The unused pages of the batch book, still stapled together, are moved forward to the next operation as soon as the first parts from the batch are sent there. The partly booked pages remain in the sections performing the operations until the last of the batch is machined. This method enables bookings against orders to be made as and when the parts are processed. When the last of the batch has been completed on the first section, the completed first page of the batch book goes forward with the remainder of the parts to the next section. After all the parts have been processed on the second section, the completed first two pages of the batch book are sent forward. In this way, all the completed batch-book pages will be collected together by the time the last of the parts arrive at the stores. This method of collecting up the batch-book pages, section by section, avoids leaving orders open for small balances of work which fail to appear.

WORKS ORDER	previous operation	next operation 20 form
part no. 78172B	description Bracket	quantity 10,500
to finish by 30/12/61 (2)	order no. 67802	min. qty. 10,000
material specification CR EN 2B 0·109" x 1·5" Coil		wt / 1000 31·8lb
op. no. 10	operation Blank and pierce CVA 10T roll feed press T 1141	m/c group PD2
minus week 2		labour grade M 4

PRODUCTION RECORD		bal.		over-produced
	def.	10,500 4,800 (300)		
	good	5,200 5,100		
	date	18/12 19/12		

	def.	good	date
	500	5,200	18/12
	-	5,100	19/12

FIG. 14.2 *One Page of Batch Book Works Order (Production Record on Reverse Side)*

MATERIAL REQUISITION

DESIGN OF REQUISITION

This, like the works order, is an essential document. The information on the material requisition should include:

1. Number and description of part.
2. Material specification.
3. Material standard weight (quantity of material to make 100 or other suitable standard quantity of parts).
4. Order quantity.
5. Amount of material authorized for issue.
6. Order number.

Space must be available on the requisition for the material weight actually issued to be recorded. Where a system of stock allocation is in operation space for a P.C.D. release stamp must be allowed. There should also be room for substitute material to be written in should the original material be out of stock and an alternative material be available. A material requisition is shown in fig. 14.3.

MATERIAL REQUISITION			
part no. 78172B	description Bracket	quantity 10,500	
to finish by 30/12/61 (2)	order no. 67802	min. qty. 10,000	
material specification CR EN 2B 0·109" x 1·5" Coil		wt./1000 31·8 lb	
alternative material (if used)		material entitlement 333·9 lb	
rec'd by T.Smith	issued by J.Hopkins	date 16/12/61	released ▽	actual issue 336·0 lb

FIG. 14.3 *Material Requisition.*

USE OF MATERIAL REQUISITION

The material requisition is usually issued to the first-operation shop at the same time as the works order. Before the job is ready to run the requisition is presented at the raw material stores and exchanged for the correct weight and type of material. The storekeeper making the issue enters the exact weight supplied and the completed requisition is then sent to the stock-records section, where the appropriate stock-record card has its balance reduced.

Should there be inadequate stock available to meet the requisition when first presented, or should only part of the material be required to start the job, then arrangements will have to be made to authorize the issue of the rest of the material. This can be done by reducing the quantity on the requisition by the amount already issued and notifying the stock-records section of the actual issue. If a system of material allocation is used adequate material should be in stock, as the material requisition would not be released without first checking that material was available to satisfy it.

PROBLEMS OF EXACT MATERIAL ISSUE
Where material is issued in bars or strips and the components manufactured are long, there may be considerable wastage unless the bar or strip is a multiple of the component's length plus an appropriate "part off" or webbing allowance. Sometimes ideal material lengths cannot be purchased, and at other times slight length variations have to be accepted. Under these circumstances the actual yield of parts may differ from that intended. Difficulty may also be experienced in producing the required number of parts when thin strip or coil material is issued by weight. Commercial tolerances on thickness are often quite wide compared with the nominal thickness and consequently appreciably different component yields can be obtained from similar weights of material.

The increased use of coil instead of strip material for press work has introduced difficulties in material issue. It is extremely unlikely that the weight of material required will be an exact multiple of the coil weight and therefore a fraction of a coil will be needed to satisfy most requisitions. Without uncoiling and recoiling facilities in stores the issue of the correct quantity of material will in most cases be impossible. One method of dealing with this problem is to issue to the nearest whole or part coil available in stores and deduct the issue from the stock balance. The quantity of parts indicated on the order is then produced in the press. When the correct quantity of parts has been produced the remainder of material is returned to stores and the balance on the stock-record card is adjusted accordingly. Material returned to stores is usually dealt with on a "Return to Stores Note" which is made out by shop supervision and accompanies the material into stores. The note, after having been checked by the storekeeper against the returned material, is sent to the stock-records section for posting.

ADDITIONAL WORKS DOCUMENTS
MACHINE-LOADING CARD
This document is required when a system of machine loading is being

P

used. One card is issued for each operation loaded and, apart from general order information, specific loading information is included, such as:

1. Machine group on which work should be processed.
2. Standard time for operation.
3. Time for complete batch at expected operator performance.
4. Expected setting time.
5. Labour grade to be used.
6. Departments performing previous and subsequent operations.

An example of a machine-loading card is shown in fig. 14.4. The use of machine-loading cards will be described in Chapter 16. When

MACHINE   LOADING   CARD

PART No.	DESCRIPTION	QUANTITY
78172 B	Bracket	10,500
To FINISH by	ORDER No.	MIN. QTY.
30/12/61 (2)	67802	10,000

Minus week	Op. No.	Operation	M/C group	Lab. grade	Std. min. 100	Op. hrs.	Setting hrs.	
2	10	Blank/pierce	PD 2	MA	0·82			Previous operation
1	20	Form	PA	F	22·5	33·0	0·8	Operation to be loaded
1	30	Tumble	BI	MA	-			Next operation

FIG. 14.4 *Machine Loading Card.*

work moves in complete batches used machine-loading cards can be made to serve a multiple purpose. Provided the next operation appears on the card it can be used to route the work to the next operation, and as an identification tally.

IDENTIFICATION TALLY

If the work moves as a complete batch a specially produced card is sometimes placed with the parts to identify them on the shop floor. The use of a polythene envelope to keep the identification tally clean and readable is desirable. In other cases a works order or route card accompanying the work is used as an identification tally.

OPERATOR TIME-CARD

Cards for booking operator production and times can often be conveniently produced with other works order documents. These cards, which can be prepared for each operation, contain standard order information which reduces the amount of shop clerical work when operators are paid by piecework-type bonus schemes. Usually only one operator time-card is printed for each operation; when more than one card is needed, as for split batches, or if several operators are engaged on the same operation, blank cards will have to be written out by the bonus clerk.

PRODUCTION OF WORKS ORDER DOCUMENTS

Works order documents are normally printed on cards with rulings and headings pre-printed on them. There are, however, considerable differences in the methods of putting order information on printed cards. Some of the commonly used methods are listed below:

1. HAND-WRITTEN

This is the best method where a small number of orders is issued, on prototype work for instance.

2. INDIVIDUALLY TYPED

Usually easier to read than hand-written documents, typed documents have little advantage except that unauthorized alteration is made more difficult.

3. SPIRIT DUPLICATED

If a large quantity of order documents is issued, then the use of masters prepared in advance speeds up order production and, provided the masters have been carefully checked, reduces the possibility of mistakes.

It will be realized that certain information such as operation sequence, minus weeks and material specification remain virtually unaltered and are not dependent on when the order is issued. The variable information consists of quantity, material weight, order number and finishing date. Both permanent and variable information has often to be written on works documents several times, particularly with systems issuing loading and operator time-cards. To avoid frequent re-writing, masters can be used from which both permanent and temporary information can be reproduced. Spirit-duplicating masters are typed or hand-written over a sheet of hectographic carbon paper. Some of the carbon is transferred to the back of the master where the writing pressure was applied. By setting the master in a duplicating machine and activating the carbon on the back of it by a spirit the master is reproduced on the forms. Duplicating machines used for production-control purposes are frequently able to select any desired line from the permanent master and reproduce it, so facilitating the production of batch books, loading cards and operator time-cards. Care must be taken in designing forms for spirit duplicating, and companies selling duplicating equipment are usually eager to advise on suitable layouts.

4. PRINTING FROM DUPLICATING PLATES

The masters used with this system are small metal plates which have order information punched into them. The raised characters on the plates are inked and can be used in specially designed printing machines to produce works order documents. Although the masters last longer than the typed ones used for spirit duplicating they occupy more storage space when not in use.

5. PUNCHED CARDS

After punched cards have been used to produce production programmes they need not be thrown away but can be used as works order documents such as identity tallies. The information punched into the cards must be interpreted, and this can be done by passing them through an interpreter which reads the punched holes and prints the information in a line along the top of the cards.

ROUTING, SCHEDULING AND DESPATCHING

These three terms are widely used in the United States to refer to specific activities connected with production control. Although this book has not been arranged so that each is treated as a major topic, it is desirable that routing, scheduling and despatching should be explained.

ROUTING

Routing consists of determining the sequence of operations by which a part is made and deciding on the method of manufacture. Routing, normally the function of the production engineering department, was described in Chapter 5. After the method of production has been specified the P.C.D. use it for works orders either in an abbreviated form or in the same form as it appears on the operation layout. The route specified by the production engineering department is also accepted as standard by the cost office after it has been proved satisfactory, and any deviations from it are classed as excesses.

SCHEDULING

Scheduling can be defined as the fitting of parts into a manufacturing time-table so that they are available, on time, to meet sales and service requirements.

In jobbing production scheduling is carried out for each order. Not only will the routing have to be determined before scheduling can start but the operation times will also either have to be known or estimated. After allowing adequate time for waiting and transportation between operations the processing time for each part can be determined. From this information and from a knowledge of the sub-assembly and final assembly build-up, a time-table for the manufacture of the whole product can be constructed. With batch and flow production, once a time-table has proved suitable it can be used repeatedly, provided it is not affected by changes in process or by significant changes in batch size.

Scheduling information appears on works orders and loading cards, often in terms of minus weeks from the completion date. The time-table thus provided for the factory is essential if batches of work are to be processed in the correct priority to meet the production programme. Charts showing manufacturing activities against a time base can be used to illustrate the principles of scheduling. A typical product schedule is shown in fig. 14.5.

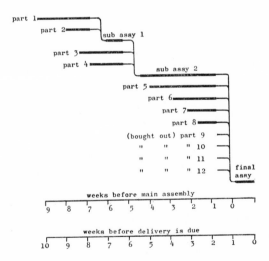

FIG. 14.5 *Scheduling of a Product (Factory Processing Time in Heavier Line).*

DESPATCHING

Despatching is the release of work to the factory in accordance with previously planned routes and schedules. Most of the despatching work is done by the P.C.D. itself and consists of:

1. The movement of work through the factory as indicated by the information supplied on works order documents.

2. Release of work to the factory in accordance with the time-table shown on works orders or loading cards.

3. Ensuring that all necessary material, tooling, layouts, and drawings are available before production is due to begin.

4. Accurately recording the progress of orders through the factory and completing operator time-cards for bonus payment purposes.

5. Acting as the custodian of works order documents.

6. Recording operator waiting time and machine idle time.

7. Reporting back on the completion of work, if a central progress record is used.

8. Shop floor machine loading.

Those parts of the despatching function not described earlier in this chapter are dealt with in Chapter 16.

Stores Organization and Control

STORES ORGANIZATION

Storekeeping normally involves the performance of five stock control functions; these are:

1. Receiving materials, finished goods and equipment, correctly identified and accompanied by the requisite documentation.
2. Locating stocks in such a way that they can be easily found and removed when required.
3. Maintaining stocks safely and in good condition by taking all necessary precautions to ensure that they do not suffer from deterioration, damage or pilfering.
4. Issuing from stock such quantities as are authorized, and providing information on shortages of parts.
5. Recording receipts and issues on stock-record cards so that the correct stock is shown at all times.

The storekeeping function is the responsibility of different executives in different companies. The works manager or production controller is usually responsible for material and component stores. However, occasionally they are under the cost accountant or the buyer. Finished product warehouses and spares stores will probably be controlled by the sales manager or the service manager.

Separate stores are usually provided for different types of supplies, the following being the main stores in use in a manufacturing company:

1. Raw material stores.
2. Component and sub-assembly stores.
3. Drawing stores.
4. Consumable supplies stores.
5. Tool stores.
6. Gauge stores.
7. Stationery stores.
8. Spares warehouse.
9. Finished product warehouse.

In addition, departments such as the tool room and maintenance section are likely to have their own material and tool stores, which are specially organized to meet their particular needs. Part-finished component stores, which are sometimes necessary for batch production, are usually the responsibility of the departments in which they are situated.

RAW MATERIAL STORES

It is desirable that raw material stores are situated near the entrance to the factory and near the shops they serve. Incorrect positioning of material stores inevitably increases handling costs, creates congestion in the factory and causes machine delays. In a large factory there are frequently a number of raw material stores situated to give the best service to particular departments. This often necessitates a number of gates and unloading bays round the perimeter of the factory.

The allocation of space in material stores is of great importance, since small increases in the quantity stored can quickly result in overcrowding, and the breakdown of the storage system. Some materials, such as chemicals, are stored in the containers in which they arrive from the suppliers, and the method of storage is usually dictated by the form of the packing. Castings can generally be stored in pallets and lend themselves to row or block stacking. Specially designed pallet racks are sometimes used to facilitate handling and location. In both these cases it is possible to estimate to fairly close limits what floorspace is required to store an adequate supply, knowing the permissible height to which containers or pallets can be stacked.

A more difficult problem is presented by bar material. Here, the older system of storage is in a near-vertical position in lean-to racks. Although this system requires a minimum of storage equipment, unnecessary handling results due to the man-handling of individual bars from a horizontal position to a vertical position for storing, and then to a horizontal position again for issuing. Also, utilization of space is poor. More recently, methods of horizontal storage of bar material have been introduced, the bars being unloaded from a lorry on to a standard stacking cradle. The bars are weighed on their cradles and transported by gantry crane or bridge crane to their location where the cradles are stacked on top of each other to give good vertical space utilization.

On receipt of a consignment, a Goods Inward Note is normally written out, quoting the name of the supplier, material and quantity received. Copies of this note are sent with the material to the stores, whence a typical distribution might be to the cost office, material progress, and inspection, the last copy being accompanied by a sample of the material. Another copy is kept with the material for identification purposes.

Inspection may involve a chemical analysis and a check on physical properties which can take several days. The system used should allow the material to be taken into stores but prevent its issue until approved by inspection. This necessitates the labelling and physical separation of the consignment from the rest of the stock. When the material has been cleared by inspection it is taken into stock and the stores copy of the Goods Inward Note is passed to the stores record section for posting on the stock-record card.

Sometimes the stock-record card is posted by the storekeepers themselves if the physical stock figure only is required, in which case it is filed in the stores and can also act as a location card. In other cases the stock-record card is actually kept at the stock location when it is frequently referred to as a bin tally. More usually, the stores keep only location cards and send their posting media to a separate section where the stock-record cards are kept. The advantages of this system are:

1 A cheaper grade of female labour can be used to perform the clerical operations.
2. Record cards are kept cleaner and are less liable to damage.
3. Posting errors are reduced as a result of specialization of labour.
4. Allocations of materials may be made to orders not yet started.
5. The cards can be sited so that they are easily available to the material planning section.
6. Mechanization of stock records is facilitated.
7. Unauthorized adjustments to stock-record cards by storekeepers are prevented.

Possible disadvantages are:

1. Increased chance of loss of posting documents.
2. When mechanized records are used, posting machine operators must be trained, and reserve operators are necessary to allow for sickness.

Material may be drawn from stores by means of a direct material requisition authorized by P.C.D. or by means of an indirect material requisition signed by a foreman or other authorized person. Indirect material requisitions may be used to make up for deficiencies in the quantity of productive material issued or for purposes not directly connected with production, such as experimental work. P.C.D. must control the issue of materials against indirect material requisitions to avoid running out of stock and stopping production. In some cases a limited quantity of stock only may be issued without P.C.D. agreement, in other cases all indirect requisitions have to be sanctioned by P.C.D. before an issue is made.

Special procedures must be observed when work is performed on A.I.D. or A.R.B. contracts. All consignments of material for this work are separately recorded and stored. Issues are made against requisitions, quoting a specific release note number which originates with the material purchase and which accompanies the components through the works. The completed batch of components can then be identified with the material consignment from which it was made.

COMPONENT AND SUB-ASSEMBLY STORES

These should ideally be situated between the manufacturing departments and the assembly shop. The form of the stores will vary considerably but in most manufacturing companies part of the stores area will be reserved for the collection of sets of parts taken from stock prior to issuing them to the assembly shop. The authority for taking these parts is generally a parts list extended to call for the total number of parts required to build the programme. Alternatively, a punched-card tabulation may sometimes be used for this purpose. Shortage notes or lists will have to be made out for items not in stock. This information is used by the progress section to expedite late orders and late deliveries. A similar shortage procedure will be used for sub-assemblies if all of the parts are not available.

In order that shortages on incomplete sets of parts are cleared when the appropriate parts are received in the stores an allocation card system is sometimes used. An allocation card (fig. 15.1) exists for every component or sub-assembly required to clear a shortage. These cards are filed in stores in part-number sequence and show the products or the spares programme on which the component in question appears as a shortage. On receipt of a batch of components in stores, the allocation card must be checked and any outstanding shortages cleared.

The method of storage depends principally on the size of components and the quantities in which they reach stores. Large components can be stored in pallets or crates as received from the last operation. This frequently necessitates storing a component in more than one location to give the best space utilization, and in these cases the loca-

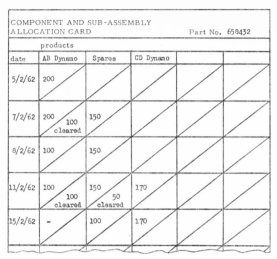

COMPONENT AND SUB-ASSEMBLY ALLOCATION CARD			Part No. 658432		
products					
date	AB Dynamo	Spares	CD Dynamo		
5/2/62	200				
7/2/62	200 100 cleared	150			
8/2/62	100	150			
11/2/62	100 100 cleared	150 50 cleared	170		
15/2/62	-	100	170		

FIG. 15.1 *Allocation Card used for Clearing Shortages of Components and Sub-assemblies.*

tion card must always be kept up-to-date by the storekeeper. Alternatively, space will be wasted if sufficient is allocated to each component to cover all contingencies.

Small components are generally best stored in sheet-metal work tins, of standard dimensions, which slide into racks. Some components may occupy more than one tin but others will occupy only a small portion of one tin. For the latter, divisions may be provided which allow a number of different components to be stored in one tin. The racks are generally arranged back-to-back so that each gangway has a row of racks on either side. To conserve space, racks are sometimes arranged in rows two deep, with the front row sliding to allow access to the back rows.

It is easier to "bulk issue" to the assembly shop than to select parts for each job, and bulk issue is often practised for inexpensive parts. If stock records are kept for bulk-issue items the storekeeper must notify the stock-records section of the quantity issued. Alternatively record cards can be dispensed with for these items if a sealed stock method of re-ordering as described in Chapter 13 is used.

Another function of parts stores is to feed assembly teams or lines. For line assembly, it is important that quantities of the larger components should be fed at the rate required by the line. Usually this amounts to loading a conveyor to capacity, but for some sorts of assembly the work stations may be supplied by box pallets. Small parts can generally be bulk issued, and line stocks periodically replenished. When assembly is by batch production a greater quantity of parts will be issued at once, although some form of control will still be needed over the issue of large components.

Items are received into stores only if accompanied by the requisite paperwork. This may take the form of a route card for parts processed in the factory, a goods inwards note for bought-out parts, or a return-to-stores note for parts issued in excess or error.

Issues from stock must only be made if correctly authorized. The authority may take the form of:

1. An extended parts list to select parts for assembly.

2. A direct material requisition stamped by P.C.D.

3. An indirect material requisition signed by a foreman or departmental manager.

4. A stores requisition to clear a shortage.

5. An inter-stores work note which serves the multiple purpose of drawing out from one stores, routing and booking into a second stores.

The time-consuming operation of writing out requisitions in stores when clearing shortages may be eliminated if the quantities called for on sets lists are posted off stock-record cards irrespective of whether or not stock is available. If there is no stock, the amount of the shortage is indicated by a red figure in the balance of the stock column. For this system to work satisfactorily, it is essential that an accurate account of shortages is kept in stores; a shortage allocation card similar to that described previously should assist in this respect.

DRAWING STORES

Sometimes a whole batch of work is scrapped through producing to an obsolete drawing. For this reason a strict control over the issue of prints is desirable. Ideally, setters should return prints to the drawing stores at the completion of their operation on each batch of work. Unfortunately, however well-intentioned setters may be, prints are not always returned and are frequently used for subsequent batches of the same components. Provided a check is kept of the names of all those in possession of particular prints, so that action can be taken to secure their return in the event of an alteration, no great harm will be done.

Control may be exercised by making setters sign, on cards filed in part number order, for prints. If three prints of a certain part are in circulation three signatures should appear on the appropriate record card. When a print is returned the signature of the setter is crossed through or cancelled by indicating the date of return. A further check against the production of scrap work from obsolete drawings is to stamp all prints issued with a drawing-stores date stamp. If, on subsequent enquiry, it is found that work has been produced from an unstamped print, it will be obvious that the print has not been obtained in the prescribed manner.

The storekeeper will be made aware of a drawing alteration when a new set of prints, accompanied by a drawing alteration note, is sent from the print room to the stores, and he will take immediate action to secure the return of obsolete prints.

CONSUMABLE SUPPLIES STORES

These are used for storing all production supplies of a consumable nature except production material. Although in a smaller company such stores may be centralized or combined with another type of store, in a large factory where distances are great it is usual to have a central supply stores which serves a number of sub-stores. This complicates the keeping of records, but reduces the time wasted by direct operators and setters in walking to a central stores. The normal procedure is to supply the sub-stores with a quantity of each consumable tool in general use so that these items can be issued to setters or operators in exchange for a loan ticket or tally. Tally systems work satisfactorily in tool rooms or short-order departments, each employee being supplied with a set quantity of tallies bearing a certain number. Tallies are often in the form of brass discs drilled for a keyring. A tally is placed in the bin from which a tool is removed; the tally is then returned to the operator when the tool is returned to stores. In this way there is a limit to the number of small consumable tools each man can draw at any time. Tool loan tickets are more popular than tallies in production shops, the normal procedure being to write them in duplicate, one copy being kept in the tool bin and the other filed in operator-number sequence. This allows an immediate check to be made against the number of tools drawn by a particular employee. Loan tickets do not limit the number of tools an operator can draw, although the hoarding of small tools by operators can be discovered by referring to the filed copy of the loan tickets. A disadvantage of loan tickets is that they involve a considerable amount of writing, which frequently leads to congestion at the serving hatch.

When breakages occur the foreman signs a requisition for a replacement, which is then charged against his department; in a sub-stores the requisition is passed to the supply stores, which issues the sub-stores with a new tool.

Non-returnable supplies such as welding rod or cutting oil are usually issued against requisitions chargeable to the department using them.

TOOL STORES

These stores contain all the larger non-consumable tools such as press tools, jigs and fixtures. The tools stored vary considerably in size and shape, the usual method of storage being on racks. Platform trucks will probably be needed to raise and lower the heavier tools. Gangways will have to be wide enough to allow the handling equipment to be manoeuvred.

Generally, for tools of this type, record cards are kept in tool-number order showing the location in which the tools are stored. The tools can be issued against a setter's signature on the location card. If the job for which tools are used is sub-contracted, the name of the sub-contractor to which the tools have been sent will be inserted in place of a setter's signature. In this way it is possible to know at all times where a particular tool can be found.

Sometimes a cutter-grinding section is provided on the shop floor to avoid sending press tools back to the tool room for re-grinding. Often, as a matter of routine, the last components produced from a tool are sent to stores with the tool so that the tool inspector can decide if a re-grind is necessary.

GAUGE STORES

If the accuracy of gauges is to be maintained they must be periodically returned to stores for checking. The gauge stores in a large factory will probably be controlled by the gauge-inspection department, which will make a routine check on all gauges returned to stores.

A suitable way of accounting for gauge issue is for them to be drawn on duplicate tool loan tickets, one of which can be filed in date sequence and the second placed in the bin. By this means all gauges not returned in a certain period will be shown up. It is desirable that the setter knows the date by which the gauge should be returned. This can be done by attaching a label with adhesive tape, or using a tie-on label, although these labels are apt to be defaced by oil or removed when in use. An alternative is for the setter to retain a third copy of the loan ticket so that he can check on the date drawn and hence know the deadline date for return.

STATIONERY STORES

Stationery supplies tend to be one of the least checked sources of expenditure in many companies. They are normally requisitioned by departmental managers or foremen and stored in the departments either as a free issue to anyone requiring them or under lock and key for issuing on request. It is important that a close check should be kept on stationery issues, otherwise there is a likelihood of unauthorized use and even pilfering on a fairly large scale. It is surprising how otherwise honest people regard pencils, rubbers, ballpoint pens and paper to be legitimate "perks".

Managers can be made aware of their responsibilities in this direction by including stationery as a separate item on departmental budgets.

SPARES WAREHOUSE

Spare parts will be required to cover orders from customers and agents and to provide a buffer stock to supply possible future orders. Buffer stocks are particularly important in the case of obsolescent parts where the procurement time is likely to be high.

Orders produced exclusively for spares, where there is no production call, may be routed direct to the spares warehouse, but most orders will have to be divided between the production and spares requirements. This is where the allocation cards described previously are of great use. The tendency to divert the spares quota for production use must be strenuously resisted, as, frequently, a company's poor reputation for service and spares causes loss of markets for complete products.

Although it is possible to send parts to the spares warehouse without any other paperwork than a spares programme or schedule, using this programme to book quantities off the stock-record card, it is wiser to book parts out of the component stores and into the spares warehouse on numbered work notes. In this way subsequent arguments on deliveries can be prevented.

FINISHED PRODUCTS WAREHOUSE

Finished products should preferably be stored near the assembly and test departments, and the warehouse should have direct access to the loading bay. In some instances a central warehouse sited separately from the factory is used. This arrangement is desirable where customers' orders are made up of sets of products supplied by several of the company's factories.

Target warehouse stocks should be calculated on the basis of adequate buffer and planning stocks. These stocks were referred to in Chapter 13.

Methods of storage will depend on the product, but if possible the finished products should be palletized to minimize handling costs.

"FIRST IN – FIRST OUT" STORAGE

It is of particular importance that with perishable commodities and other products liable to deterioration, the first consignments received into stores should be the first issued. Often the latest deliveries are stored in front of or on top of previous deliveries, because it is usually much easier to put them there, and the only way really old stock ever comes to be issued is when a nil stock position is being reached.

"First in – first out" systems are unpopular because they require more work from the storekeeper, and space utilization often suffers. However, often this system can prevent considerable financial loss due to deterioration. There is a number of ways in which first in –first out systems can be operated. Occasionally, when space and other conditions allow, gravity conveyors are used; the oldest stock will then always be at the lower end of the conveyor. Another method is to store consignments individually labelled to show the date of arrival in stores. If bulk storage is used, successive consignments can be stored next to each other until the storage area allocated has been filled. New stocks are then placed in the position where the oldest stocks have been drawn out, the old and new being separated by a movable partition. A further method is to use a double storage area for each part; the first area being cleared while the second is filled and vice versa. Although this does not ensure a strict first in – first out system it prevents very old stocks from being left in stores, which is good enough in most instances. Unfortunately this method often results in poor space utilization.

STOCK RECORDS

Although many companies still post stock records manually, the work can be speeded up and made more accurate by using accounting machines. It is possible to prove that the correct balances have been picked up by using a check total. This total, when correctly picked up with the balances for the next posting will give a zero proof. If the part number or material code number is also included in the check total it is possible to prevent errors through postings being made on the wrong card. The zero proof method is not the only accuracy check that can be exercised on accounting-machine operations, but it is the most widely used. A recent development in accounting machines enables the balances from the previous posting to be picked up automatically from a magnetic strip on the reverse side of the card.

By pre-listing, the chance of posting a wrong quantity can be greatly minimized. Pre-listing consists of sorting the documents for posting into their posting categories, typical categories being:

1. Receipts into stores.
2. Withdrawals from stores.
3. Manufacturing scrap.
4. Returns to stores.

The quantities on the posting media for each category are then totalled on an adding machine. Normal posting procedure is performed on each batch of documents, the accounting machine accumulating the quantities posted. The total is cleared from the machine after the last posting and compared with the pre-list total. Should these totals disagree the individual stock-record card postings must be checked.

The four main types of stock records are:
1. Material stock records.
2. Component and sub-assembly stock records.
3. Warehouse stock records.
4. Stock records for consumable tools and consumable materials.

MATERIAL STOCK RECORDS

Every item of material normally has a stock-record card. The record card shows the stock and may also show orders outstanding or allocation of stock against orders not yet drawn. A card suitable for showing allocations as well as stock balances is shown in fig. 15.2.

date	code	reference	recpts.	part no.	week no.	alloc-ation	date released day	mth	issues	surplus or deficit after allocating	stock bal.	check total	proof
15/5	372240	GI 48762	24000							24000	24000	420240	0
20/5	372240	V 26842		385846	40	15500	20	5		8500	24000	404740	0
26/5	372240	V 26842		385846	40				15500	8500	8500	389240	0

RAW MATERIAL STOCK RECORD CARD
Card No. 1
material code 372240
form no. 268
description steel bar (bright) width - dia. or thickness 1 in. grade 1

FIG. 15.2 *Raw Material Stock Record Card for use on an Accounting Machine.*

It will be seen that the heading panel is reversed at the foot of the card. This panel, which contains the material code, is not visible when the card is being posted, thus avoiding the temptation of posting the material code number from the card instead of from the posting medium. The possibility of selecting a wrong card on which to post can be eliminated if the code number is included in the check total. This check can be exercised, however, only if a suitable system of material coding is in use.

COMPONENT AND SUB-ASSEMBLY STOCK RECORD

The records are used to show the balance of stock in stores; some also show the total of outstanding manufacturing orders, and others indicate the balance of stock surplus to assembly requirements. A card which shows stock and orders outstanding is illustrated in fig. 15.3.

JOURNAL SHEET

Reorder level 200
Reorder quantity 500

date	part no.	order	week no.	ref.	receipts	issues	orders o'stdg.	stock	check total	proof	1 stock and orders o'stdg.	2 reorder level	bal. 1-2
11/5	642822	500	30				500		643322		500	200	300
20/5	642822		30		300		200	300	643322	0	500	200	300
22/5	642822		30		100		100	400	643322	0	500	200	300
28/5	642822			R28622		350	100	50	642972	0	150	200	50
28/5	642822	500	33				600	50	643472	0	650	200	450

Part No. 642822   Description washer

COMPONENT STOCK RECORD CARD

FIG. 15.3 *Component Stock Record Card with Journal Sheet for use with Stock Level Ordering System.*

This type of stock card is suitable for use in a stock-level ordering system. There is no correction for over-deliveries, so in the event of an order being over-delivered a fictitiously low outstanding order position would be shown, which must be corrected by a "dummy posting". Scrap and other losses in production are recorded from waste tickets or works' orders. The effect of scrap is to reduce the outstanding order position, whereas issues from stores will reduce the stock.

When parts are ordered on a stock-level basis a total of stock plus outstanding orders is required. This can be obtained if a carbon paper and a plain sheet of paper called a journal sheet are inserted behind the record card in the accounting machine. The three additional columns on the journal sheet enable stock plus outstanding orders to be compared with the re-order point, the result being printed as a debit or credit balance in the third column of the journal sheet. When a red balance occurs it is a signal that a new order should be issued, and the new order can be posted without removing the card from the machine. At the completion of the day's postings, the journal sheet is passed to the ordering section for them to issue new orders. The use of journal sheets makes it unnecessary to remove stock-record cards from the file when raising new orders. A less satisfactory alternative is to arrange for the sum of stock and outstanding orders to appear in a column on the stock-record card itself. This enables stock plus outstanding orders to be compared with the re-order point and for the card to be taken from the file and sent to the ordering section, if the part requires to be re-ordered.

Another type of stock-record card used with ordering systems based on an analysis of the assembly programme is one which shows free stock. Free stock is the difference between the total outstanding requirements and the total of stock plus outstanding orders. The card, indicating its essential features, is shown in fig. 15.4. The operation of this sort of record depends on a summarized tabulation of requirements, such as that obtained by a punched-card breakdown.

FREE STOCK RECORD CARD						
Description - BODY			Part No.	512871		
entry	date	qty.	o'stdg. assy. rqmt.	o'stdg. mfg. order	stock in stores	free stock
planned rqmt.	1/1	400	400			- 400
order	1/1	440	400	440		40
mfg. scrap	7/1	20	400	420		20
rcpts. into stores	14/1	200	400	220	200	20
issued to assy.	15/1	100	300	220	100	20
assy. scrap	17/1	10	310	220	100	10
issued to assy.	17/1	10	300	220	90	10

FIG. 15.4 *Typical Postings on a Free Stock Record Card.*

WAREHOUSE STOCK RECORDS

The stock and order records for finished products will usually be kept by the sales department, while those for spare parts will be maintained by the service department. Since individual customers are to be supplied, we need to know the total orders outstanding against each customer, the stock available, and the quantity programmed on the

WAREHOUSE RECORD CARD								PRODUCT X Y CONTROL BOARD					
Outstanding Customer Requirements								Programme Requirements					
rqmts.	date	Jones	Robinson	Smith	Dunn			total	date	program	del'd	o'stdg.	stock
Bt. Fwd March	27/2	50	100	-	80			230	Bt.fw Mar.			250	
	1/3	200	200	400	--				27/2	1000		1250	
		250	300	400	80				1/3			1000	250
	4/3	200	200	380	--				4/3		250	1000	
	6/3	100	100	280	--				6/3		300	700	300
									6/3			700	

FIG. 15.5 *Record Card for Warehouse Records and Customer Allocations.*

factory but not yet delivered to the warehouse. Allocations to customers must be individually considered, particularly when output is lagging behind demand, so that the requirements are met in the correct priority. Under these circumstances mechanization loses some of its advantages. A hand-posted record card suitable for this purpose is shown in fig. 15.5.

STOCK RECORDS FOR CONSUMABLE TOOLS AND CONSUMABLE MATERIALS

These fall into two main categories, materials or tools which are ordered for one purpose and which are unlikely to be required again in the foreseeable future, and those which are regularly required and for which there is a stock-level ordering system. The cards for items regularly required must show the re-ordering level and will record stock and orders outstanding. For items not ordered on a stock-level system the same type of card may be used, but the re-ordering information will be left blank, orders being placed on receipt of the appropriate request. This type of stock record is also frequently hand-posted.

ERRORS IN STOCK RECORDS

Accurate stock records are vital to the correct operation of any system of production control. If the record shows too low a stock, parts will be ordered unnecessarily and excessive stocks will be built up. Should too large a stock balance be shown on the record card then requirements will not be ordered and shortages will be created. If these shortages are not cleared in time the factory output may be brought to a halt or machine and labour utilization may suffer due to the panic measures necessary to maintain production. There are many sources of error and it is important that these are appreciated so that their occurrence can be minimized or averted. The main causes of error affecting stock and outstanding order balances are as follows:

1. Illegible information on posting media.
2. Over-issuing or under-issuing parts from stores.
3. Incorrect location causing parts to be lost for long periods in stores.
4. Posting errors such as incorrect copying or posting on wrong cards.
5. Unauthorized removal of stock, including pilfering.
6. Loss of posting media.

7. Over-deliveries of orders, which incorrectly reduce the outstanding order balance.

8. Undisclosed scrap causing the outstanding order position to appear fictitiously high and producing too high a free stock balance.

9. Incorrect stocktaking returns from which wrong balances are posted.

10. Incorrect stock checking.

11. Issuing wrong parts from stores.

12. Incorrect counting of parts received into stores.

Errors can be brought to light by periodic stock checks, when the stores stock is counted and compared with the balances on the stock-record cards. This procedure enables an accurate perpetual inventory to be maintained, and the knowledge that a systematic effort is being made to discover and track-down the reasons for discrepancies can have a marked effect in reducing them. Provided an efficient system of stock checking is used, the Companies Act does not require the auditors to demand a physical check of stock for the preparation of the annual accounts.

Machine Loading and Progressing

MACHINE loading and progressing are concerned with the execution of the production plan so that parts are produced according to the time-table indicated on the works order documents. Progressing, which is the maintenance of the planned production schedule, is recognized as an essential P.C.D. function, but machine loading is an aspect of production control which, in many companies, has received little attention. Where machine loading is not in operation shop supervision usually allocates work to machines, often with little regard to order priorities. Progressing and machine loading are so closely connected on the shop floor that it is advisable to make both functions the responsibility of a single senior member of the P.C.D., as shown in the organization chart fig. 12.1.

FACTORY WORK LOAD

Machine loading has two distinct aspects, the prior comparison of load with capacity, a clerical function, and the allocation of work to machines, a task carried out on the shop floor. In this section consideration is given to the calculation of machine and labour load from the production programme and to its comparison with the manufacturing facilities available.

CALCULATION OF LOAD

The calculation of load is basically a matter of multiplying the quantity of parts ordered by the operation time per part for each manufacturing process. These operation batch times will, when adjusted and collected together under the appropriate machine groups and operator grades, provide the basis of a machine and operator load for the factory.

Assuming that the operation time for a part is 1 minute 29 seconds at 100 B.S. rating and the batch quantity is 550, then, if the expected average level of operator performance is 105 on the B.S. scale, the processing time for the batch will be $550 \times \dfrac{100}{105} \times \dfrac{89}{60 \times 60} = 12 \cdot 9$ hours.

To find the number of operators required it is necessary to collect together the processing times under each grade of labour and to adjust for the anticipated waiting time and absenteeism. If the total hours required from a particular grade of labour is 1,520 and if it is expected that 80 hours will be spent on unmeasured work, the clock hours required will be 1,520+80 = 1,600. If these 1,600 hours represent one month's work, and if arrears are negligible, then, assuming a 160-hour working month, 10 operators of this grade will be required. A further allowance will have to be made for absence from work, for instance if the average rate of absenteeism is 3 per cent, a payroll of eleven (10·3) operators will be required to deal with the load.

Machine load is considered next. Most machine operating times can be calculated by multiplying batch quantities by standard times adjusted for expected operator performance, as in the processing time example already calculated. If, however, the machine is operating on a fixed cycle time, as for an automatic lathe, the batch time is calculated by multiplying batch size by cycle time and operating efficiency. Operating efficiency is used to allow for material replenishment, setting and other production stoppages. Assuming a cycle time of 15 seconds, a batch size of 18,000 and an operating efficiency of 85 per cent, the machine operating time for the batch will be:

$$18,000 \times \frac{15}{60 \times 60} \times \frac{100}{85} = 88·2 \text{ hours.}$$

If the machine load is calculated for each order and then analysed by machine group, by department and by the week in which the work falls due, a comprehensive machine load statement can be built up.

A load calculation in most factories is a tremendous task if clerical methods are used. However, when punched-card equipment or computors are available load statements can be more quickly and economically produced. The calculation of machine load using punched cards is described in the next chapter. If the assembly programme is issued periodically then the calculation of load is undertaken as a single operation soon after a programme is issued. Where orders are issued at random times, the factory load must be compiled on a running total basis. In this method the load generated by each new order is added to the current factory load, and as orders are completed the current load is appropriately reduced.

COMPARISON OF LOAD AND CAPACITY

By comparing load with capacity it is possible to predict the ability of the factory to meet the work load placed on it. If capacity and load differ significantly action can be taken so that the two can be brought into balance, thus avoiding a factory overload or minimizing the ill effects of under-capacity working. The capacity of a factory to do work is usually limited either by the production equipment available or by the direct labour force employed and, less frequently, by such factors as shortage of material or setters.

Let us now examine the courses of action which can be taken when machine or labour load does not correspond with the capacity available.

If the machine capacity falls short of the load the difficulty may be overcome by:

1. Overtime working.
2. Shift working.
3. Using alternative equipment.
4. Purchasing additional equipment.
5. Method improvement.
6. Sub-contracting surplus work.

Overtime or shift working can be an effective and immediate remedy provided the equipment is not already fully utilized. The purchase of additional equipment is usually a longer term measure, as are most method improvements. Sub-contracting can often be arranged within a few days, with deliveries following soon afterwards.

Should labour capacity be insufficient the following courses of action are possible:

1. Overtime working.
2. Engaging additional operators.
3. Increasing operator output by work study techniques, or purchasing new equipment.
4. Sub-contracting the overload.

When the machine capacity exceeds the load it is first necessary to find whether the surplus of capacity is likely to be permanent or temporary. If it is temporary then very little can be done, unless there is an overload to be absorbed from some other section of the factory. When surplus machine capacity is likely to persist it may be possible to secure sub-contract work; alternatively, the surplus equipment can be sold and profitable use made of the floor area released.

Should the load statement indicate a surplus of labour every effort must be made to find work elsewhere in the factory. Redundancy should be avoided whenever possible by allowing natural wastage of labour to reduce the size of the working force. In the event of dismissals becoming necessary the company must act impartially so that there is no suspicion of unfairness or lack of consideration.

Although a detailed and regular comparison of load with capacity may be desirable, the number of factories where this is done is comparatively small. The main reasons for load capacity statements not being more widely produced are the clerical work involved and the large amount of development work necessary to produce reasonably accurate results. Machine and operator load are, however, frequently calculated for certain sections of the factory when they fail to meet their commitments, or when the purchase of new equipment is being considered.

Counting orders provides an approximate method of comparing load and capacity. If a weekly count is made of the number of overdue orders on each section and this count is divided by a moving average of the number of orders processed each week by the section, then an estimate of the backlog of work, in terms of weeks of work, can be obtained. By graphing the weekly arrears it is possible to see whether progress is being made in the clearance of overdue orders. The method just described will not indicate surplus capacity although this can be found by activity sampling, referred to in Chapter 8.

CONTROL AND LOADING OF FACTORY ORDERS

We will now consider the second aspect of machine loading, the use of loading cards in the factory to give the requisite priority to works orders. There is a number of factors essential to the success of any loading system; they are summarized below.

1. *Flexibility.* This is particularly important in batch and jobbing production work where changes are frequently made in order priority to meet changes in assembly programme.

2. *Simplicity.* The system should be simple and rugged. To plan the progress of orders through a batch production factory on a strict time-table is almost impossible. Each time a machine breaks down or an operator works at a different speed from the average an elaborate loading scheme has to be adjusted, whereas a simple scheme can take these changes in its stride.

3. *Accuracy.* The machine loading system must accurately reflect the position of orders in the section. Nothing will bring machine loading into disrepute quicker than a scheme which fails to show correctly and promptly what is happening on each machine being loaded.

4. *Control of Processing Priority.* For a loading scheme to be effective it must indicate which job is to be set on each piece of equipment after the order being processed has been completed. If P.C.D. staff determine order priority, shortages caused by the neglect of unpopular work will be largely eliminated.

5. *Planning Ahead.* By planning ahead, a loading scheme can improve machine utilization. Often tooling is common to a number of jobs and setting time can be minimized by choosing a suitable job sequence. Setting times can also be minimized if tools, gauges and materials are immediately available to the setter; apart from improving machine utilization, setter's time is more effectively employed.

A large number of different loading schemes is in use, many of which are proprietary ones. Some of the more popular systems are described below.

LOADING CARD RACKS

Machine loading cards similar to those in fig. 14.4, or interpreted punched cards carrying similar information, are used to control the processing of work; the works order itself serving only a recording and, sometimes, a routing function. Loading cards are arranged in racks, similar to those used to hold operators' clock cards; one of these racks is shown in fig. 16.1. Each machine being loaded has a horizontal line of four pockets allocated to it. The vertical columns made up by the pockets are used as follows:

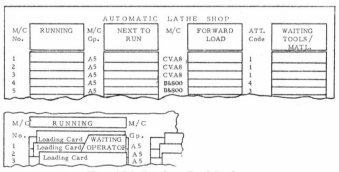

FIG. 16.1 *Loading Card Rack.*

column one   – orders running
column two   – next orders to run
column three – orders with tools and materials or parts available
column four   – orders not yet cleared for tools, materials or parts.

The loading racks are mounted at a convenient location in the section of the factory they control, if possible alongside the wages booking position. A desk should be provided for the loader and a low barrier built round the loading station to keep out unauthorized persons.

The loading cards are inserted in the appropriate pockets of the board and each time a setter wants to know which job should be set next on any one of his machines he reports to the loader for instructions. The loader finds the appropriate machine reference on the board and then takes out the loading card in the "next to run" position; the availability of material on this job will have been checked and the tools made ready. When the machine is vacant the loading card is moved from the "next to run" to the "running" position, and a "setting" signal is placed in front of it. The setter informs the loader when the tools have been set and a "waiting for operator" signal replaces the "setting" one. When the operator starts the job the "waiting operator" signal is removed, but if during the production run work is interrupted an appropriate signal indicating the cause of delay is used. In this way the first column on the loading board reflects the current position of each machine. If setters are required to come to the loading position for instructions, and the loading and wages booking positions are adjacent, it is possible to keep the loading board information in line with what is happening in the factory. When the "next to run" pocket becomes vacant it should be filled by a card selected from column three.

The fourth column has been used to house the cards for which tools or materials are not yet available. Other uses can be made of the fourth column and in some cases loading boards with only three columns are employed. Although batch processing times are shown on the loading cards, as a guide to the loader, this is not a time loading system; it is, however, a simple and effective method of loading, particularly suitable for batch production.

GANTT CHARTS

This method displays the load against a time scale with one horizontal line allocated to each piece of equipment or assembly line. A Gantt chart suitable for loading an assembly line is shown in fig. 16.2. The completion of orders can be shown on the chart and a new load added as the orders are issued. A cursor moved across the chart each day shows whether orders are being cleared on time. A new Gantt chart is prepared when the period covered by the old one has expired, arrears from the old chart being transferred to the new one. Various forms of chart can be used, from simple ones designed and made in

LINE	WEEK 1				WEEK 2				WEEK 3				WEEK 4			
	M	T	W	T	F	M	T	W	T	F	M	T	W	T	F	M T W T F
A							152				1286				·	
B							169 12							1281		
C							582				1175				1151	
D							1915				1012					
E							1082									

completed work ──┘　　　　↑── cursor

FIG. 16.2 *Gantt Chart for Loading Assembly Line.*

the factory, using strips of coloured paper stuck on a white paper base, to elaborate proprietary charts.

Gantt chart loading is inflexible and a considerable amount of replanning is necessary each time the original plan is changed. Even if there is close similarity between the time plan and its execution in first operation shops, the similarity becomes progressively more difficult to maintain as further operations are performed. Gantt charts are suitable for loading flow production lines, the inflexibility of the chart being compatible with the inflexibility of the manufacturing layout.

FLEXIBLE GANTT CHART

If the processing and setting time for each job is marked off to scale on a horizontal line along the top of the loading card a Gantt chart capable of easy re-arrangement can be compiled. Each machine station on the loading board has a horizontal channel into which the loading cards are placed. These cards are arranged from left to right in order of processing and overlapped so that the marked-off load

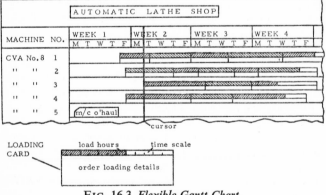

FIG. 16.3 *Flexible Gantt Chart.*

times show the total load against each machine. The rest of the loading card can carry additional loading information such as part number, machine group, setting time and labour grade. An example of this type of loading board is shown in fig. 16.3.

WORK RELEASE

This is a simple type of loading where work is released by the loader from the main bank of work in regulated quantities. The work released is just adequate to keep the section fully-occupied, but insufficient to allow setters and supervision to select popular work and avoid processing unpopular parts or small batches. A sub-stores is normally necessary to hold the main bank of work for processing. This type of loading is suitable for sections of the factory where processing times are short, such as heat treatment, short run press shops, plating and painting.

TOOL KITS

Much time can be spent by setters in tool stores collecting their requirements before they start setting. For a single spindle automatic lathe a set of cams, about half-a-dozen small tools, gauges, a drawing and a tooling layout will probably be required. Often, on collecting the tools, the setter finds that he cannot use them in the machine until some have been sharpened. A system which provides setters with a complete set of sharpened tools not only makes the most efficient use of setters' time, but increases output and machine utilization. Such a system can be integrated with a loading scheme. A tool-kit procedure suitable for an automatic lathe shop is described below.

A tooling layout for each part is prepared by the Tool Drawing Office; this layout is stuck on a board and covered with a transparent plastic sheet to protect it from oil. The tool stores, on receiving a new layout, collect the special tools, cams and gauges and place them with the layout in a suitably located box. The shop loader notifies the tool stores when a job has been selected as next to run and the store-keeper collects the necessary standard tools and puts them, with a copy of the part drawing, in the tool box to complete the kit. The tool kit is now ready for issue; when the setter draws the kit from stores he checks it against the tooling layout and signs a receipt. At the end of the run the tool kit is returned to stores, the tools are checked to see if they require attention and the standard tools are removed for use on other jobs.

PROGRESSING

Progressing ensures that work is given due priority so that the production plan is completed on time. Delays are averted by speeding the passage of late work through the factory and urging delivery of raw material, bought-out and sub-contract parts from the purchasing department. Although routine progressing is the responsibility of P.C.D., works supervision often involve themselves in progress work when a shortage is likely to reduce output from their section of the factory. When there is a serious failure to meet delivery promises almost everyone, from the managing director downwards, may be concerned with progressing late work.

In our consideration of progressing we will confine ourselves to P.C.D. progress work. When machine loading is in operation the progress staff should work closely with the machine loaders. If work is required from a part of the factory which has been loaded the progressmen indicate their requirements to the loaders who arrange the necessary priorities. In the case of an urgently-required part which is not yet running, another job may have to be broken down so that the required parts can be set up. Sometimes there will be insufficient time to wait for a complete batch of the urgently required parts to be processed and the batch has to be split. Sufficient parts to keep production going are hurried forward by the progressman through the remaining operations to the assembly line. Although vigorous progressing will be necessary in emergencies, such as the complete rejection of stores stock or an ordering omission, it disrupts production and if practised on a large scale will bring chaos to the factory.

A valuable warning of impending shortages is provided by the collection of parts in stores prior to their despatch in sets to the assembly section. Often the production controller holds daily meetings with his progress staff using the clearance of stores shortage lists as the main item of discussion. In other companies progress meetings are held with the factory manager in the chair and with foremen as well as progress staff present. If meetings are held with foremen present they should be brief to avoid keeping supervision away from the shop floor for extended periods.

Some P.C.D.s maintain a central record of order progress, thus enabling any uncompleted order to be located in the factory. A suitable method of producing such a record is to print a duplicate route card for use as a progress card; these cards are held in a central file while the jobs are being manufactured. As the batch of work is processed its progress from one operation to the next is reported back and recorded on the central file. The reporting back can be effected economically by the use of spent loading cards or from wages booking documents. A progress record is valuable to P.C.D. staff, who can quickly locate any order on which there is a shortage. Such a record however, is expensive to maintain and for this reason not always used. The display of order progress on wall charts cannot usually be justified in batch production factories due to the volume of work involved, although they are sometimes used for jobbing production.

Punched-card Equipment
for Production Control

PRODUCTION control by normal clerical methods involves recording the same facts many times over. Basic facts are arranged and re-arranged, grouped together and selected from each other for convenience of arithmetical manipulation. This results in laborious analysis and synthesis.

The same procedures can be vastly speeded up by means of punched-card systems. In principle, the facts are recorded in machine language once only by punching holes in a card and thereafter the arrangement, selection, grouping, addition and printing of data is carried out automatically by machines.

The basic approach, sometimes referred to as the punch-sort-tabulate technique, involves the punching of information into cards followed by a series of sorting, reproducing and arithmetical operations. Data is then extracted from the cards during the tabulating operation and printed out in detail or total form to provide results such as schedules of raw materials and machine loading or component and sub-assembly requirements to effect a production plan.

PUNCHED-CARD INSTALLATIONS

THE PUNCHED CARD

Punched cards are rectangular, of standard sizes, containing information in the form of punched holes. The holes are so arranged that they fall in vertical columns across the width of the card, there being, usually, twelve possible positions in each column, ten of these positions representing the digits from 0 to 9 and the other positions being used for double punching so that alphabetical characters or other symbols to control machine operation can also be represented. Figure 17.1 shows a typical 40-column card with digits and alphabetical characters punched in it. Different installations use cards having different numbers of vertical columns, the greatest number in common use being eighty or with some equipment, ninety. This allows at least eighty digits or letters to be represented on any one card,

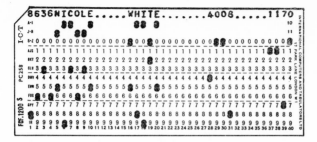

FIG. 17.1 *Typical Forty Column Punched Card.* (I.C.T. Ltd.)

although by "interstage" punching the capacity of the eighty column card can be increased to one hundred and sixty characters.

Adjacent groups of vertical columns may together represent items such as a part number or a quantity, these groups being known as "fields". When designing a card for a particular use the information must be so arranged that the digits do not exceed the number of vertical columns on the card. Figure 17.2 shows a 40-column card divided into fields.

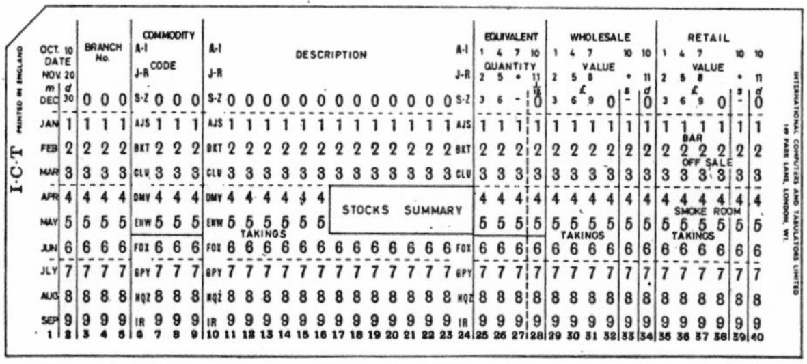

FIG. 17.2 *Forty Column Card Divided into Fields.* (I.C.T. Ltd.)

PUNCHED-CARD EQUIPMENT

A comprehensive range of equipment has been developed to process punched cards; the functions of the most important items are described below:

1. *Punching and Verifying Equipment.* These machines convert basic information into punched-card form and check the accuracy of the information punched. Holes are initially punched by an operator depressing keys on a manually operated or power-assisted machine.

R

The method of verification depends on the type of installation used, but essentially the punching operation is repeated by a second operator reading from the original document. One method, employing a hand verifier, uses a sensing mechanism which compares the punched information with the key depressions made by the verifying operator. If the punching is correct the carriage automatically advances to the next column. If the sensing device reveals an error the carriage locks, ensuring that corrective action is taken. The other method of verifying uses the key punch with the card position slightly displaced so that the original holes are elongated by the check punch. Any error in punching results in round holes appearing in a column instead of one elongated hole. This can be sensed by an automatic verifier through which the cards are subsequently passed.

Some key punches also type the punched information in plain language along the top edge of the card at the same time as the holes are punched. Punched cards not already interpreted in this way can have their punched information subsequently printed by a machine known as an interpreter.

2. *Processing Equipment.* The most important machines in this range are the reproducer, sorter, collator and electronic calculator. They perform a variety of operations on cards which have already been punched and verified. Punched information in one pack of cards can be reproduced in another pack or, alternatively, the information punched in one card can be reproduced in each card in a pack by means of a reproducer or gang punch.

Cards can be sorted one digit at a time, in a sorter, at rates up to 120,000 per hour. The sorter has thirteen pockets, one for each punching position in a given column, and one for unpunched cards. Cards are automatically fed, one at a time, in rapid succession, over a sensing device which guides the card into the pocket corresponding to its punching.

Two batches of pre-sorted cards can be "married" so that cards containing a particular similarity are brought together for comparison by using a collator or interpolator. This machine senses up to sixteen columns at a time, and the columns being sensed need not be the same in both cases, so it is possible to intermingle different card forms.

The electronic calculator is capable of performing relatively complex arithmetical calculations at high speeds and punching the result into a given card. This machine can add, subtract, multiply or divide and can be programmed to make simple decisions. Calculations of the form $\frac{a+b}{c} \times (d+e-f)$ can be performed at the rate of about 6,000/hour.

3. *Tabulating Equipment.* Having processed the cards in the required manner the resulting information must be tabulated and summarized This is done, after sorting, by a tabulator, which can add or subtract amounts punched in the individual cards. If totals only are required, the printing of individual items can be suppressed until all the cards containing a particular code have been processed, when a single summary line is printed on the tabulation sheet. A summary punch can be fitted to the tabulator so that a summary card is punched every time the tabulator strikes a total. By this means a set of summary cards can be produced for future information, or as a source of input information to a subsequent process.

ECONOMIC ASPECTS OF PUNCHED-CARD EQUIPMENT

The advantages of punched-card equipment are increasingly attracting smaller firms, so that this form of data processing has ceased to be the prerogative of large companies. However, to derive the maximum economy from a punched-card installation high utilization is necessary. Improved utilization can be obtained from shift working, a day shift and an evening shift often being employed; if a night shift is operated, male labour will have to be used. For efficient utilization the flow of work through the machine room must be properly planned, and a competent staff trained to operate the machines.

Frequently, accounting and payroll applications and sales statistics occupy most of the equipment time but production control applications can make up an important proportion of the total work load. In many medium-sized companies the processing of data from several departments helps to raise the utilization of punched-card equipment to an economic level. This fact must not be allowed to result in the production of data irrespective of its subsequent usefulness; information should be provided only if it is necessary for the exercise of effective control.

PRODUCTION CONTROL APPLICATIONS

The use of punched cards for production control provides a rapid means of performing simple clerical operations and results in the following benefits:

1. Clerical labour is reduced.
2. Possibility of errors is minimized.
3. Quicker breakdown of the sales programme enables planning time to be reduced and increases planning flexibility.
4. Production of load statements is facilitated, thus providing an earlier opportunity of bringing load and capacity into balance.

5. Tabulations of material and bought-out parts requirements can be rapidly produced for the purchasing department.

Most of these benefits cannot be assessed financially, nevertheless their value may be considerable. For example, the competitive advantage due to reducing the time between receipt of order and despatch of goods may make the difference between gaining or losing markets. The vast amount of preparatory work required to set up a punched-card system is sometimes quoted as a disadvantage, but in many cases it can be proved that much of this work is due only to the inadequacy of existing information.

The use of punched cards does not achieve anything which cannot be done by clerical methods; it simply allows existing operations to be performed at a higher speed and with greater accuracy. Realizing this, it is not surprising that punched-card systems applied to production control are usually essentially similar in operation to manual systems. Some of the most important applications are as follows:

1. Tabulation of component and sub-assembly requirements.
2. Calculation of future material requirements.
3. Calculation of work load on the factory.
4. Production of works documents.
5. Inventory control.
6. Preparation of lists of parts required by the assembly department to build the production programme.

COMPONENT AND SUB-ASSEMBLY REQUIREMENTS

For every model and spares sub-assembly manufactured a master pack of punched cards is stored, each card in the pack representing a component or sub-assembly on the parts list. A typical arrangement of fields on such a card would be:

1. Model number or symbol.
2. Part number.
3. Description of part.
4. Quantity of the particular part required to complete one unit.
5. A number of fields representing the current and forecast assembly or spares programmes divided into suitable manufacturing periods.

The master pack information is punched into the first four fields only.

The procedure for obtaining component and sub-assembly requirements could then be as follows:

1. Using a reproducer, produce a duplicate master pack for each model programmed; then return the master pack to the file.

2. Punch a header card for each model on the programme showing model number, the current assembly requirements and the estimated requirements for a given period ahead. Cards should also be punched for spares component and sub-assembly requirements.

3. Multiply the model requirements by the number off and punch the resulting component requirements into the respective duplicate master packs.

4. Collect all the reproduced packs together, and sort them into part number order.

5. Pass the sorted cards through a tabulator to tabulate component and sub-assembly requirements.

Summary cards showing total current and estimated requirements of each part or sub-assembly can be produced automatically at the same time as a total is struck on the tabulator.

The tabulation so obtained can be used for ordering purposes after adjusting for free stocks and scrap allowance. If economic batch quantities of sub-assemblies are ordered the above process will need some modification due to surplus sub-assembly stocks and orders. Cards for components used in sub-assemblies will then have to be removed from the master packs, so that only the sub-assemblies and components actually used in the final assembly are initially tabulated. The sub-assembly requirements shown on this tabulation are then reduced by the amount of any sub-assembly free stocks. Next the net sub-assembly requirements are broken down by use of reproduced sub-assembly master packs into component requirements. A combined tabulation of component requirements can now be obtained and adjusted for component free stocks and scrap allowances.

Although the basic idea of punching requirements into reproduced assembly master packs is common to almost all punched card methods for obtaining component and sub-assembly requirements, considerable variation exists between individual systems. Some allow corrections for free stocks and scrap allowances to be made on

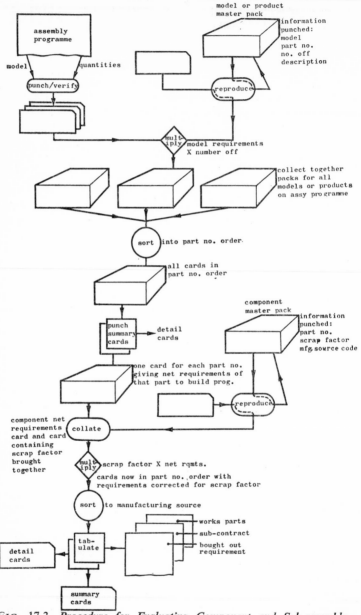

F IG. 17.3 *Procedure for Evaluating Component and Sub-assembly Requirements.*

punched cards before finally tabulating requirements, thus eliminating subsequent clerical operations. Other systems produce tabulations which show in coded form the routing of the parts; sometimes
this routing is shown in terms of weeks before final assembly, thus
providing a complete manufacturing time-table.

Figure 17.3 shows a procedure for tabulating gross component
requirements according to source of manufacture, allowing a suitable
scrap percentage.

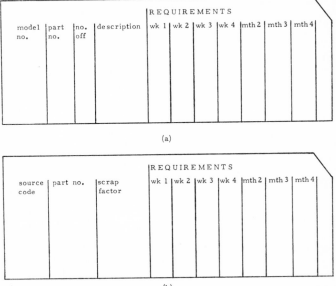

(a)

(b)

FIG. 17.4 *Master Pack Cards for Calculating Component and
Sub-assembly Requirements.*
(a) *Product Master Pack,* (b) *Component Master Pack.*

RAW MATERIAL REQUIREMENTS

Material requirements can be obtained by interpolating the component requirement summary cards with a reproduced material master
pack consisting of a card for every component part number in use,
each card being punched with the material code and the standard
weight of material for that component. The cards are passed through
a multiplier where the component requirements are multiplied by the
standard material weights and are then sorted into material code
sequence and the material requirements are tabulated; the procedure
is illustrated in fig. 17.5.

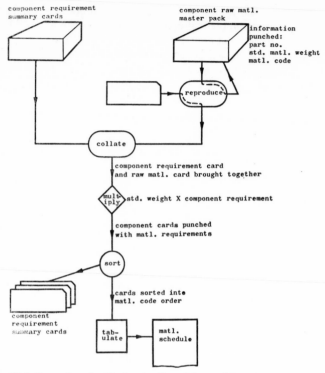

FIG. 17.5 *Procedure for Evaluating Raw Material Requirements.*

	material code	part no.	material std. wt.	MATERIAL REQUIREMENTS						
				wk 1	wk 2	wk 3	wk 4	mth 2	mth 3	mth 4
0										
1										
2										
3										
4										
5										
6										
7										
8										
9										

FIG. 17.6 *Raw Material Requirements Card.*

MACHINE LOAD CALCULATION

A loading master pack is punched containing a card for every operation loaded. Thus there may be ten or more cards for some scheduled parts. This pack is sorted in part-number sequence. Typical information contained on loading cards would be:

1. Part number.
2. Operation number.
3. Allowed processing time (at B.S.100 performance).
4. Expected operator performance (usually shop average performance).
5. Machine group (coded).
6. Department (coded).

There are also blank spaces for punching the processing time required.

The machine load master pack is reproduced and the component requirements from the summary cards are multiplied by the allowed time and divided by the performance to give processing times; now the cards are sorted by shop and by machine group. Shop load tabulations can then be prepared showing the load on machine groups in various parts of the factory. If the first sorting is by machine group and not by department then the total load against each group of machines can be found. Figure 17.7 shows the procedure adopted in chart form.

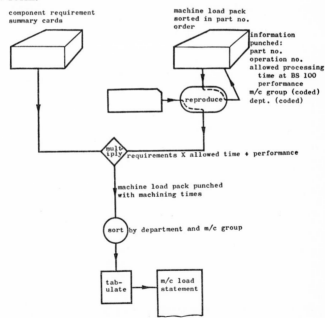

FIG. 17.7 *Procedure for Tabulating Machine Load.*

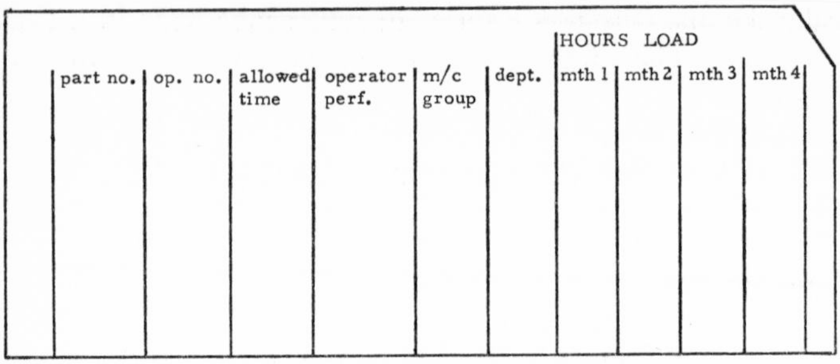

part no.	op. no.	allowed time	operator perf.	m/c group	dept.	HOURS LOAD			
						mth 1	mth 2	mth 3	mth 4

FIG. 17.8 *Machine Load Card.*

After adjustment for such factors as machine efficiency, setting time and labour utilization, statements of machine and labour load can be prepared. The tabulation does not take varying lead times into account although more elaborate systems can do so.

PUNCHED CARDS AS WORKS DOCUMENTS

Punched cards can be used after punching and interpreting as works documents. They can also be used unpunched to feed written information to a punched-card system, the written information being subsequently punched into the card.

Typical documents in the first group may be used for raw material requisitions or identification tallies. These are obtained as by-products of component and material tabulations. It is also possible to use punched cards for a variety of other purposes such as loading cards or operators' time-cards. Although punched cards are sometimes an inexpensive way of producing works documents (fig. 17.9) they may give the impression of being the "left overs" from another

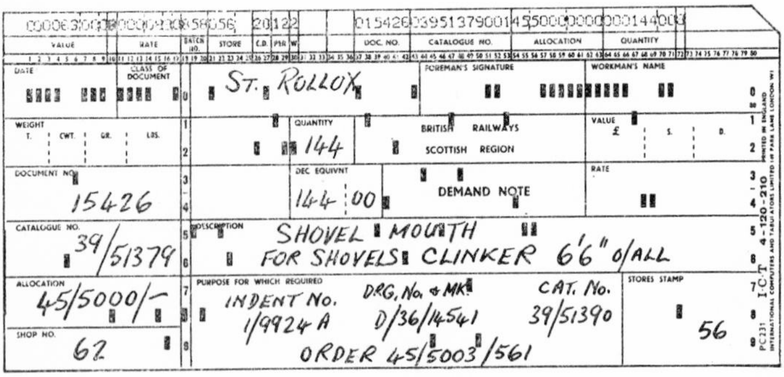

FIG. 17.9 *Eighty Column Card Punched after use as a Works Document.* (I.C.T. Ltd.)

application and therefore do not command the necessary respect in the factory. Also their size may not be convenient for certain applications.

Typical uses of unpunched cards are for requisition forms and operators' time-cards. After serving their original purpose the information written on the cards is punched into them and processed as a part of a normal punched-card application such as inventory control or wages computation. A development in this field is "mark sensing", the information being entered in the factory on the card by means of a pencil mark in the relevant punching space. The cards are later mark-sensed and the holes are automatically punched (fig. 17.10). A disadvantage of mark-sensed cards originating in the factory is that if they are received bent or dirty, duplicates may require punching before processing.

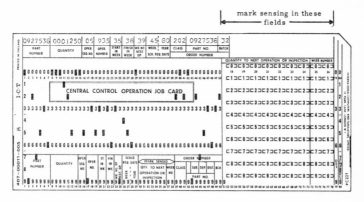

Fig. 17.10 *Eighty Column Mark Sensed Card.* (I.C.T. Ltd.)

INVENTORY CONTROL

Punched cards can be applied to the control of raw materials (fig. 17.11) or parts stocks. A card is punched for each stock transaction and at regular intervals these cards are processed to obtain a stores inventory tabulation, and a file of stores balance cards summarizing the stock, order and allocation position for each type of material. A typical card for raw material stores records has the following fields:

1. Material Code.
2. Date of transaction.
3. Requisition or Goods Inward Note number.
4. Supplier (suitably coded).

5. Quantity received or issued (or stores stock on the stores balance cards).

6. Quantity ordered or allocated (or available stock on stores balance cards).

7. Current price per unit of material.

8. Value based on current price.

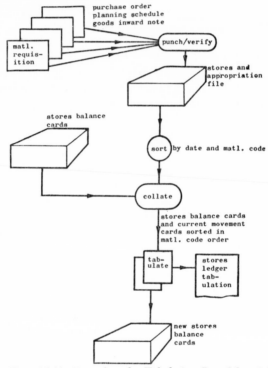

FIG. 17.11 *Procedure for Tabulating Raw Material Records.*

A card is punched for every consignment of goods ordered or received, and for every allocation or withdrawal from stores. These cards are then filed in material code sequence. At regular time intervals they are interpolated with the file of stores balance cards and a stores ledger tabulation is obtained, summary cards giving the new stores balances being automatically produced.

The main advantage of such a method is that the value of stock can be readily obtained using a "standard price" system, but its principal disadvantage is its inflexibility; any stock position which is required between processing periods must be manually computed from the pack of cards in the file. Also there is a likelihood of errors resulting from the removal of cards.

This system can be adapted to components and sub-assemblies to record stocks, orders and, if necessary, stock allocations.

PREPARATION OF STORES SET LISTS

When selecting sets of parts in the component stores for issue to the assembly department to build the production programme a tabulation can be obtained from the same product master packs which are used for calculating component requirements for ordering purposes. This method saves a laborious clerical extension of parts lists which is otherwise necessary, and is particularly useful if a number of different models of a product is to be built during the same assembly run.

OTHER APPLICATIONS

Some companies have developed punched-card systems for recording the progress of work through the factory, for calculating direct labour performance, and for compiling production statistics. Another use of punched cards is as an input to an electronic digital computer or as an instruction document for an automatically controlled machine tool. Alternatively, they can be used as intermediate documents which are converted to a tape before use in a computer.

18

Operational Research

EARLIER chapters have shown how control information can be compiled to assist managements in their task of decision-making. It is only, however, in the simplest situations that control information can indicate how best to use resources, and guesswork is often necessary when determining the most profitable use of capital, labour and equipment. Optimization demands a quantitative basis for setting targets and making decisions. A new and growing branch of applied science, called operational research, is now available to managements to provide them with quantitative assessment of complex situations and so help them to arrive at the best decisions.

Operational research was first used in World War II to find optimum solutions to problems of military strategy and tactics. Usually the work is performed by teams drawn from different scientific disciplines to ensure a balanced and comprehensive approach, although this diversity of background may become less important as formal training in operational research is developed. The industrial uses of operational research have been comparatively slow to develop. Often its potentialities are not fully realized by managements and it is frequently difficult to find staff of adequate calibre to form operational research teams. A wide range of techniques is employed, some being of a general purpose nature, such as probability and servo theory, others, like linear programming, have been specifically developed for operational research use.

As operational research provides optimum solutions to organization problems it can be of great value in production management. Some of its applications in this field are listed below:

1. Determination of the optimum size of inventory.

2. Siting of factories and warehouses to minimize distribution costs.

3. Allocation of work to machines to minimize production time or manufacturing costs.

4. Efficient organization of materials handling equipment and personnel.

5. Preparation of minimum cost production plans.

As linear programming is likely to be of importance to many readers, some aspects of it are discussed in the rest of this chapter. Space does not permit a description of other techniques, but the bibliography lists a number of textbooks which provide more complete information. Most of those included require only limited mathematical knowledge.

LINEAR PROGRAMMING

Linear programming deals with the interaction of two or more variable factors, the effect of which can be expressed as a number of linear inequalities and from which optimum conditions can be deduced. A linear inequality is a mathematical expression whose variables are all to the first power. Non-linear relationships cannot usually be solved by this method.

A few simple examples of linear programming will now be considered to illustrate some of the principles involved.

TRANSPORTATION METHOD

This type of problem occurs when seeking the most economical method of supplying warehouses from factories. The following example shows one method by which an optimum solution can be obtained.

Example. A company has factories at York, Oxford and Bedford, with warehouses at Chester, Bristol, London and Norwich. Only one product is manufactured and the factory capacities, which need not be fully utilised, are York 100, Oxford 80, Bedford 120. Warehouse requirements are Chester 80, Bristol 40, London 90, Norwich 60. If the transport charges per unit of production are as indicated in the table below, find the most economical allocation of factory output to the warehouses.

From	To: Chester	Bristol	London	Norwich
York	£13	£27	£25	£23
Oxford	£17	£9	£8	£19
Bedford	£18	£14	£7	£12

A table known as a distribution matrix, showing factory output, warehouse requirements and transport costs is next constructed. This table, which acts as a framework for allocating output, is shown in fig. 18.1. It will be noticed that a slack column has been included.

This is to allow for a 'dummy allocation' of products to account for the total available supply which in this case exceeds demand.

To From	Chester	Bristol	London	Norwich	Slack Column	Supply
York	13	27	25	23	0	100
Oxford	17	9	8	19	0	80
Bedford	18	14	7	12	0	120
Demand	80	40	90	60	30	300

FIG. 18.1 *Distribution Matrix*

To make the initial allocation from the factories to the warehouses the procedure is as follows:

1. Multiply the difference between the maximum and minimum unit costs in each column by the total demand in that column. For example, in the column 'To Chester' this gives a value of $(18 - 13)\,80 = 400$.

2. Number each column in descending order of the numbers obtained in the previous step.

3. Allocate to each column, starting with Col. 1, filling in the squares which incur the least transport cost.

4. When the allocation to any column results in using up the total supply on any line renumber as in step 3, the columns with an unsatisfied demand.

5. Continue the allocation until all demands are satisfied. The completed initial allocation is shown in fig. 18.2.

	(18–13)80 =400 Col. 4	(27–9)40 =720 Col. 2	(25–7)90 =1620 Col. 1	(23–12)60 =660 Col. 3	(0–0)30 =0 Col. 5	
To From	Chester	Bristol	London	Norwich	Slack Column	Supply
York	13 80	27 —	25 —	23 —	0 20	100 20 0
Oxford	17 —	9 40	8 —	19 30	0 10	80 40 10 0
Bedford	18 —	14 —	7 90	12 30	0 —	120 30 0
Demand	80	40	90	60	30	

FIG. 18.2 *Initial Allocation*

It is now necessary to test for optimum conditions. This is done as follows:

1. Construct a matrix of costs, C (fig. 18.3) consisting of the unit transport costs shown in the small squares in fig. 18.1.

13	27	25	23	0
17	9	8	19	0
18	14	7	12	0

Fig. 18.3 *Matrix C*

2. Construct a second matrix C^1, starting with the costs relating to squares in which an allocation has been made, and adding an extra column U and an extra row V (fig. 18.4).

	1	2	3	4	5	U
1	13				0	
2		9		19	0	
3			7	12		
V						

Fig. 18.4

3. Insert a zero in any space in either the U column or V row (say in the V1 square), then complete all the U and V squares so that the sum of any pair of U and V values equals the cost which lies in the square which is common to both the row and column. For example V1 + U1 = 13. Hence U1 = 13. The rest of the squares in the matrix can now be completed by selecting new combinations of U and V values. (fig. 18.5).

13	9	14	19	0	13
13	9	14	19	0	13
6	2	7	12	−7	6
0	−4	1	6	−13	

Fig. 18.5 *Matrix C^1*

S

4. Subtract each element in C^1 from the corresponding element in C (fig. 18.6).

0	18	11	4	0
4	0	−6	0	0
12	12	0	0	7

FIG. 18.6 *Matrix* $C - C^1$

5. If a minus figure appears in the $C - C^1$ matrix allocate the maximum possible quantity to this square. Where more than one minus figure appears a choice must be made; in this case there is only one minus figure. The re-allocation will be as shown in fig. 18.7, and the effect on transport cost of moving one unit into this square will be £8 — 19 + 12 — 7 = £ — 6 i.e. a reduction of £6.

The maximum number of units which can be moved is 30.

From \ To	Chester	Bristol	London	Norwich	Slack Col.
York	80				20
Oxford		40	30(+30)	0(−30)	10
Bedford			60(−30)	60(+30)	

FIG. 18.7 *Second Allocation*

6. Repeat the complete procedure until no minus figures occur in the revised $C - C^1$ matrix.

13	9	8	13	0		13
13	9	8	13	0		13
12	8	7	12	−1		12
0	−4	−5	0	−13		

Second Matrix C^1

0	18	17	10	0
4	0	0	6	0
6	6	0	0	1

Second Matrix $C - C^1$

It will be seen that all the numbers in matrix C — C^1 are now positive and the optimum solution has been obtained. The total transport cost of £2,780, is found by multiplying the quantities allocated by the unit costs.

GRAPHICAL METHOD

Example. Two products *A* and *B* are each produced by a capstan lathe operation followed by a milling operation. The capstan and milling machine are each available for 50 hours (3,000 minutes) per week. Details of the production times and profit per piece are shown below:

	Capstan operation	Milling operation	Profit each
Product *A*	6 min	3 min	10*d.*
Product *B*	2 min	3 min	4*d.*

What combination of products *A* and *B* produces maximum profit?

LIMITS SET BY MACHINE CAPACITY

On a graph, fig. 19.8, a line is drawn for each process showing the limits of production imposed by the process times. For instance when the capstan is used only for product *A* it will produce $500 \left(\frac{3,000}{6} \right)$ parts and when used only for product *B* $1,500 \left(\frac{3,000}{2} \right)$ parts will be produced. If half the week is spent on each product, $250 \left(\frac{1,500}{6} \right)$ of part *A* and $750 \left(\frac{1,500}{2} \right)$ of product *B* will be available.

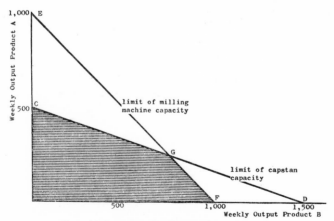

FIG. 18.8 *Limits Set by Machine Capacity.*

It will be seen that the capstan output, represented in fig. 18.8 by *CD*, and the milling machine output, represented by *EF*, intersect at point *G*. At this point the product combination fully utilizes both capstan and milling machine capacity. Other product combinations along *EG* and *GD* cannot be produced due to a lack of capacity of the capstan and of the milling machine respectively. The feasible limits of production are indicated by lines *CG* and *GF*.

PROFIT

Profit can now be considered. As all the relationships are linear, profit at points *C*, *G* and *F* only need be calculated.

Point *C*

Production	500 product *A*
	nil product *B*
Profit	$500 \times 10d. = £20.8$

Point *G*

Production	250 product *A*
	750 product *B*
Profit	$(250 \times 10d.) + (750 \times 4d.) = £22.9$

Point *F*

Production	nil product *A*
	1,000 product *B*
Profit	$(1,000 \times 4d.) = £16.7$

Profit for the various combinations of product *A* and *B* are shown in fig. 18.9. The maximum profit of £22.9 occurring at point *G*.

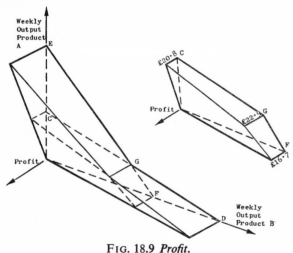

FIG. 18.9 *Profit.*

LIMITATIONS DUE TO CAPACITY OR SALES CEILINGS

Sales ceilings or fixed-capacity special-purpose equipment impose different types of limitation which are indicated by vertical or horizontal lines. If the maximum number of products *A* and *B* which can be sold are 300 and 700 respectively, production will have to be bounded by these limits, unless stocks are to be built up. The effect of these restrictions is shown in fig. 18.10 and possible combinations of products are now bounded by points *H*, *I*, *J* and *K*. It will be seen that simultaneous production of 300 product *A* and 700 product *B*

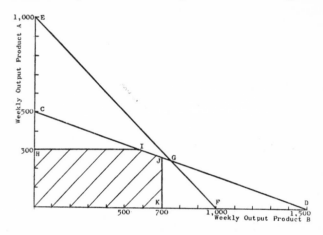

FIG. 18.10   *Additional Limitations Imposed by Sales Ceilings.*

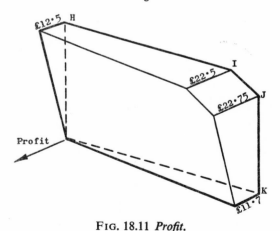

FIG. 18.11 *Profit.*

cannot be attained due to lack of machine capacity. To find the maximum profit it is now necessary to calculate profit at points H, I, J and K. Profits for these points are shown in fig. 18.11, the maximum of £22·75 occurring at point J.

SIMPLEX METHOD

Graphical solutions would be impractical for the complex problems encountered in practice where a large number of products and production facilities are usually involved. Here the normal method is to form and solve a number of simultaneous equations. This procedure is known as the simplex method. The following example involves the manufacture of two products on three machines and although a graphical solution would be possible, it will be solved by the simplex method.

Example. Two products A and B, are each made in three operations on machines I, II and III. The process times for component and the available machine capacity are as shown:

	Process Times on Machines (hours)		
Product	I	II	III
A	3	3	4
B	4	5	2
Available capacity (hours)	3,000	3,500	2,500

Product A yields a profit of £2/unit and product B yields a profit of £3/unit. Find the quantities of each product which will provide the greatest profit.

To form the equations it is necessary to introduce the concept of imaginary products being manufactured on each of the three machines. For convenience, each imaginary product is assumed to take one hour to manufacture and yields no profit. It is assumed that imaginary product S is made on machine I, imaginary product T on machine II and imaginary product U on machine III. The equations for time and profit will then be as follows:

$$3Q_A + 4Q_B + Q_S \qquad\qquad = 3,000$$

$$3Q_A + 5Q_B \qquad + Q_T \qquad = 3,500$$

$$4Q_A + 2Q_B \qquad\qquad + Q_U = 2,500$$

$$\text{Profit} = 2Q_A + 2Q_B + 0Q_S + 0Q_T + 0Q_U$$

where Q is the quantity made of each product.

The initial assumption is that *only* the imaginary products are made and the tableau shown in fig. 18.12 can be constructed from the above equations.

Production Times

		A	B	S	T	U	Production
	S	3	4	1	0	0	3000
Product made	T	3	5	0	1	0	3500
	U	4	2	0	0	1	2500
Profit		2	3	0	0	0	0

FIG. 18.12 *First Tableau.*

Now consider the product which will yield the greatest unit profit, in this case *B*. To find the maximum possible production of this product divide the times needed to make *B* on each of the three machines into the respective numbers in the right hand column. The minimum value, of 700, occurs in the second row.

The next step is to divide the second row in the tableau by 5, so that the value in the *B* column becomes unity. This row now reads:

$$\frac{3}{5} \quad 1 \quad 0 \quad \frac{1}{5} \quad 0 \quad 700$$

The other three rows are now operated on in such a way that each of the values in the *B* column are reduced to zero. To achieve this in the first row, multiply the new second row by 4 and subtract the values so obtained from the old first row, thus:

$$\frac{3}{5} \quad 0 \quad 1 \quad \frac{4}{5} \quad 0 \quad 200$$

Similarly, the new third row is obtained by multiplying the new second row by 2 and subtracting the values obtained from the old third row. Finally, the new profit row is found by multiplying the new second row by 3 and subtracting the values obtained from the old profit row.

The revised tableau is shown in fig. 18.13. Note that column *B* now corresponds to the original column *T*.

The largest profit is now in column *A*. A similar procedure is adopted to that which was used for column *B*, the figures in column *A* being divided into the corresponding figures in the right hand

		A	B	S	T	U	Production
	S	$\frac{3}{5}$	0	1	$-\frac{4}{5}$	0	200
Products made	B	$\frac{3}{5}$	1	0	$\frac{1}{5}$	0	700
	U	$\frac{14}{5}$	0	0	$-\frac{2}{5}$	1	1100
Profit		$\frac{1}{5}$	0	0	$-\frac{3}{5}$	0	-2100

Fig. 18.13 *Second Tableau.*

column to give the maximum number of product *A* which can be made. This is found to be $333\frac{1}{3}$ in row 1, so the next move is to shift the figures from column *S* into column *A*. The third tableau is shown in fig. 18.14.

		A	B	S	T	U	Production
	A	1	0	$\frac{5}{3}$	$-\frac{4}{3}$	0	$333\frac{1}{3}$
Products made	B	0	1	-1	1	0	500
	U	0	0	$-\frac{14}{3}$	$\frac{10}{3}$	1	$166\frac{2}{3}$
Profit		0	0	$-\frac{1}{3}$	$-\frac{1}{3}$	0	$-2166\frac{2}{3}$

Fig. 18.14 *Third Tableau.*

There are no positive profits to be obtained so the optimum solution has been achieved. Rounding to the nearest whole number it will be most profitable to make 333 of *A* and 500 of *B*, yielding a profit of £2,166.

In view of the considerable labour involved in these fairly trivial problems it is not surprising that for practical problems involving many more variables a computer is necessary, and it is convenient that linear programming problems are easily optimised by this means.

OPTIMUM SITING FOR A FACTORY

A problem which arises frequently is how to position a factory or warehouse so as to minimise transport costs between *N* customers.

This problem can be solved by first plotting the co-ordinates of the factory and each of the customers from an arbitrary datum on a map, as in fig. 18.15.

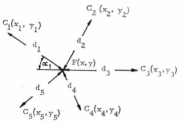

FIG. 18.15 *Locations of Factory and Customers, showing Coordinates.*

Assuming the requirements of customers C_1, C_2 C_3, etc. to be R_1, R_2, R_3, etc., transport routes to be straight lines, and the transport costs per unit of output to be k per mile, the total cost of transport will then be

$$\sum_{i=1}^{N} k.R_i.d_i,$$

where d is the distance of individual customers from the factory.

Expressing distances in co-ordinates,

$$\text{Total cost, } K = k.\sum_{i=1}^{N} R_i.[(x-x_i)^2 + (y-y_i)^2]^{\frac{1}{2}}$$

To optimise cost it is necessary simultaneously to optimise distances in the x and y directions.

$$\frac{\partial K}{\partial x} = k\sum_{i=1}^{N} R_i \frac{(x-x_i)}{[(x-x_i)^2 + (y-y_i)^2]^{\frac{1}{2}}} = 0 \text{ for minimum cost.}$$

$$\frac{\partial K}{\partial y} = k\sum_{i=1}^{N} R_i \frac{(y-y_i)}{[(x-x_i)^2 + (y-y_i)^2]^{\frac{1}{2}}} = 0 \text{ for minimum cost.}$$

If the angular directions of C_1, C_2, etc. in relation to F, measured from the x direction are α_1, α_2, etc.

$$k \sum_{i=1}^{N} R_i \cdot \cos \alpha_i = 0$$

$$k \sum_{i=1}^{N} R_i \cdot \sin \alpha_i = 0$$

For a large number of customers this problem is best solved by an iterative procedure on a computer, but for small numbers of customers a mechanical model can be constructed. This is similar to the force board used in mechanics problems to find the equilibrium of a number of co-planar forces passing through a point. Small pulleys are fastened to the board to represent the locations of the customers and a string is taken over each and joined at a common point as shown in fig. 18.16. Weights proportional to customer

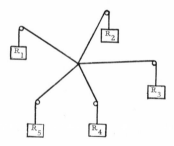

FIG. 18.16 *Force Board Representation of Factory Location.*

requirements are then fastened to the free ends of the strings. The system will come to rest so that the position of the joined ends of the strings represents the optimum site for the factory. For this method to be accurate the frictional resistance of the pulleys must be negligible compared with the torque exerted by the weights.

[19]

Network Analysis

Network analysis is a method of charting which is of particular value in complex one-off jobs such as shipbuilding and factory construction. A chart called a network diagram is drawn to show the inter-relationship of the tasks comprising the total project. From this diagram the overall time for the project can be found as well as the times at which particular resources will be required. A basis is thus provided for resources to be reallocated depending on the relative importance of cost and time. As network analysis is a disciplined appraisal of work to be done, it forces management to think logically and to plan thoroughly before the job starts. When the network diagram has been drawn in its final form it serves as a master plan which can be updated and amended as work proceeds.

ORIGIN OF NETWORK ANALYSIS

In the late 1950s a number of new charting techniques were evolved and applied, some in the U.S.A. for shipbuilding and constructional work and one in the U.K. for the maintenance of electrical generating equipment. These were an improvement on the Gantt chart, previously used for planning, as they not only showed the time occupied by the various activities but closely defined their inter-relationship. The methods of charting are somewhat different in detail, P.E.R.T. (Programme Evaluated Review Technique) and C.P.M. (Critical Path Method) being the two original American systems. Another commonly used name for network analysis is critical path analysis.

NETWORK CONVENTIONS

Tasks, usually mental or physical work, are called activities and are indicated by arrows ———→. The termination of activities are referred to as nodes or events and are shown by circles. ———→○. Those at the start of an activity are called tail events and those at the finish head events, corresponding to the tails and heads of the arrows. The activities and events from start to finish of a job are put together in a network diagram of arrows and circles which precisely define the task. When drawing a network the sequence of events should progress from left to right and the numbering of events should preferably be such that tail events have lower numbers than head events, thus: ④———→⑤ In large networks gaps are sometimes left between groups of event numbers, enabling some re-arrangement of the network without having the tedious jobs of re-numbering every event.

If an activity cannot be started until two earlier activities have each been completed it is shown as in fig. 19.1.

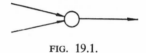

FIG. 19.1.

Also if a number of activities cannot start until a previous single activity has finished it is represented as in fig. 19.2.

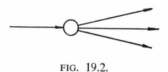

FIG. 19.2.

Sometimes broken lines called dummies are drawn. These are activities of zero time duration which are used to further define the sequence of activities; for instance if activity N depends on the completion of activity L and activity M cannot start until activities K and L have been finished, a dummy is drawn as in fig. 19.3.

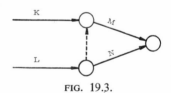

FIG. 19.3.

DRAWING THE NETWORK DIAGRAM

The first step is to determine the logical sequence and interdependence of the activities. The size of the network will depend on the complexity of the job and on the amount of detail included. One of the difficulties in producing a network is to decide how many elements of work should be bracketed together to form a single activity. If too much sub-division occurs the significance of the main activities may become lost in a fog of detail.

The next stage is to estimate the time likely to be taken by each activity and from this information to calculate the earliest and latest event times. Consider the simple network shown in fig. 19.4 where the activity times in days have been indicated.

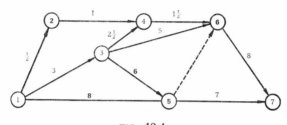

FIG. 19.4.

EVENT TIMES

If event 1 occurs at time zero the times of the other events can be found by following the arrows and summing the activity times. However it will soon be seen that some events have different times depending on how they are approached through the network. For instance event 5 has a time of 9 days (3 plus 6) if approached via activity 1—3 and 3—5, or 8 days if activity 1—5 is considered. As event 5 depends on the completion of both activity 1—5 and 3—5 the earliest completion time must be the longer time path. The earliest completion time for each event is tabulated below:

Event No.	Earliest Completion
1 (start)	0 days
2	$\frac{1}{2}$ day
3	3 days
4	$5\frac{1}{2}$ days
5	9 days
6	9 days
7 (finish)	17 days

The total time for the project is 17 days.

THE CRITICAL PATH

There is a path through the network on which any delay will immediately lengthen the completion time. This is called the critical path and can be found by working back against the direction of the arrows so that the latest finishing time for each event is determined. These latest finishing times are obtained by subtracting activity times from the total project time, again taking the longest time path available. Event 6 is straightforward having a latest finishing time of 9 days (17 minus 8). Event 5 can be reached in two ways, either directly via activity 7—5, giving a latest finishing time of 10 days (17 minus 7), or via activities 7—6 and 6—5 which gives a latest time of 9 days (17 minus 8). The latest finishing times for the rest of the network have been calculated and added to the table.

Event No.	Earliest Completion	Latest Completion
1	0 days	0 days
2	$\frac{1}{2}$ day	$6\frac{1}{2}$ days
3	3 days	3 days
4	$5\frac{1}{2}$ days	$7\frac{1}{2}$ days
5	9 days	9 days
6	9 days	9 days
7	17 days	17 days

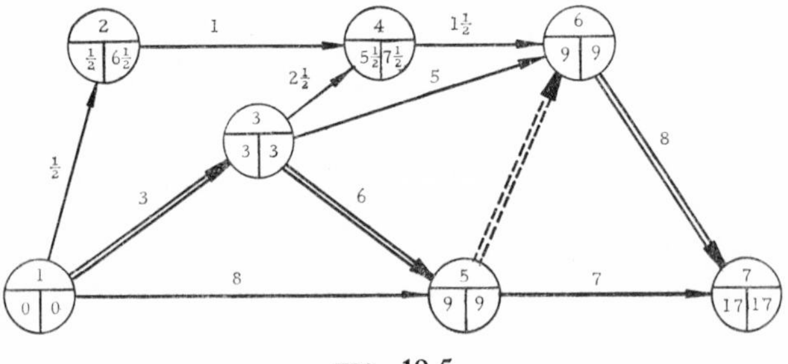

FIG. 19.5.

In fig. 19.5 the earliest and latest times have been entered in the lower halves of the event circles and the critical path indicated by a double line. It will be noticed that the head and tail events of activities on the critical path have identical earliest and latest completion dates and the difference between event times is the duration of the activity lying between them.

ACTIVITY TIMES

Activities off the critical path are not trapped in time between their head and tail events but have some freedom of movement. For instance activity 2—4, which occupies only 1 day, can start as early as half-way through the first day, yet as late as half-way through the sixth day. The earliest finishing time for this activity is therefore day $1\frac{1}{2}$ and the latest is day $7\frac{1}{2}$. Fig. 19.6 shows the range of times for starting and finishing activity 2—4.

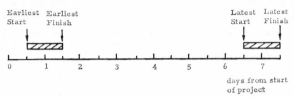

FIG. 19.6 *Starting and Finishing Times: Activity 2-4.*

The earliest and latest starting and finishing times for all of the activities have been calculated and are tabulated below:

Activity	Duration	Start Earliest	Start Latest	Finish Earliest	Finish Latest
1—2	$\frac{1}{2}$ day	0	6	$\frac{1}{2}$	$6\frac{1}{2}$
1—3	3 days	0	0	3	3
1—5	8 days	0	1	8	9
2—4	1 day	$\frac{1}{2}$	$6\frac{1}{2}$	$1\frac{1}{2}$	$7\frac{1}{2}$
3—4	$2\frac{1}{2}$ days	3	5	$5\frac{1}{2}$	$7\frac{1}{2}$
3—5	6 days	3	3	9	9
3—6	5 days	3	4	8	9
4—6	$1\frac{1}{2}$ days	$5\frac{1}{2}$	$7\frac{1}{2}$	7	9
5—6	0 days	9	9	9	9
5—7	7 days	9	10	16	17
6—7	8 days	9	9	17	17

SLACKS AND FLOATS

Slack is the difference between earliest and latest event times. If activity 2—4 is considered it will be seen that there is a tail slack of 6 days and a head slack of 2 days. Slack enables activities to float between time limits.

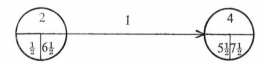

Total float is the maximum time available in which an activity can take place minus the length of time occupied by the activity itself. The total float for activity 2—4 is 6 days (7 minus 1). The float will be cut if the following activity (4—6) starts before the latest finishing time of activity (2—4). The greatest reduction in float occurs when the subsequent activity absorbs the whole of the head slack. The resultant float is called free float and is 4 days (6 minus 2) for activity 2—4. A further reduction in float will result if the tail slack is absorbed by the preceding activity. The residual float, which is sometimes negative, can be found by subtracting the tail slack from the free float. It is called independent float and for activity 2—4 is —2 days (4 minus 6). Floats and slacks for activity 2—4 are shown in fig. 19.7. Floats have been calculated for all activities and are shown below. Note that critical activities do not have any float.

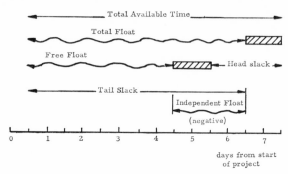

FIG. 19.7 *Floats and Slacks: Activity* 2-4.

| Activity | Duration | Start | | Finish | | Floats | | |
		Earliest	Latest	Earliest	Latest	Total	Free	Independent
1—2	$\frac{1}{2}$ day	0	6	$\frac{1}{2}$	$6\frac{1}{2}$	6	0	0
1—3	3 days	0	0	3	3	0	0	0
1—5	8 days	0	1	8	9	1	1	1
2—4	1 day	$\frac{1}{2}$	$6\frac{1}{2}$	$1\frac{1}{2}$	$7\frac{1}{2}$	6	4	—2
3—4	$2\frac{1}{2}$ days	3	5	$5\frac{1}{2}$	$7\frac{1}{2}$	2	0	0
3—5	6 days	3	3	9	9	0	0	0
3—6	5 days	3	4	8	9	1	1	1
4—6	$1\frac{1}{2}$ days	$5\frac{1}{2}$	$7\frac{1}{2}$	7	9	2	2	0
5—6	0 days	9	9	9	9	0	0	0
5—7	7 days	9	10	16	17	1	1	1
6—7	8 days	9	9	17	17	0	0	0

PROJECT TIME

Once the network diagram has been drawn, the critical path found and the floats calculated the activities are examined to see if any can be completely eliminated or combined with others. The critical path is of particular interest because any reduction of time here will reduce the overall project time. It may be imperative that the overall time is reduced to meet a contract completion date and extra resources will have to be concentrated on the critical activities to shorten them.

COST

Typical variations in activity cost against time are shown in fig. 19.8. Cost variations are not normally linear but an approximation over a limited range can be obtained by assuming linearity and drawing an

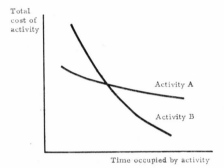

FIG. 19.8 *Cost/time Curves for Activities.*

appropriate tangent to the curve. This is referred to as the cost slope of the activity. When faced with having to reduce time by increasing resources employed those activities with the least cost slopes should be chosen. Sometimes costs and not time have to be minimised and in these instances critical activities with the steepest cost slopes should be extended. Worthwhile cost reductions can always be obtained by increasing the time of non-critical activities which have steep cost slopes.

LABOUR AND RESOURCE LOADING

This is frequently called smoothing in network analysis and is a similar problem to the loading of production facilities in a factory. It is possible in some simple problems to optimise the use of resources by means of linear programming. The number of ways in which resources can be used in the average network of several hundred activities is astronomically large and the use of a computer

T

for a linear programming solution would be impracticable. However, approximate methods have been devised and one of these is explained below.

A representation of how resources are used can be obtained by converting the network diagram into a Gantt chart and from this compiling a histogram of each resource. The Gantt chart is drawn by indicating each activity by a horizontal line, the length of which is proportional to the duration of the activity.

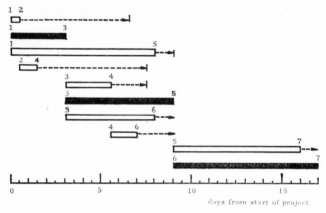

FIG. 19.9(*a*) *Gantt chart of activities.*

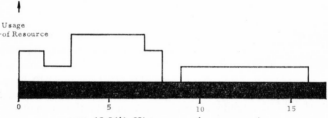

FIG. 19.9(*b*) *Histogram of resource A*

In fig. 19.9(*a*) the critical activities have been shown shaded; non-critical activities are positioned at their earliest starting times and broken lines have been used to show how far the latest finishing times extend. Below the Gantt chart a histogram, fig. 19.9(*b*) has been drawn to show the usage of a hypothetical resource A. For simplicity it has been assumed that each activity utilises resource A at a common rate. Resource histograms normally show peaks and valleys in demand and by making use of the floats on non-critical activities it should be possible to adjust the activity times so that some of the peaks are used to fill in the valleys. It is frequently impossible to completely level the load but with resources such as labour it may be possible, and even desirable, to gradually increase them to a maximum and then taper them off towards the end of the job. The availability of certain resources may be strictly limited and this will necessitate action to balance load with capacity by extending the duration of activities or having work sub-contracted. If equipment or services have to be hired it is usually desirable that they are continuously employed over as short a period of time as possible in order to minimise cost.

CONTROL OF THE PROJECT

Once the network diagram has been finally amended it becomes the timetable to which work proceeds. Let us consider the network diagram for the introduction of a new product shown in fig. 19.10 (overleaf).

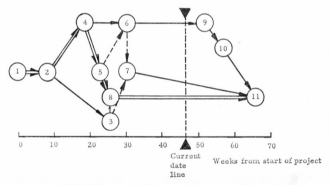

FIG. 19.11 *Network Diagram drawn to Time Scale*
(*Introduction of new product*).

This network can be redrawn as in fig. 19.11 so that the events are shown against a time scale at their latest finishing times. If any of these times are exceeded there is a risk that the planned completion date will not be met.

Mapping pins can be used to indicate progress by inserting them at the appropriate points along the activity lines; any pins to the left of current date line indicate that certain activities are behind schedule and time will have to be made up if the job is to be finished on time.

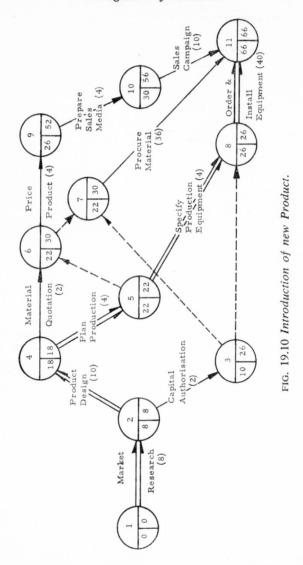

FIG. 19.10 *Introduction of new Product.*

Another method of showing the plan and recording progress against it is to use a Gantt chart. Such a Gantt chart is shown in fig. 19.12, completion or partial completion of an activity is indicated by a double line and, as in fig. 19.9, the latest completion date by a broken line.

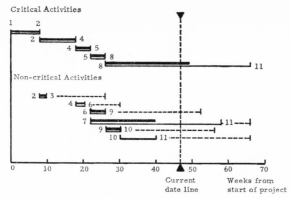

FIG. 19.12 *Gantt chart of network diagram (Introduction of new product).*

By attaching a cost to each activity, or group or activities, it is possible to find when expenditure will be incurred. It is often found that rate of expenditure rises slowly at first, reaches a maximum and then reduces towards the end of the project. Typical cumulative cost curves are shown in fig. 19.13, line A representing the original planned expenditure. If work falls behind the original timetable and the lost time cannot be regained, expenditure will have to be spread over a longer period. This re-scheduling is shown by line B on the graph.

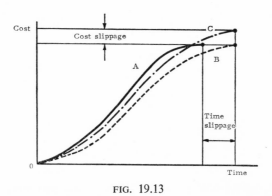

FIG. 19.13

Costs may also increase during the course of the project and this will result in an upward revision of estimated expenditure. Graph C shows such a revision when the work is also running behind schedule.

Computer programmes can be written to process data which are used periodically to indicate actual progress against time and cost plans. New critical paths may occur when non-critical activities are delayed beyond their latest completion dates and in complicated networks a computer will be required to determine the current critical path.

Although network analysis is a new and powerful technique, it is not a substitute for good management. Management decision will still have to be made in the planning and operational stages. If the original plan is a poor one or if the right corrective action is not taken the project can still end in failure.

Systems Engineering and Computers

SYSTEMS ENGINEERING

Systems engineering has not yet been developed to the stage at which it is widely used in the management of production. It is, however, a valuable approach as it enables the manufacturing unit to be considered as an integrated system in which the consequence of change in one part can be measured elsewhere. Thus an overall optimisation of the firm can be attempted.

Systems engineering theory has developed from control theory and makes use of operational research techniques. When operational research is used to optimise the various isolated sections of a firm it is frequently found that the total manufacturing unit does not function optimally, because of the interdependence of the various parts. If a systems approach is used the interdependence can be determined and the operational research models modified accordingly.

Space does not allow an explanation of basic control theory but books dealing with it are mentioned in the bibliography and an introduction to operational research appears in Chapter 18.

CYBERNETICS

The most broadly based approach is that of cybernetics which relates to all self-regulating systems, whether they are man-made or biological processes. Cybernetic systems do not behave in a purely deterministic manner but have a range of responses which correspond to a probability distribution, i.e., they are stochastic. Truly cybernetic models should have the ability to regulate themselves to changing environmental conditions; they are endowed with the ability to learn and to develop as a result of past experience. On this basis it is possible to conceive a machine which could produce another machine having superior performance to its own by a process of trial and error. When applied to organisational systems it is possible that a more efficient self-regulation can be achieved and the individual parts of the system can be optimised so as to improve overall performance.

MODELLING AND SIMULATION OF PERFORMANCE

In order that a system may be studied it is necessary to construct a model having similar objectives and environmental conditions, the action of which simulates that of the system. Such models are usually imperfect because of the simplification involved in their construction, and frequently considerable modification is necessary before their predictions are sufficiently accurate.

The systems approach emphasises the need to work from the general to the particular, but however large the unit considered it is still a part of a larger unit which creates the environment of the smaller unit. In considering, for instance, a model of the national economy, if the model is to be accurate the impact of the international economic situation must be considered and subjective considerations, such as the effect of social change on spending patterns, should also be allowed for. However, even when the environmental conditions are not incorporated in a model, useful trends can be predicted which are not strictly accurate but provide a good basis for calculation.

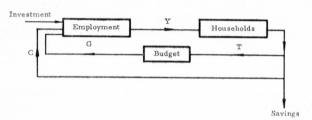

FIG. 20.1 *Simplified Model of National Economy.*

Let us, then, consider the following simplified model of the national economy. Figure 20.1 shows the essential parts of the model where

Y = Total income to all households.

C = Amount spent on consumer goods.

A = Exogenous expenditure, e.g. savings, taxation, etc.

G = Government expenditure.

T = Taxation.

$Y = C + A$

Nett wages = $(Y - T)$

Assuming a linear relationship between nett wages and consumer expenditure,

$C = a(Y - T) + b$ where a and b are constants.

Over a small range of Y we can say that $T \propto Y$

Hence $T = t.Y$.

$C = a(l - t) Y + b = Y - A$.

$$Y = \frac{A + b}{l - a(l - t)}$$

It is seen from fig. 20.1 that under conditions of steady production, Y can be controlled by controlling government expenditure G, and consumer expenditure C can be controlled by increasing or decreasing taxation T.

Assuming that $a = 0.8$ and $t = 0.3$, $\quad \delta Y = 2\frac{1}{4} \delta A$.

Hence a variation of taxation or government expenditure of £1m. can affect nett income by £$2\frac{1}{4}$m. This multiplier effect, if correctly applied, enables the government to exert a stabilising effect on the economy by its fiscal policies. One does not need to be an economist to see that this model is grossly over-simplified, but it can be used as a starting point from which to construct a more complex model in which the environmental factors are incorporated.

Unfortunately the economic system has a high inertia, which means that the full effect of changes will not be felt for several months. It is the time lag which produces difficulty in determining the cause—effect relationship and the taking of appropriate corrective action.

Time lags occur in all dynamic systems and are important when considering manufacturing units. They are found in both the feedback loops and in the response of the system to a given unput signal. In the feedback loops, the time taken to measure the output and take the appropriate corrective action can be of such a magnitude in a rapidly changing situation that the actual output is vastly dissimilar from that predicted. Errors due to time lags in feedback loops can be reduced by reducing the time lag in a minimum or by anticipating the effect of time lag. The anticipated effect of time lag can be calculated by considering the rate of change of the controlled variable at the time when output is monitored, fig. 20.2. Thus, the value of y at time t, $\quad y(t) \simeq y(t_o) + \dot{y}(t_o) \cdot (t - t_o)$.

The resulting error in output will be dependent on the processing time, $(t - t_o)$, and on the frequency with which the output is varying.

Similarly, the volume and flow rate of material in a system between the input point and the monitoring point will affect the response time to a given signal. Ideally, this is reduced by reducing throughput time or process time, but there is a limit to the time reduction which can be effected.

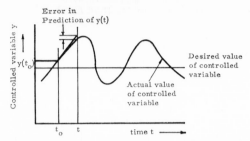

FIG. 20.2 *Variation of Controlled Variable with Time.*

Production controllers are well acquainted with the situation which requires the balancing of work load against factory capacity. Assuming that the load of work is increasing at a faster rate than factory capacity then a backlog of work will accumulate. This backlog can become excessive unless there is a feedback from the machine loaders which can be used to appropriately reduce the incoming workload by sub-contracting or spreading orders over a longer period. If the time lag of the feedback loop is too great and the corrective action too severe, the system can become unstable.

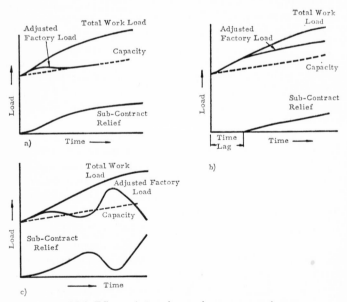

FIG. 20.3 *Effect of time lag and over-correction on factory load.*

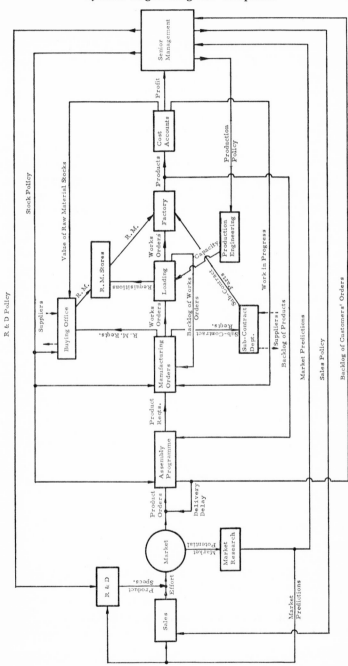

FIG. 20.4 *Flow of information and materials in a batch manufacturing company.*

Figure 20.3(*a*) shows a stable condition, where load is brought quickly into line with capacity. Conditions shown in fig. 20.3(*b*) and (*c*) indicate respectively less stable conditions caused by an excessive time lag and by over-correction. It is in the reduction of time lags of this sort that the rapid data processing possible with digital computers can be of great assistance.

A block diagram showing the main flows of information and materials in a manufacturing unit is shown in fig. 20.4. The company's input to the market consists of the sales effort to sell the products which have been developed. If we consider the time relationship of the various factors affecting the placing of an order, an increase in sales effort is unlikely to have an immediate effect on orders, but after a short period, t, sales can be expected to rise until a new sales equilibrium level is reached as shown in fig. 20.5.

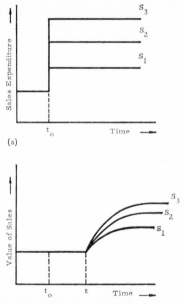

FIG. 20.5 *Response of Orders Received to Sales Effort.*

Sales expenditure will yield diminishing returns, and if too much is spent on sales promotion a point is reached where the increase in sales revenue no longer exceeds the marginal cost. Increased research and development expenditure should also yield an increase in sales, but the time lag is likely to be much greater than for sales expenditure.

Also, the rate of increase in sales due to research and development expenditure can be expected to be lower unless an important breakthrough is achieved, and the effect will probably be more long-lasting than with sales expenditure which usually has a large advertising content.

The volume of customers' orders will be further affected by the delivery time quoted. This delay can be reduced if a suitable buffer stock of finished products is held, but if this stock is consumed the delay will then be a function of manufacturing time and the backlog of outstanding orders. All of these factors, together with the selling price, combine to determine the proportion of the total market which the company commands.

Internally, the assembly programme reflects the balance between production capability of the firm, customers' orders and stock policy. The amount of work sub-contracted is determined by the overload situation in the works and by the total assembly capacity, while the manufacturing orders passed to the works are determined by the assembly programme and the monitored value of work-in-progress. Raw material requirements are similarly coupled to the size and product mix of the assembly programme. Factory capacity is determined by production policy which specifies the amount of plant and labour available and the efficiency with which they are used.

The separation and evaluation of the various factors affecting the performance of the system present considerable problems, but if they can be evaluated with reasonable accuracy the model can be used to optimise profitability at differing levels of production. Although this is essentially an analogue model, digital computer programmes have been developed for simulation and this is how such simulations are usually performed.

OTHER TYPES OF MODELS

Operational routines have been rigorously analysed due to the introduction of mechanised data processing methods. Figure 20.6 shows a typical block diagram from which a computer programme can be written for the ordering and allocation of components and subassemblies required to build a given assembly programme. Block diagrams of this type are the essential models from which to test the logic of a computer routine.

Network diagrams, described in Chapter 19, are another form of model in which time is the variable to be controlled. It has been explained how a network diagram can be used to optimise cost and to smooth resources. Another form of network diagram, where the

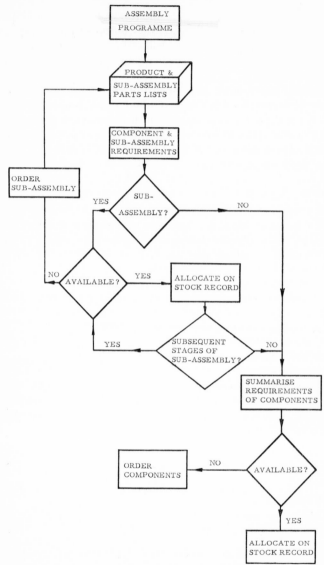

FIG. 20.6 *Block Diagram for Component and Sub-assembly ordering Procedure.*

links represent dependent functions instead of time, can be used to assess the overall reliability of a system when the probability of failure of the individual functions is known from performance tests.

COMPUTERS

Computers provide a valuable service to management over a wide field, and their uses are increasing rapidly. They can be divided into two main groups, analogue and digital, each type operating on different principles. Exaggerated claims are sometimes made for computers, but it must be understood that they can do nothing except perform routines developed by human brains. Their main asset is the great speed at which they operate which allows calculations which would take hours by clerical methods to be performed in seconds. There are some applications for which either analogue or digital methods can be used.

ANALOGUE COMPUTERS

These are devices which are built to simulate mathematical equations. Their input and output is in the form of a physical quantity such as a voltage or the angular rotation of a shaft. The analogy to a given mathematical equation may be created by means of electrical, mechanical, hydraulic or pneumatic circuits, although in practice electrical circuits are generally used.

A circuit consists of a number of units, each of which performs what amounts to a mathematical operation on the output from the previous unit. The units are designed to perform operations such as addition, multiplication, sign changing, integration and function generation, and are interconnected (programmed) to suit the particular problems.

The accuracy obtainable from an analogue computer depends upon the accuracy with which the parameters are set and on the operating accuracy of the circuit components. The total error is usually of the order of 0·1 to 1·0 per cent, although greater accuracy is possible if the additional cost can be justified.

The main uses of analogue computers are:

1. Solution of research and design problems, particularly of differential equations where the independent variable is time. Computers used for this work are general purpose machines, sometimes called 'differential analysers.'

2. Automatic control of processes and machine tools.

3. Simulation of dynamic systems such as production control, using a mathematical model of the system being studied. Variation of the factors involved in the problem enables optimum conditions to be determined. This application can be used to solve a variety of problems in operational research.

DIGITAL COMPUTERS

Digital computers operate by counting numbers. Simple manually operated machines such as desk calculators and summing cash registers work on this principle, although the word 'computer' is usually reserved for electronic machines. These are complex switching devices performing simple arithmetical operations at very high speeds and in which a control unit replaces the human operator.

A digital computer consists of the following essential parts:

1. Input unit.
2. Storage unit.
3. Arithmetic unit.
4. Control unit.
5. Output unit.

The input unit receives information and codes it in a suitable form for use by the computer. Input can take the form of punched cards, punched tape, magnetic tape or typescript. Punched card inputs can be only comparatively slowly digested by the computer and for this reason punched paper tape or magnetic tape is often used.

The storage unit consists of a large number of locations in which data and instructions are stored. Each location is suitably coded for rapid access. Information can be stored by different means, depending on how rapidly it is required. Usually a system of internal and external storage is used, the internal storage frequently only being large enough to contain the data and results required for a single series of calculations. For high-speed internal storage magnetic cores or acoustic tubes (delay lines) can be used; low-speed storage may be effected on magnetic tapes, magnetic drums or magnetic discs. Magnetic tapes are of use only if the supply of information is sequential, the data on the tape being stored in the same sequence as the input information. Strict sequence of input is of less importance if drum or disc storage is used.

The arithmetic unit performs the necessary arithmetical operations on numbers fed to it by the control unit. Any problems which are not arithmetical in character can be solved only by converting them to arithmetical form. For instance, differential equations can be solved by using finite differences and treating them as problems in arithmetic.

The function of the control unit is to obtain and dispose of the data stored as dictated by the computer programme, and to instruct the arithmetic unit which operations are to be performed. Computer languages have been developed which allow programmes to be written in a form which approximates to normal algebraic expressions.

This has greatly simplified programming and enables it to be performed by relatively untrained labour. However, a considerable amount of experience is still needed if an efficient programme is to be written. A typical computer programme to find the optimum parameters in a metal machining operation is shown in fig. 20.7.

Fortran Coding Form

NAME J. BLOGGS	PROGRAM TITLE MACHINE PARAMETERS	DATE
ADDRESS	Label 73 ___ 75	Page 76___77 of

C = Comment

Statement Number	FORTRAN STATEMENT
9	READ(5,1)V1,V2,F1,F2,A,X,B,P,R1,R2,R3,C1,D,RAD,SC
1	FØRMAT(2F6.2,2F4.4,4F5.3,3F4.0,F6.0,2F5.4,F2.0)
	READ(5,23)FO,FF,F,T,S,Y,W,U,Q,TIP,EDGES
23	FØRMAT(3F3.3,F3.1,F4.4,F2.0,2F5.1,F2.2,F1.0,F2.0)
	AA=SC*3.142/180.
	G=D/((D-RAD*(1.-SIN(AA)))/COS(AA)+(90.-SC)*3.142*RAD/180.)
	WRITE(6,2)G
2	FØRMAT(18H0THE VALUE OF G IS F20.6)
	Y=Y*3.142/180.
	IF(TIP-1.)7,8,7
7	H=(R1*T+W/EDGES)*(FO-FF)/(F-FF)
	GØ TØ 10
8	H=W/(1.+Q/(F*SIN(Y)+S))
	H=(H+R1*T+R2+R3*S+R3*F*SIN(Y))*(FO-FF)/(F-FF)
10	WRITE(6,3)H
3	FØRMAT(18H0THE VALUE OF H IS F20.6)
13	VP=330000.*P/(C1*D*F2**X)
	V=U*(R1/(H*(1./B-1.)))**B*(1./(F2*G))**A
	IF(VP-V)4,5,5
4	WRITE(6,6)VP,F2
	GØ TØ 9
5	WRITE(6,6)V,F2
6	FØRMAT(26H0THE VALUES OF V AND F ARE 2F12.4)
	GØ TØ 9
	STØP
	END

Form 20

FIG. 20.7 *Typical Computer Programme in Fortran.*

Computers can have their sequence of operations varied according to the results produced by previous operations. This is known as 'branching,' and allows a computer to make certain decisions and to vary its programme.

Finally, the output unit decodes the answers and produces them in one of a number of forms such as a printed tabulation, punched cards or magnetic tape.

Electronic computers usually adopt the binary system of expressing numbers. Whereas in the decimal or denary system numbers are made up of symbols representing increasing powers of ten, the binary system is based on powers of two. An example showing how 569·5 can be converted to its binary number 1000111001·1 is shown below.

Decimal system

10^2	10^1	10^0	10^{-1}			
9	9	(9)	9			
8	8	8	8	5×10^2	$=$	500·0
7	7	7	7	6×10^1	$=$	60·0
6	(6)	6	6	9×10^0	$=$	9·0
(5)	5	5	(5)	5×10^{-1}	$=$	·5
4	4	4	4			
3	3	3	3			569·5
2	2	2	2			
1	1	1	1			
0	0	0	0			

Binary system

2^9	2^8	2^7	2^6	2^5	2^4	2^3	2^2	2^1	2^0	2^{-1}
(1)	1	1	1	(1)	(1)	(1)	1	1	(1)	(1)
0	(0)	(0)	(0)	0	0	0	(0)	(0)	0	0

		Decimal		Binary
1×2^9	$=$	512·0	$=$	1000000000·0
1×2^5	$=$	32·0	$=$	100000·0
1×2^4	$=$	16·0	$=$	10000·0
1×2^3	$=$	8·0	$=$	1000·0
1×2^0	$=$	1·0	$=$	1·0
1×2^{-1}	$=$	·5	$=$	·1
		569·5		1000111001·1

It will be seen that every digit of a binary number is either 1 or 0. This simplifies electronic calculating as the components doing the arithmetic are usually two-state devices. These devices act as 'on' or 'off' switches and represent at any given moment either 1 or 0. Input information may be either in binary or denary form. If input is supplied in denary form the machine automatically converts it to binary numbers before using it.

The main uses of digital computers are:

1. Solving operational research problems.
2. Control of machine tools.
3. Data processing.
4. Calculations based on scientific formulae.

Digital computers are particularly suited to data processing, which requires both highly accurate solutions to arithmetic problems and a very large memory storage.

The use of computers for data processing has led in many instances to the collective processing or integration of data used for control purposes.

INTEGRATED DATA PROCESSING

This is the collection and processing of information by the most effective and automatic means practicable, thereby eliminating clerical duplication. Data integration can take two main forms:

1. The information coming into the organization can be presented in such a way that the processing of data and the final production of control information is derived directly from the original documents.

2. Data used by different departments, which are often derived from the same basic information, can also be integrated so that duplication of processing is eliminated.

When mechanized office methods are used it is sometimes possible to integrate the complete flow of data from receipt of a customer's order to the final costing and invoicing. A further stage is possible where the receipt of information from customers is itself standardized. For example, some hire-purchase companies supply prepunched cards for customers to return with their remittances.

If data processing is to be effectively integrated, some form of "common language" is necessary throughout the organization, and departmental barriers have to be broken down. This, however, is likely to have beneficial effects, as departmental managers and their assistants will develop a broad knowledge of the functioning of other departments, and the interchange of staff between departments will be facilitated.

As has already been mentioned the most efficient use will be made of computers only if the data processing systems are carefully designed. The programming of existing procedures, if indeed possible, will in most instances not result in the best use being made of a computer, so considerable thought should be given at the planning stage to the best means of integration. The system employed to process data will depend largely on the type of production and on the degree of automation achieved in the production processes. Often digital computers are used for payroll and production control applications which are only extensions of existing clerical procedures. In many of these applications computers are not used to their full potential, but are none-the-less of great value as they can perform simple clerical operations at great speed and with a high degree of accuracy. The use of computers for data processing has resulted in the following benefits:

1. Mathematical methods of production planning hitherto impractical for clerical staff are now possible. For instance, the more elaborate economic batch formulae can be used to calculate order quantities if desired.

2. Greater integration of planning and control functions is facilitated; the high speeds attained with electronic data processing enable the manufacturing plan to be compared frequently with achievement, and exception reports prepared on divergencies from plan.

3. Duplication of processing can be avoided by combining operations in a way hitherto impossible, using clerical methods.

4. Demand and capacity can be rapidly compared for both short- and long-term sales forecasts, enabling effective action to be taken in good time.

5. A quick feed-back of work-in-progress and finished stock values is possible, so that the working capital position can be studied as a current statement instead of as a historical document.

Before a computer is installed its value to the company must be subjected to a detailed study. Usually only the larger companies have sufficient applications to justify the purchase or hire of a computer. Companies which require less computer work may find it more economical to hire time from a computer centre.

Bibliography

Chapter 1
Brech, E. F. L., *Principles and Practice of Management* Longmans 1963
Brech, E. F. L., *Organisation: The Framework of Management* Longmans 1965
Brown, W., *Exploration in Management* Heinemann 1960
Burns, T., and Stalker, G. M., *Management of Innovation* Humanities 1961
Cole, G. D. H., and Postgate, R., *The Common People 1746–1946* Methuen 1948
Drucker, P. F., *Managing for Results* Heinemann 1964
Drucker, P. F., *The Practice of Management* Heinemann 1961
Litterer, J. A., *Organisations: Structure and Behaviour* Wiley 1963
March, J. G., and Simon, H. A., *Organisations* Wiley 1958
Revans, R. W., *Science and the Manager* Macdonald 1965
Richards, M. D., and Greenlaw, P. S., *Management Decision Making* Irwin 1966
Trevelyan, G. M., *English Social History* Longmans 1946

Chapter 2
British Standard 308: 1964, *Engineering Drawing Practice*
Buck, C. H., *Problems of Product Design and Development* Pergamon 1963
Carter, T. M., *The Cost Aspects in Designing for Reliability of Products* Journal I.Prod.E. **46** 3
Cockcroft, J. (Ed.), *The Organisation of Research Establishments* Cambridge U.P. 1965
Collinson, H. A., *Management of Research and Development* Pitman 1964
Johnson, D. L., *Product Design for Automated Production* Journal I.Prod.E. **36** 8
Paine, F. A. (Ed.), *Fundamentals of Packaging* Blackie 1962
Patents Office, *Instructions to Applicants for Patents* Patents Office 1956
Niebel, B. W., and Baldwin, E. N., *Designing for Production* Irwin 1963
Stanley, A. O., and White, K. K. *Organising the R. and D. Function* A.M.A. 1965

Chapter 3

Allen, W., *Factory Design for the Future* Journal I.Prod.E. **39** 6

Carter, F., *Heating and Ventilation of Factories* Journal I.Prod.E. **37** 8

D.S.I.R., *Factory Building Studies* (Series of 12) H.M.S.O. 1959–62

Faber, O. and Kell, J. R., *Heating and Air Conditioning of Buildings* Architectural Press 1957

Hopkinson, R. G., *Lighting* H.M.S.O. 1963

Norris, G., and Small, B. W., *Planning a New Factory* Chartered Mechanical Engineer May 1967

I.E.S. Code, *Illuminating Engineering Society* 1961

Myers, D. T., *Investing in Better Factory Design* Journal I.Prod.E. **35** 7

Chapter 4

Broster, E. J., *Investment Criteria and Cost Analysis* Journal of Management Studies **3** 2

Merritt, A. J., *Investment in Replacement: the Optimal Replacement Policy* Journal of Management Studies **2** 2

Moore, J. M., *Plant Layout and Design* Macmillan 1962

Morrow, L. C. (Ed.), *Maintenance Engineering Handbook* McGraw Hill 1957

Muther, R., *Practical Plant Layout* McGraw Hill 1955

Stewart, H. M. V., *Efficient Maintenance Management* Business Publications 1963

Carson, G. B. (Ed.), *Production Handbook* Ronald 1958

Chapter 5

Brierley, R. G. and Siekmann, H. J., *Machining Principles and Cost Control* McGraw Hill 1964

De Groat, G. H., *Metal Working Automation* McGraw Hill 1962

Gadzala, J. L., *Dimensional Control in Precision Manufacturing* McGraw Hill 1959

Parsons, S. A. J., *Production Tooling Equipment* Macmillan 1960

Schaller, G. S., *Engineering Manufacturing Methods* McGraw Hill 1959

Chapter 6

Davies, B. T., *Better Manual Handling and Lifting* Journal I.Prod.E. **43** 8

Hoefkens, L. J., *Materials Handling and the Production Engineer* Journal I.Prod.E. **42** 8

Immer, J. R., *Materials Handling* McGraw Hill 1953

Organ, P. M., *Some Users' Comments on Reach Fork Lift Trucks Available in the U.K.* Journal I.Prod.E. **45** 6

Reimert, R. P., and Gambrell, C. B., *Minimising Materials Handling with Flexible Plant Layout* Journal of Prod. Eng. Research **5** 1

Young, T., *Materials Handling* Journal I.Prod.E. **45** 10

Chapter 7

Binney, H. A. R., *A British Viewpoint on International Standards* Journal I.Prod.E. **38** 5

Brisch, E. G., *Maximum ex Minimo* Journal I.Prod.E. **33** 6

Conway, H. G., *Simplification by Selection* Journal I.Prod.E. **33** 8

Falcon, W. D. (Ed.), *Value Analysis and Value Engineering* A.M.A. 1965

Taylor, N., *Maximum Production—Minimum Cost via Value Analysis* Journal I.Prod.E. **42** 3

Woodward, C. D., *Standards for Industry* Heinemann, 1965

Chapter 8

Barnes, R. M., *Work Sampling* Wiley, 1957

Brown, W., *Piecework Abandoned* Heinemann 1962

Chapanis, A., *Man Machine Engineering* Tavistock 1965

Currie, R. M., *Financial Incentives* B.I.M. 1963

Karger, D. W., and Bayha, F. H., *Engineered Work Measurement* Industrial Press 1966

Kellerman, F., van Wely, P., and Willems, P. *Ergonomics* Cleaver Hume 1963

Klein, M., *A Note of Wage Incentive Plans* Journal of International Production Engineering Research **4** 4

Milward, G. E. (Ed.), *Organisation and Methods* Macmillan 1960

Morgan, C. T., Cook, J. S., Chapanis, A., and Lund, M. W. (Eds.), *Human Engineering Guide to Equipment Design* McGraw Hill 1963

Murrell, K. F. H., *Ergonomics* Chapman Hall 1965

Sury, R. J., *A Survey of Time Study Rating Research* Journal I.Prod. E. **41** 1

Welford, A. T., *Ergonomics of Automation* D.S.I.R. 1960

Chapter 9

British Institute of Management *Job Evaluation* B.I.M. 1961

British Institute of Management, *Merit Rating* B.I.M. 1954

Brown, J. A. C., *Social Psychology of Industry* Penguin 1954

Constable, J. and Smith, D., *Group Assessment Programmes* Business Publications 1966

Fraser, J. M., *Handbook of Employment Interviewing* Macdonald and Evans 1954

Kahn, H. R., *Repercussions of Redundancy* Allen and Unwin 1964

Kellog, M. S., *What to do about Performance Appraisal* A.M.A. 1965

Klein, L., *Multiproducts, Ltd.* D.S.I.R. 1964

Lupton, T., *Money for Effort* D.S.I.R. 1961

Marsh, A., *Industrial Relations in Engineering* Pergamon 1965

Mayo, E., *Social Problems of an Industrial Civilisation* Routledge 1949

Seymour, W. D., *Industrial Skills* Pitman 1966

Woodward, J., *Industrial Behaviour; Can it be Studied Scientifically* Journal I.Prod.E. **43** 12

Woodward, J. *Industrial Organisation: Theory and Practice* Oxford University Press 1965

Chapter 10

D.E.F. 131, *Sampling Procedures and Tables for Inspection by Attributes* H.M.S.O. 1961

Dudding, B. P., and Jennett, W. J., *Quality Control Charts* British Standard 600 R 1942

Dudding, B. P., and Jennett, W. J., *Control Chart Techniques* British Standard 2564 1955

Glass, H. M., *Standards and Quality Control* Journal I. Prod. E. **43** 6

Grant, E. L., *Statistical Quality Control* McGraw Hill, 1964

Griffin, R., *Quality, Assurance and Control of Incoming Material* Journal I.Prod.E. **43** 9

Juran, J. M. (Ed.), *Quality Control Handbook* McGraw Hill 1962

Summerscales, E., *Quality and Automatic Assembly* Journal I. Prod. E. **38** 10

Chapter 11

Batty, J., *Management Accountancy* Macdonald and Evans 1964

Bostock, C., *Management Accounting and Profitability* Pitman 1960

Paula, F. C. de, *Management Accounting in Practice* Pitman 1964

Scott, J. A., *Budgetary Control and Standard Costs* Pitman 1962

Sizer, J., *The Accountant's Contribution to the Pricing Decision* Journal of Management Studies **3** 2

Chapters 12, 13, 14 and 16

Brown, R. G., *Statistical Forecasting for Inventory Control* McGraw Hill 1959

Eilon, S., *Elements of Production Planning and Control* Macmillan 1962

Cox, G. E., and Ralston, D. H., *The Application of Computers to Shop Control* Journal I.Prod.E. **46** 1

King, J. R., *Machine Supervision* Journal I.Prod.E. **46** 2

Lockyer, K. G., *Production Control in Practice* Pitman 1966

Magee, J. F., *Production Planning and Inventory Control* McGraw Hill, 1958

Mellor, P., *Job Shop Scheduling* Journal I.Prod.E. **46** 2

Moore, F. G., *Production Control* McGraw Hill 1959

Raymond, F. E., *Quantity and Economy in Manufacture* McGraw Hill 1931

Rhodes, J., *The Control of Variety and Stocks in Manufacturing Industry* Journal of Management Studies **4** 2

Scheele, E. D., Westerman, W. L., and Wimmert, R. J., *Principles and Design of Production Control Systems* Prentice Hall 1960

Chapter 15

Baily, P. J. H., *Purchasing and Supply Management* Chapman Hall 1963

Burton, J. H., *Stores Accounts and Stores Control* Pitman 1956

Kay, F., *Purchasing* Pitman 1960

Melnitsky, *Industrial Storekeeping Manual* Exposition 1956

Chapter 17

McGill, D. A. C., *Punched Cards* McGraw Hill 1962

Chapter 18

Adelson, R. M., *Application of Queuing Theory in Production Engineering* Journal I.Prod.E. **46** 2

Eilon, S., *On the Theory of Games* Journal I.Prod.E. **46** 2

Rivett, P., and Ackoff, R. L., *A Manager's Guide to Operational Research* Wiley 1963

Salkin, G. R., *Linear Programming and its Applications* Journal I.Prod.E. **46** 2

Sasieni, M. W., Yaspan, A., and Friedmann, L., *Operations Research Methods and Problems* Wiley 1959

Chapter 19

Battersby, A., *Network Analysis for Planning and Scheduling* Macmillan 1964

Greene, D. E., *Critical Path Scheduling* Journal I.Prod.E. **42** 12

Lockyer, K. G., *An Introduction to Critical Path Analysis* Pitman 1964

Walton, A., *Application of Network Analysis to Various Fields* Journal I.Prod.E. **45** 12

Chapter 20

Barr, A. E. De, *Automatic Control* Chapman Hall 1962

Bryen, F., and Kease, W. J., *Controlling Inventory—A Computer System* Journal I.Prod.E. **43** 6

Kease, W. J., and Bryen, J. F. A., *Data Processing for Quantity Production* Journal I.Prod.E. **44** 8

Mansell, B., *Materials Planning by Computer* Journal I.Prod.E. **45** 12

Rivett, B. H. P., *What is Operational Research?* Journal of Management Studies **4** 2

Roots, W. K., *Industrial Systems Analysis* Journal I.Prod.E., **46** 3

Starr, M. K., *Production Management: Systems and Synthesis* Prentice Hall 1964

Smith, P. T., *How to Live with your Computer* Bailey Bros. & Swinfen 1965

West, J. C., *A Textbook of Servomechanisms* English Universities Press 1954

Westwater, F. L., and Waddell, W. A., *An Introduction to Servomechanisms* English Universities Press 1961

Authors and publisher would welcome suggestions towards future editions, or the pointing out of any misprint or obscurity. Please write to the Technical Editor, Macmillan & Co. Ltd., Little Essex St., London W.C.2.

INDEX